HOPALONG CASSIDY COLLECTIBLES

by Joseph J. Caro

WITH CONDITION SCALE
AND CURRENT VALUES

Cowboy Collector Publications
P.O. Bx. 7486
Long Beach, CA 90807

E MAIL ADDRESS: HOPPY@HOPALONG.COM WEBSITE: HTTP://WWW.HOPALONG.COM

ISBN: 0-89538-013-8

Library Of Congress Catalog Number: 542-644

Published by
Cowboy Collector Publications
P.O. Bx. 7486
Long Beach, CA 90807
(562) 428-6972

Original "Hoppy art" shown on this and the previous page was provided by the original, and only Hoppy cartoonist, Mr. Dan Spiegle.

First Printing 1997 00701

Printed and Manufactured in the United States of America

Printed by: Image Graphics, Paducah, Kentucky

TABLE OF CONTENTS

INTRODUCTION

"Howdy Pardner!

I see you've finally found us! Well, mosey on over to the collectors' campfire, take off your boots and sit a spell. The boy's and I . . . well, we've been wait'n for you to join us. Glad you could make it. Want some "hardtack" and a cuppa coffee? Good, ain't it? . . . You look familiar, didn't our trails cross back in "92" with the first Hoppy collector's book? That would be "Collectors Guide to Hopalong Cassidy Memorabilia." Quite a mouthful, I know. The Boy's and I, we trimmed the new book name a little to "Hopalong Cassidy Collectibles," kinda catchy, don't you think?

You're here for the Hoppy round-up no doubt. What round-up you say? Why, just the biggest gol' darned Hoppy collectibles round-up there ever was, is what! Behind this here "introduction" page . . . and a few others, you will set your eyes on the biggest and the best assortment of Hoppy treasures that ever were! Me'n the boy's here, why we "wrangled" for the better part of a year puttin' this here book-map together just for you and a few others from the old Bar-20. You best get some rest tonight pard, at sun-up tomorrow we all hit the trail . . . first findin' then roundin'-up the best Hoppy treasures there is!"

"Hopalong Cassidy Collectibles" is designed as a fully usable reference guide or directory, replete with current values, conditions and color photographs of over 1,100 Hoppy collectible items. It is the most extensive collectors book ever assembled on the subject of collecting Hoppy items. According to Jerry Rosenthul, President of Hopalong Cassidy Enterprises, Inc. there were 2,400 license agreements for Hoppy products and endorsements contracted during the "Hoppy era" on a world-wide basis. We have made a great effort to provide the majority of Hoppy collectible items made in North America during this period, along with realistic and timely values that these items hold.

Restricted to space as we are, we have opted not to relate much of the history and background of Bill Boyd and the "Hoppy" persona. That is a writing that may be undertaken in the future. This book was designed for the "novice" collector through to the most advanced Hoppy collector, antique and collectible dealers, cross-collectors, auction houses and collectible item value researchers. There is no one person who could have written a book nearly as extensive as this is . . . this book is the result of the combined efforts of many, many Hoppy collectors who, like you, enjoy the thrill of the hunt and the joy of the next "treasure" purchase! I am very proud to be a part of it.

COLLECTOR SHOCK

The first thing a collector will do after buying this book is immediately flip through the pages, check-out a few items, glance at the listed values . . . and nearly have heart seizure! The values *appear* to be quite high. If you look a little closer, you will quickly understand why. When writing the first Hoppy collector book, I used condition levels from #1. mint, or mint-in-box to #5. which is "poor" condition, where, out of a possible 100 condition points (100 being highest) a #5. would rate somewhere around a '30.' This book however, has eliminated condition levels #4. & #5. and therefore stated values shown *seem* to be much higher at first blush. The reason that these two condition levels were eliminated is (a.) to save valuable room to show more items and (b.) because most collectors wouldn't be caught dead with a #4. or #5. condition item in the first place.

INTRODUCTION

COLLECTING AN INVESTMENT

There are only two ways to view collecting anything: collect it because its a fun, enjoyable past-time, or collect it because it qualifies as a sound investment. Most Hoppy collector's creatively combine these two elements and deal with both the inner "child" and the responsible "adult" by both having fun and collecting a great investment! Hoppy is Hot! When I first started collecting Hoppy items twenty years ago, the "adult" side of my brain insisted in keeping track of my modest "investment" as with all others. Believe me when I say that Hoppy collecting has out performed all other investments, with the exception of California real estate! In 1976 I wisely invested $500 in assorted #3. condition or better, Hoppy "collectibilia" (a word that I now use). Current value of these items is over **$8,500.!!** Lets look at a few randomly selected pieces: Hoppy alarm clock (in box) #1. condition: 1976 **$75.** 1985 **$150.** 1990 **$450.** 1995 **$1,200.** and in this book (1997) that clock is valued at $1,400! Okay, how about the gun/holster ceramic nite lite: 1976 **$30.** 1985 **$70.** 1990 **$150** 1995 **$325.** and in this book you will find that it has again increased to $395. The list and investment "profitability" has grown on an average, more than 25 % per year!

In any investment there are "danger signs" where investors are wise to take heed when an investment hurricane approaches. Collecting Hoppy is no exception. Over the last ten years the value of Hoppy items far outvalued those of "Roy" or "Gene." This is especially important to note because there are much more Hoppy items to collect than both "Roy" and "Gene" combined. What this simply means is that even with such a large supply of licensed items to collect, Hoppy items continue to maintain a much higher value because of the law of Supply and Demand! Simply put . . . there are more people collecting Hoppy overall, than Gene or Roy. My opinion of an "investment" hurricane of destruction in this instance, is when Hoppy items start loosing ground and diminish in "collectibility" to the levels of Roy, Gene, or below. The law of Supply and Demand, if watched closely, will tell you all you really need to know.

FLUID VALUES

Collectors who have used my first Hoppy book are invited to compare "values" with those listed here and will quickly understand the importance of "Fluid Values" and how it affects collecting anything. About fifteen years ago, two Texas millionaires named the Hunt brothers attempted to "Lock Values" on silver bullion. During a three year period they were very successful and the value of silver skyrocketed from $7.00 per ounce to nearly $40.00! They were then found-out and the "Liquid Value" of silver was restored (to my dismay) and silver sought its uncontrolled value of where it is now, around $4.80 per ounce. The point here is simply that many Hoppy items have continued to increase, some remained stable in value over this period and some have declined. These "fluid" market actions should make investors comfortable because it clearly shows Hoppy values are not "Locked." A quick example of the "Liquid" Hoppy value market would be the recent discovery of Hoppy new-old-stock (NOS) potato chip bags. When they were first exposed to the "market" the bags sold for $250 each, and most collectors thought that just a few had been discovered. When 100 chip bags hit the market, the value tumbled down to where it is today, around $50 each. This reaction element shows both "Liquid" values at work in addition to "Supply and Demand." It is not my intention to turn this lovely book into an "Introduction to #101 Economics" but some collector's need and want to know things that motivate value changes. I have a few more technical areas to relate to you, but I promise, not many.

INTRODUCTION

DEFINING ITEM CONDITION

When a person looks to buy a collectible item, or a used car, there are generally two principal areas of interest: condition and price. Without a clear understanding of an item's actual condition, the stated price of an item is almost meaningless. My general impression of an item in "good" condition, is sure to be different than yours. The use of an adjective such as "good," "great," "wonderful," etc. is much too subjective to have *any* real meaning. While many traditional collectors (coins & stamps) use an item condition formula that would confuse Albert Einstein, I decided to devise my own system which is as simple as 1-2-3. While many use a reverse system based on the popularity of Bo Derek (#10 which like the actress, is about as *good* as you can get)! As old fashioned as I am, I agree with Harley Davidson motorcycles - - #1. can only be the absolute best! Following this philosophy, a definition of this condition scale is as follows:

#1. Mint or Mint-in-box. This condition generally means new-unused condition, new-old-stock (NOS) showing no wear or use, having appropriate warranty papers, price stickers, packaging. Some slight allowance is made for "patina" or age coloring and a small box abrasion or two is also okay. Out of a possible 100 points, my #1. condition would rank '95.' (Serious collectors can extend this condition scale to #1+ [100 points] or #1- [90 points] when dealing with "Investment Value" items which will be described a little later).

#2. Excellent. Applies to items that have been slightly used, showing little wear or use. For those who like using the term **Near-Mint**, that application would be scaled as: #1- or: 90 out of 100 points. Out of a possible 100 points, a #2. condition item would rank at '85.'

#3. Good. Showing some wear or use but still very presentable and in good working order, light scratches are allowable and in some cases, a little surface rust or paint discoloration. Out of a possible 100 points, #3. condition would rank at '75.'

The first page of each chapter in this book contains a brief definition of the three condition scales used to help you, as a guide, and to further establish the level of item condition. This is done so that you can clearly see and understand the differences in stated "current market values" on each page.

VALUES - IN GENERAL

In the world of appraising there are many applications of the word "value," most of which have no real impact on the collector. Being that appraisers do this for a living, they have defined "values" to avoid confusion about what "values" they are talking about; starting at the beginning with the term "value" itself. The American Society of Appraisers (ASA) defines it as: "The cash or cash equivalent that a buyer is willing to exchange for some object or thing." Based on this basic "value" definition, many nuances of "value" spring forth: "Investment Value," "Market Value," "Replacement Value," "Orderly Liquidation Value" and "Forced Liquidation Value." Believe me when I tell you, it is important for a collector of anything to know at least the basic definition of what these terms mean.

INVESTMENT VALUE

Many collector's and collectible dealer's often use the term "investment value" when attempting to use this term to describe their opinion of an item that they feel will appreciate higher and faster than other similar pieces. What they really mean to say is something else entirely.

INTRODUCTION

The National Society of Real Estate Appraisers (NSRE) and other appraisal institutions have this to say about the "investment value" term: "Investment Value is the estimated value to a particular investor. Investment Value is seldom the same as Market Value. Market Value represents an impersonal synthesis of sellers and buyers, whereas Investment Value is the estimated value for one individual." A good but extreme example of how investment value would work is: You are the grandchild of General George M. Patton and your family has kept and cherished *one* of the two nickel-plated 45 caliber pistols that he wore strapped on him throughout the war. You heard there was an auction that was featuring his other nickel-plated 45 pistol. What would you pay for it? What would you pay for it if it wasn't a part of your family heritage? You would pay "Market Value." Being that you already had one of the two guns, (and he was a member of your family) you would be willing to pay more for it than anyone else. That would be "Investment Value." A Hopalong Cassidy can of Green Beans, or a Hoppy wading pool, or a Hoppy tent, are other examples of investment value items, because there are so few of them around, with so many collector's who would like to own them.

MARKET VALUE

"The most probable price which an item should bring in an competitive and open market under all conditions requisite to a fair sale, both buyer and seller acting prudently and knowledgeable and under no duress to either buy or sell." This is the definition that the ASA uses and it works well for collector's as well. Most items found in this book have been researched to find the current selling price in an open market and is related to you as market value. Extremely rare pieces carry "investment value" estimates of worth, just to give you a rough idea of where it will be. Those collectors who like auctions will be glad to hear that in general, auctions offer most *all* value ranges stated on this page!

AUCTIONS

Attending collectible auctions or participating in "call-in" or "mail-in" auctions is a lot of fun and can certainly get your collection into high-gear in a short period of time. I have personally gotten some excellent items at excellent prices at auctions and strongly recommend most "established" auction houses dealing with collectible items, such as Hoppy stuff. The biggest advantage that attending an auction in-person has over other kinds, is that you get to see and examine the items you are interested in purchasing. Just remember to have fun and keep in mind the importance of item conditions. Hoppy Hunting!!

SUMMARY

I wish I would have had a book like this when I started collecting Hoppy items over twenty years ago, it would have saved me ten times the price of the book in the first year alone! I doubt that I, or any Hoppy collector will ever be able to amass all the great collectibles there are in the "Hoppy" field, as new unknown "treasures" are found, seemingly, on a weekly basis! This book, you may be surprised to read, is dedicated to all the "new" Hoppy collectors that are just starting to build their fine collections. In all likelihood, they are the ones who will be finding most of the rare Hoppy "treasures:" tents, fishing poles, pogo sticks, wading pools, outfits and cap guns that are pretty much unknown to the Hoppy collectors today. Like the recently discovered Hoppy Green Beans can, I have heard that there are more Hoppy canned vegetables and canned fruit yet to be found! Not to mention the 1936 Hoppy fountain pens! Or the 1952 Hoppy & Topper child's wading pool that has three inflated Topper musical heads that came boxed with a repair kit and a 5' shower attachment! I know there is a boxed one around, I just know it!

ACKNOWLEDGMENTS

The thoroughness and completeness of this book is the direct result of the efforts of many fine Hoppy fans and collectors throughout the country. They weren't paid to do it, and as a matter of fact, many invested hundreds of dollars and many hours of work to produce the majority of the photographic images found throughout the book. Many other kind folks submitted good photos that did not make the final selection process due to space restraints and image duplication. While not mentioned by name, I want each and every one of them to know that their efforts are warmly appreciated.

You will no doubt notice the hundreds of wonderful items submitted by Jon and Charlie Cheek from Pleasant Garden North Carolina, as you view this book. Charlie and Jon are a father & son team of avid "Hoppy" collectors who were willing to share their great treasures with all of us. Jon Cheek has recently been elected as president of the Hopalong Cassidy Fan Club and although he holds two jobs, always found the time and the energy to support the development of this book. My deepest thanks to two of the most enthusiastic Hoppy collectors it has been my pleasure to know. I warmly thank each of the following supporters for their great contributions.

John Abramson
Porter Albin
Steve Axelson
Brian Beirne
Garry Bondy
Garry Bondy Jr.
Pamela C. Brand
Dave Brobeck
Aileen Buck
Steve Castelli
Doug Candler
Jon &
Charlie Cheek
Lee Davidson
Sharon Delaney
Robert Donovan
Gene Douglass
Phil & Rose Ellis
Mike Forthun
Ted Hake
Bill Hamburg
John Hirsch
Bill Hoffman
Ron Johnson
John Kennedy
Terry Klepey
Corky Leigh
Bill Larzelere
Charles Lombard
Boyd Magers
Charlie &
Jean Mattoe
Charlotte &
Lenny Marcinkowski
James McLoughlin
Mike Merryman
Lee &
Sharon Mitchell
John Mlachnick
Mike Pellow
Ron Pieczkowski
Bob Reed
Charles Ringhel
Howard Reidinger
M. Saxer
Larry Seymour
"AJ" Siarkowski
Dennis Smith
Frank Smith
Chet &
Marge Tkach
Gary Nichols
Pete & "The
Princess" Woebcke

HOPPY FILMS

FILM	RELEASE DATE
Hop-A-Long Cassidy (Enters)	July, 1935
The Eagles Brood	October, 1935
Bar 20 Rides Again	November, 1935
Call Of The Prairie	March, 1936
Three On The Trail	April, 1936
Heart Of The West	July, 1936
Hopalong Cassidy Returns	October, 1936
Trail Dust	December, 1936
Borderland	February, 1937
Hills Of Old Wyoming	April, 1937
North Of The Rio Grande	June, 1937
Rustlers' Valley	July, 1937
Hopalong Rides Again	September, 1937
Texas Trail	November, 1937
Partners Of The Plains	January, 1938
Cassidy Of The Bar 20	February, 1938
Heart Of Arizona	April, 1938
Bar 20 Justice	June, 1938
Pride Of The West	July, 1938
In Old Mexico	September, 1938
The Frontiersman	December, 1938
Sunset Trail	February, 1939
Silver On The Sage	March, 1939
The Renegade Trail	July, 1939
Range War	September, 1939
Law Of The Pampas	November, 1939
Santa Fe Marshall	January, 1940
The Showdown	March, 1940
Hidden Gold	June, 1940
Stagecoach War	July, 1940
Three Men From Texas	November, 1940
The Doomed Caravan	January, 1941
In Old Colorado	March, 1941
Border Vigilanties	April, 1941
Pirates On Horseback	May, 1941
Wide Open Town	August, 1941

HOPPY FILMS

FILM	RELEASE DATE
Stick To Your Guns	September, 1941
Twilight On The Trail	September, 1941
Riders Of The Timberline	September, 1941
Secrets Of The Wasteland	November, 1941
Outlaws Of The Desert	November, 1941
Leather Burners	October, 1942
Undercover Man	October, 1942
Hoppy Serves A Writ	November, 1942
Border Patrol	April, 1943
Colt Comrades	June, 1943
Bar 20	October, 1943
False Colors	November, 1943
Lost Canyon	December, 1943
Riders Of The Deadline	December, 1943
Texas Masquerade	February, 1944
Lumberjack	April, 1944
Mystery Man	May, 1944
Forty Thieves	June, 1944
The Devil's Playground	November, 1946
Fool's Gold	February, 1947
Unexpected Guest	March, 1947
Dangerous Venture	May, 1947
Hoppy's Holiday	July, 1947
The Marauders	July, 1947
Silent Conflict	March, 1948
The Dead Don't Dream	April, 1948
Sinister Journey	June, 1948
Borrowed Trouble	July, 1948
False Paradise	September, 1948
Strange Gamble	October, 1948

In 1948, Bill Boyd saw the future of a new generation of Hoppy viewers via the television screen. "Strange Gamble" would be his last "Hoppy" film. In 1951 Hopalong Cassidy was the first "cowboy hero" to have his own TV show. The show ran until 1954 and co-starred Edgar Buchanan.

ABOUT THE AUTHOR

oppy is never far from Joe Caro's view. he Hoppy oil painting on the wall was ed on the cover of this book and has storic value. It was commissioned by Bill oyd himself, in 1949 to be taken as a gift Clarence Mulford in Fryburg, Maine as "peace offering" to help Bill negotiate e remaining "rights" to the Hoppy character.

Joseph J. Caro is a well known writer and photographer who has written many feature "collector" articles for national and international magazines for many years. A skilled appraiser, arbitrator and businessman, Joe works as a business development consultant in Southern California, when he isn't busy writing.

A Hoppy collector for over 20 years, Joseph Caro has written the first Hoppy collector's book: "Collector's Guide to Hopalong Cassidy Memorabilia" published in 1992 by L -W Books, Inc. A skilled consumer arbitrator, Joe also wrote: "Consumer's Guide to the California Lemon Law" published in 1990. An avid classic car enthusiast with several unique cars of his own, Joe's latest hobby is restoring antique pedal cars when he isn't working with Cowboy Collector Network or his Hoppy newsletter.

Joe and Grace (Mrs. Hopalong Cassidy) Boyd in Lone Pine, California during the Hoppy Film Festival in 1991.

A "Hoppy's Kid" from childhood, the photo on the left shows Joe, his father Jim and his brother Bob (playing with his prized Hoppy gun) at home in Plainfield, NJ in 1952. The photo on the right is Joe trying to master Hoppy's trick lariate. Notice the Buster Brown Black & white shoes . . . he was not allowed to wear Hoppy boots.

Joe & Bob actually met Hoppy and talked to Him at Madison Square Garden, NY during a Cole Bros. Circus held there in 1952.

HOPPY DAYS

These great comic illustrations are a loan from Jerry Rosenthul, President of Hopalong Cassidy Enterprises, Inc. in Tarzana, California. They represent all "Hoppy's Kids" at their best and funniest!

"The kids? They're ***thrilled*** *- - I told them Hopalong Cassidy caught you."*

"But darling, I'm Sure Mr. Cassidy wouldn't consider you disloyal just because you ate one LAMB chop."

"Come along now and stop worrying about what Hopalong Cassidy would think."

Dennis the Menace By Hank K

"Gosh! No wonder Hopalong Cassi dosen't smoke!"

"No question about it, the only man who can lick Truman in 52 is Hopalong Cassidy. But how do we know he's a Republican?"

"Well, whats it going to be Thompson - - Hopalong Cassidy or Troup Nine?"

"HOPPY'S KIDS"

There was something very special about Hopalong Cassidy that captured the hearts and imaginations of millions of kids growing-up in the 1950's that defies explanation. Maybe it was a more "friendly" time in this country, or, as some say, maybe it was the "best" time that America ever had. Things were either black or white, right or wrong - good or bad. These important lessons were learned at home, in school, or in church, and was confirmed by the people that we as children, admired and tended to emulate. It is true that all kids have "heroes" at one time or another while on the shaky road to adulthood . . . but there was something special, almost magical, that "Hoppy" had, that has not been equaled then, or since. Yes, he was a "father figure" with white hair and a warm smile and magnetism - so much so, that it would reach out from the theatre or television screen and capture most young viewers in a heart-beat. That explains then . . . but what about now? Why for example, does Producer's Dairy in Fresno, California continue to place the Hoppy image on milk, butter, eggs and cottage cheese when few customers know or care to remember who Hoppy is? Why do grown men today proudly wear custom made Hoppy outfits, build wagons and bicycles, paint Hoppy pictures or sculpt full-size images of Hoppy and his horse Topper? Why have I spent 20 years collecting Hoppy memorabilia and a year writing this book? I'll be darned if I know, but I'll tell you *one* thing . . . I doubt that in twenty years or so, you will see a whole lot of grown people running around in green "ninja" turtle suits, karate-kicking *their* way into retirement!

Here is a small sampling of "Hoppy's Kids" then and now, who were kind enough to allow me to grace these few pages with their images or activities. Hoppy Trails to you all!

The most famous of all "Hoppy's Kids" was a boy named Billy who closely adhered to the Hoppy Creed. He grew-up to be President of the United States. His full name is Bill Clinton (photo, 1955)

With both guns blazing you may recall Roger Hall. He posed with Hoppy for the cover of Look magazine. This photo is from his home in Bergenfield, NJ in 1950.

Roger Hall eventually married another "Hoppy's Kid" named Gail. This photo, taken in Attleboro, Mass. in 1954, shows that Roger also had an eye for beauty!

"HOPPY'S KIDS"

Current photo of Roger Hall holding the Look Magazine that he shared with Hoppy himself.

Childhood actor Gary Gray talks with Grace (Mrs. Hopalong Cassidy) Boyd and shows a now famous photo of a young Gary during the start of his acting career.

Lifetime Hoppy fan "AJ" Siarkowski is still a won derful (but slightly grown up) "Hoppy's Kid."

Francis Reeves at the Cambridge Hoppy Festival.

A current day "Hoppy" both in spirit and looks is Francis Reeves who reveres in being Hoppy for the Cambridge, Ohio Hoppy Festival. The kids love him as much as if he were Hoppy himself. Thank you for your kindness Francis.

Norman Parvis from Conner ville, IN traveled to Cambridg Ohio for the May Hoppy Festiv proudly sporting his custo Hoppy shirt and hat. A great far

"HOPPY'S KIDS"

here else would a grown man openly walk around vn with "loaded" Hoppy cap-pistols? Why Cam-idge, Ohio of course, during the Hoppy Festival!

Red Moore from Mountainburg, AR, is another life-time Hoppy fan/collector who just can't get "The Man" out of his mind. Shown above is a life-size sculpture Red has just completed of Hoppy & Topper. What great talent going to such good use!

.rtist Melvin Phillips brings to the canvas a great keness of our hero "Hoppy."

Child star five year old Gary Gray poses with Hoppy in 1942. Gary went on to appear in many films and TV shows including "Lucy," "The Jackie Jenson Story," The Danny Thomas Show, "Man Without a Gun," "The Outlaw Kingdom" and many, many more. Thanks Gary, for your support.

"HOPPY'S KIDS"

Larry Martin, a Pensacola, FL, life-long "Hoppy's Kid" takes Hoppy wherever he goes in his converted van. Hoppy cap guns are Larry's favorite.

While not nearly as mobile as a "Hoppy" van, "Hoppy's Finer Diner" graced the streets of Boone IA, from 1988 to 1990. The brain-child of Ken Hopkins and Bobby, both of whom are "righteous" Hoppy fans and collectors.

Shown above, is the rare "Hoppy Harley" designed and ridden by John Kennedy from Orange, CA. Powered by a genuine "Whizzer" motor, the bike is a thing of beauty and one can only wonder why a "real" version was never produced.

Another very mechanical "Hoppy's Kid" is Robert Simpson from Phoenix, AZ, who has built several versions of his "Hoppy Harley" right in his kitchen! Needless to say, his wife must really be an avid Hoppy fan just to put up with it!

"HOPPY'S KIDS"

PALONG CASSIDY, JR.—That's how Bruce Perkins of Fry rg, grandson of Clarence E. Mulford, creater of the Hopalo ssidy stories, feels now that he owns the sharp cowboy outi.. s sporting here. It was a gift from Screen Actor William yd, is an exact replica of the outfit Boyd wears on the screen Hopalong Cassidy.

opalong Cassidy Jr. was really Bruce Perkins ho is Clarence Mulford's grandson. Hoppy mself brought him the "outfit" in 1949 while siting Mr. Mulford.

Wes Stigen (L) and brother Wayne, were great "Hoppy's Kids" in the 50's. Wayne was killed in Viet Nam. Photo was taken in Iola, WI.

Byron Beam in 1952. Today, this serious looking youngster owns a very prosperous Orange County, California law firm. The photo was taken in Hollywood, Calif.

This famous photo of Hoppy embracing two "Hoppy's Kids" is rumored to have been taken by the children's mother when they saw Hoppy during filming. The photo seems to be 1953 vintage.

A devote Hoppy fan/collector today, "AJ" Siarkowski started as an egar, enthusiastic "Hoppy's Kid" back in the early 50's.

Ted Hake, from Hake's Americana, was a two-gun totin' "Hoppy's Kid" for years!

"HOPPY'S KIDS"

Two great looking "Hoppy's Kids" are sadly, unknown. I bought the photo in a Long Beach, California antique swap-meet.

This shy-looking "Hoppy's Kid" is well known to me. The beautiful woman is my grandmother, Rose Caro. Photo was taken in 1952, in Plainfield, NJ.

The photo here (L) is of another unknown "Hoppy's Kid."

Fuzzy and out of focus, Mike Forthun of South Pasadena California started collecting "Hoppy" at a young age.

John Rizzo, Danvers, Maine in June of 1952. "Hoppy's Kid" and collector.

Christmas, 1955 in the house of Danny VanLuven, Owosso, MI. Submitted by his cousin, Bear Saunders.

"HOPPY'S KIDS"

Tommy Slater, age 4, in 1951 Living in Tracy, California. Tom was killed in Viet Nam.

3 year-old Johnny Haufe at his grandparents house in Dover Plains, NY in July, 1950. It was his birthday; he got "Hoppy's Kids" stuff!

A new "Hoppy's Kid" is Haley Ellis, age 4, and grandaughter of Phil & Rose Ellis, Santa Rosa, California. She is standing next to a genuine 12" Hoppy trike.

Krista Abramson from Moreno Valley, Calif. has helped her father John, by modeling this rare Hoppy outfit making her an honorary member of "Hoppy's Kids."

Miss Chris Proffitt, her brother John (middle) and their childhood friend D.B. Garrison were on vacation with their parents traveling through Palm Desert, California. They stopped by a local drugstore for a soda and were amazed to see "Hoppy" in street clothes walking out. Their parents took this great photo of them in 1955.

Cory Ellis, grandson of Rose & Phil Ellis is wearing some great Hoppy stuff making him an honorary "Hoppy's Kid" too.

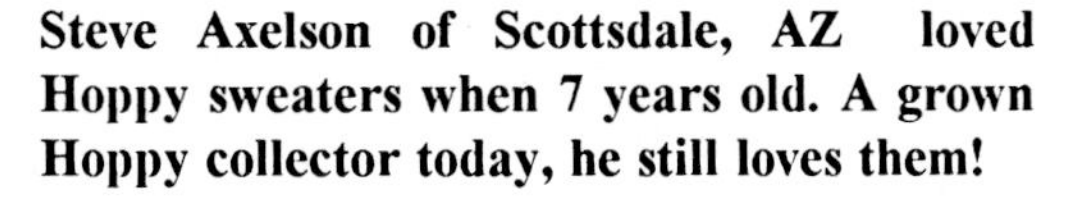

Steve Axelson of Scottsdale, AZ loved Hoppy sweaters when 7 years old. A grown Hoppy collector today, he still loves them!

"HOPPY'S KIDS"

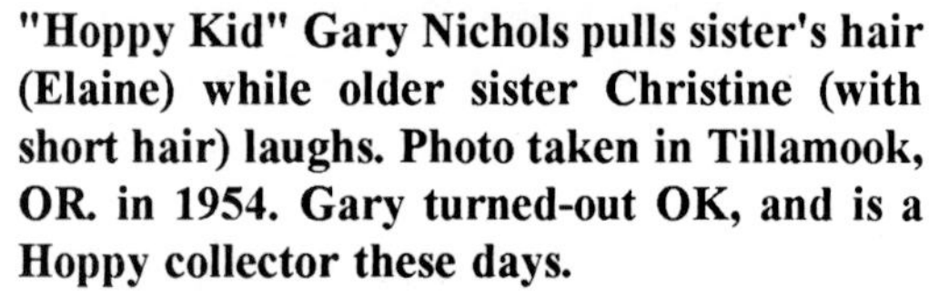

"Hoppy Kid" Gary Nichols pulls sister's hair (Elaine) while older sister Christine (with short hair) laughs. Photo taken in Tillamook, OR. in 1954. Gary turned-out OK, and is a Hoppy collector these days.

"Its Hoppy Time" is the only thing that wou make the youngest "Hoppy's Kid" known get worked-up. Photo is dated 4/6/51 but the gre looking (slightly chubby) young cowboy unknown to us. Love that tee shirt!

I snapped a candid photo of a baby picture sitting on a "genuine" Hoppy desk, when visiting the home of radio "DJ" Brian Beirne. Brian will probably kill me when he finds out, but I couldn't resist . . . those dimples are just too much! Notice the Hoppy sweater under the winter coat.

The "After" picture as the famous "Mr Rock & Roll" and K-EARTH 101 "jock," still can't hide those great dimples can they? Brian doesn't talk much about it, but he also has a star on the Hollywood Walk of Fame, not far from where Hoppy has his!

Robert Boldman is wearing a unique Hoppy tee shirt while discussing cowboy life with a very well dressed Easter Bunny. Bob was 6 years old in 1951 and a card-carrying member of "Hoppy's Kids." His home town is West Unity, Ohio.

John Dodge guards his grandmothe Donna, while dressed in the "Hoppy' Kids" latest outfit. Notice the hand-cuf on his belt. Are they real?? Maybe. Phot taken in Palm Springs, Calif. in 1953.

BATH - PERSONAL

#1. condition: mint, showing no use #2. condition: excellent to near mint #3. condition: good to very good

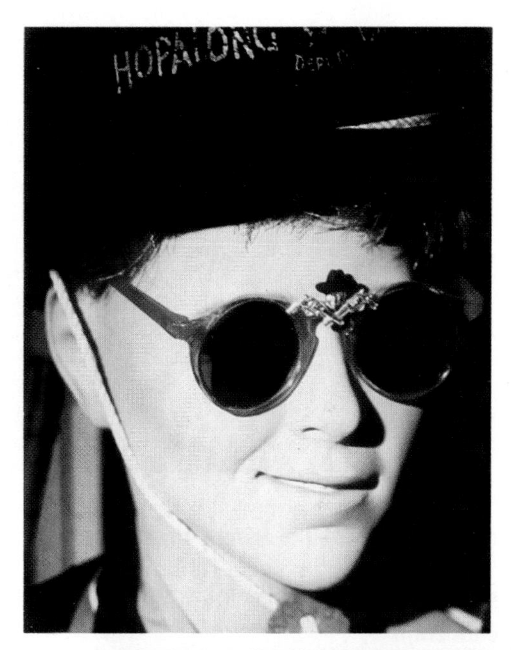

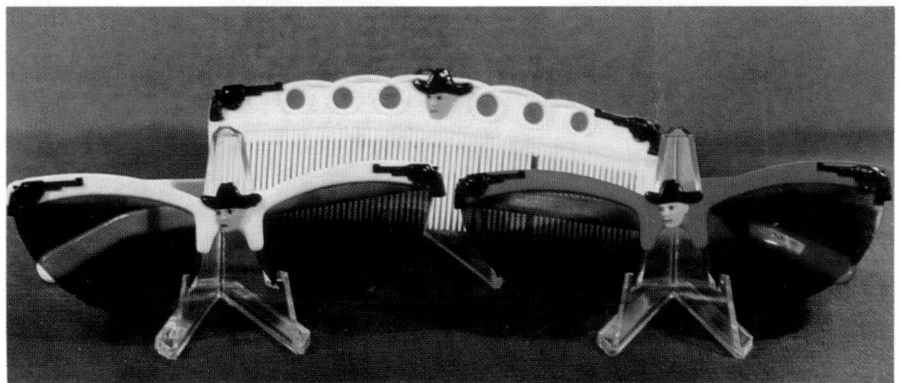

While a few experts doubt the reality of Hoppy sunglasses, the actuality is that there are quite a few pair around, both boy's and girl's. The top photos show mannequin displays of both sets. The bottom photo shows the girl's glasses in red and white, along with a rare Hoppy girl's comb for good measure. Lenses in both pair are a tinted plastic. #1. $300 #2. $250 #3. $225. (girls) #1. $350 #2. $300 #3. $250 (boys). The white comb is also plastic: #1. $300 #2. $275 #3. $250. The comb and two girl's glasses are from the Jon & Charlie Cheek collection.

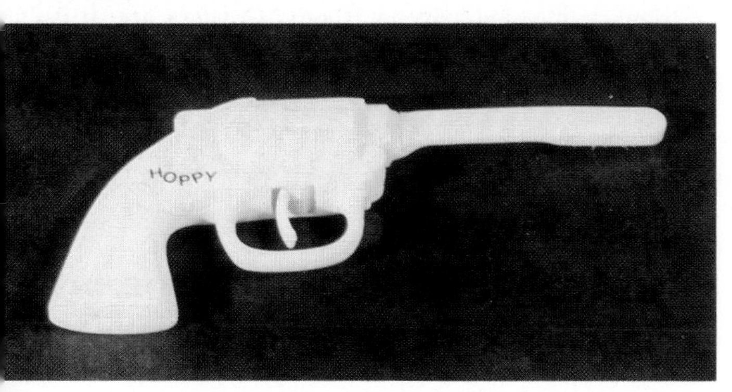

Another extremely rare Hoppy item is the gun-brush (L). This small plastic "clicker" tooth brush gun is the only one known to exist. Gun-brush came with white plastic holster that hung on wall. #1. $425 #2. $350 #3. $275 (includes holster)

The blue Hoppy "trail knife" is a difficult find even for advanced collectors, especially in this condition: #1. $375 #2. $330 #3. $285. (without fob, deduct $30.) From the Phil Ellis collection.

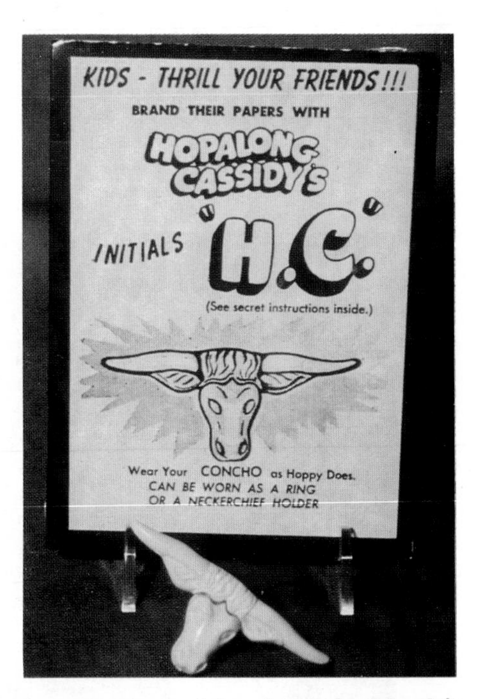

Steerhead paper stamp (also shown in school items chapter) is called a concho on the card, that can be worn as a ring or neckerchief holder. #1. $150 #2. $125 #3. $100. From the Jon & Charlie Cheek collection

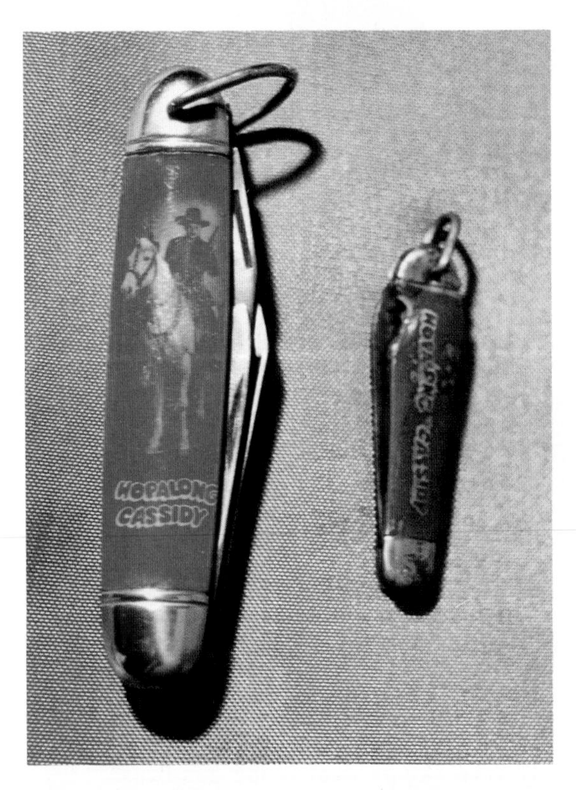

Rarer than the blue, is the red Hoppy "trail knife" shown with the blue single blade "mini" knife, also very rare. (red): #1. $450 #2. $340 #3. $300 (without fob, deduct $30). (mini blue): #1. $275 #2. $230 #3. $200. From the Jon & Charlie Cheek collection.

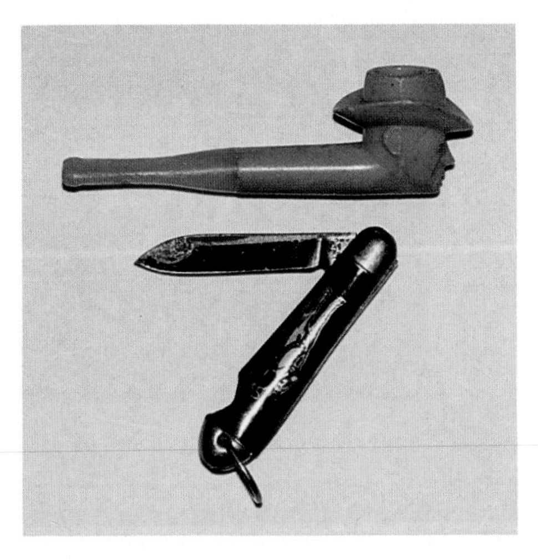

Black "mini" Hoppy single blade knife is shown with an interesting small blue plastic bubble pipe with a remarkable similarity to Hoppy. Chances are, it isn't. The black knife however, is authentic: #1. $225 #2. $185 #3. $150.

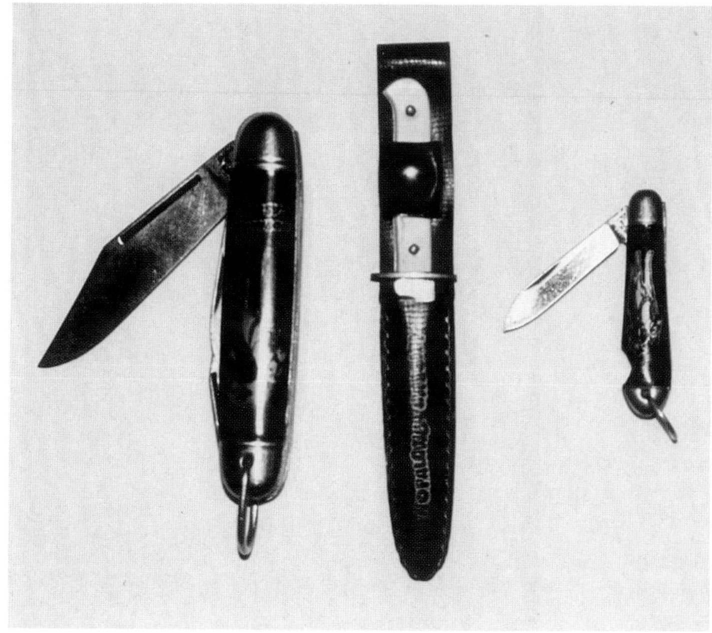

The black Hoppy "trail knife" (three bladed) is shown with a small Hoppy sheath knife in a vinyl sheath, and another view of the "mini" single blade knife. The black "trail knife" is the most common and is: #1. $250 #2. $200 #3. $175. (deduct $30 without fob). Sheath knife: #1. $190 #2. $140 #3. $110. (There is another Hoppy sheath knife -- look in "guns & outfits" chapter).

Store display card with 12 Hoppy three-bladed knives is a great collector's find. There are several around. Investment value is in the $3,500 area.

hile this leather Hoppy travel kit was advertised in Ward's and ars catalogs, the above set is the only one known to exist. To make atters worse, there is a different travel kit that was made that has t been found at all! From the Phil Ellis collection.

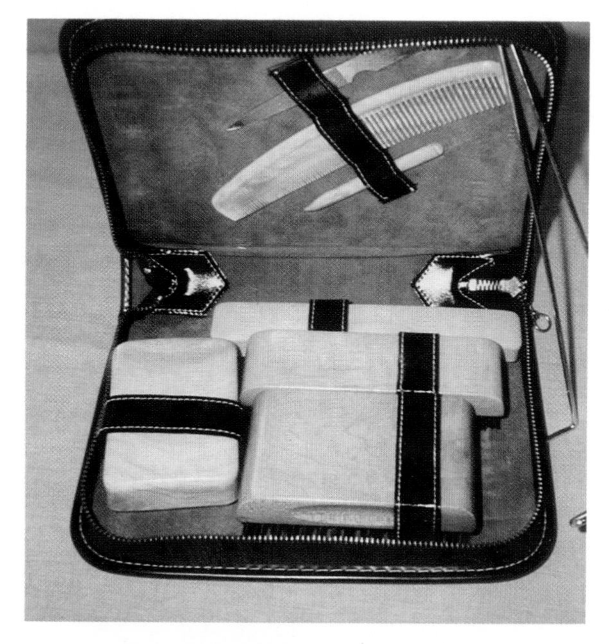

Shown in #1. unused condition, this rare kit is certainly investment value grade which may range from $2,800-$3,500. The Phil Ellis collection.

Hoppy towel set (above) is mint in the box, containing a "Bar-20" face cloth and Hoppy bath towel. It is investment grade with a value estimate of: $450. The other "name" Hoppy towels on this page are more common, but still a challenge to find: #1. $260 #2. $210 #3. $185. From the Bill Larzelere collection.

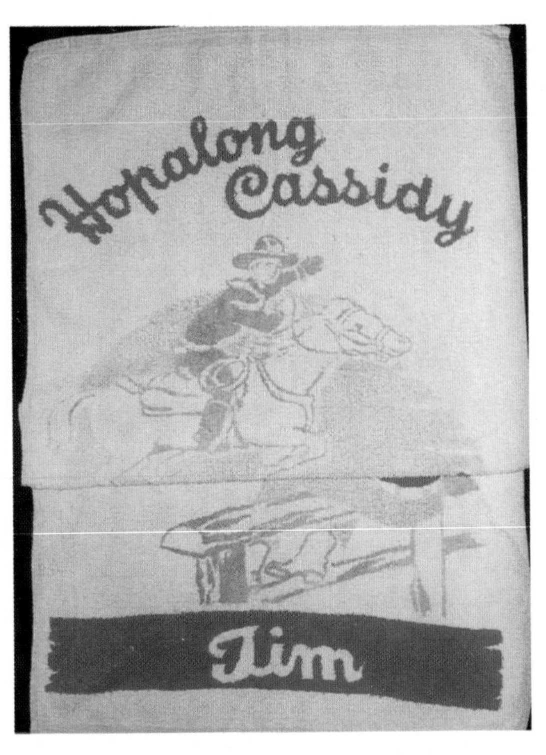

Hoppy pre-named towels were stocked in stores and a great selling item in the 50's. I wonder where the girl's towels are?

It is quite easy to tell a #1. condition towel from those used. The "Sonny" towel is in #1. condition, Arthur has been used and is #2. "Tim" was the cleanest, as his towel is a #3.

The Hoppy light wool blanket (R) is made from quality material and a great collector find. Made by the Bellcraft company, it is not easy to find. #1. $450 #2. $375 #3. $325. From the Bill Larzelere collection.

other colorful towel design is the one pictured above. It might 'e been part of a set but this is the only one of its type that could found. #1. $285 #2. $225 #3. $200.

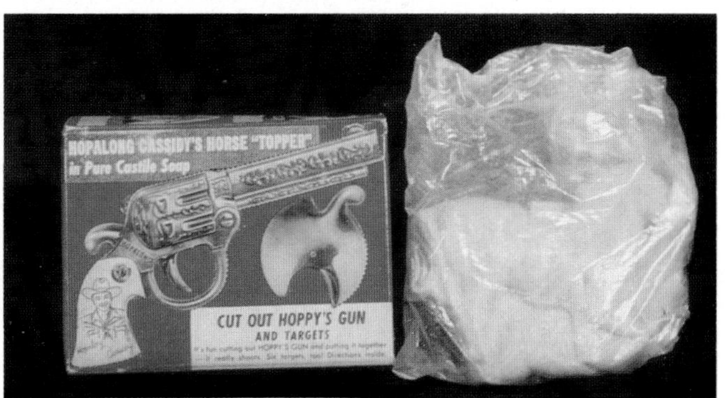

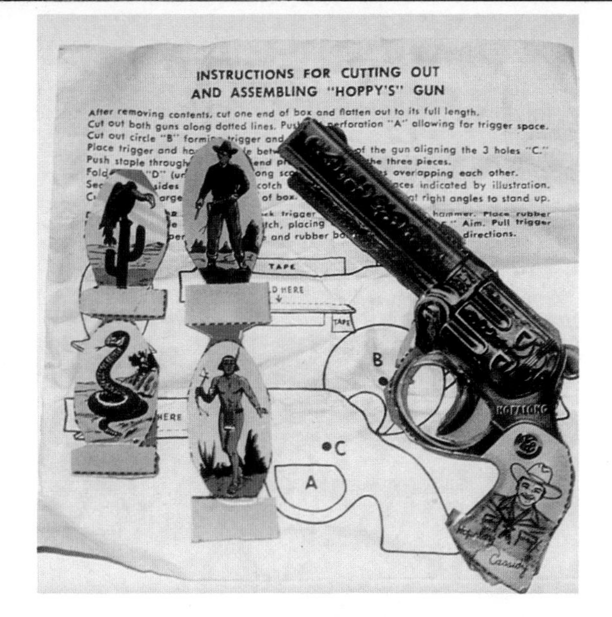
INSTRUCTIONS FOR CUTTING OUT AND ASSEMBLING "HOPPY'S" GUN

After removing contents, cut one end of box and flatten out to its full length.

The above photo is of the Topper soap & box and instructions for the Hoppy target game that is included. Soap is wrapped in wax paper bag. #1. $350 #2. $300 #3. $265.

Four bar set of Hoppy soap (by Castile) is a great find. Soap bars have color decals on top. Box back (R) has punch-out cards. #1. $395 #2. $345 #3. $300 (caution: soap decals stick to box cellophane).

Soap box back showing different Hoppy cards. One card came with each box.

One of the rarest Hoppy bath items is the "Bath Round-up" shown above. The soap horse is a Topper, which is also found in the Topper box on the previous page. The other two items in this box is bubble bath and a container of bath powder. #1. $750 #2. $650 #3. $525. From the Phil Ellis collection.

Not quite as rare as the "Bath Round-up" but in great collector demand is the "Dudin'-up Kit" shown above. Containing a plastic comb, hair trainer and shampoo, it was quite the rage. #1. $575 #2. $500 #3. $400. From the Phil Ellis collection.

Dr. West's Dental Kit is an excellent collector's find and quite novel. There are many sets available. Contains a glass tubed black tooth brush, a boxed tube of Hoppy tooth paste and a small mirror with Hoppy drawn in red or black on the background. #1. $450 #2. $375 #3. $300.

Unusual bottle of Hoppy hair trainer has the same label as Associated Brands, Inc. but is a different color and has a different top. May be a phoney?

Three sizes of Hoppy hair trainer are pictured above: (L) $55 (C) $65 (R) $85 (all with contents and top) They are NOS (new old stock) with quite a lot having been found.

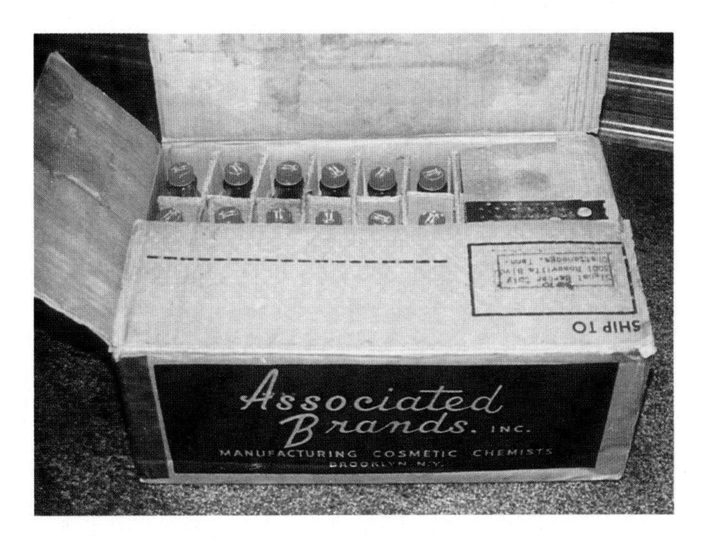

If you look hard and are so inclined, you may run across a full case of Hoppy's hair trainer from Associated Brands, Inc. Packaged 36 to a case, it will keep your hair slicked back for quite a while. Investment value is in the area of $1,000 to $1,200.

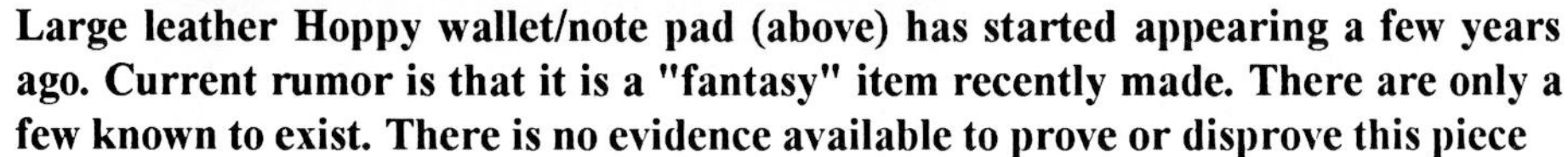
Large leather Hoppy wallet/note pad (above) has started appearing a few years ago. Current rumor is that it is a "fantasy" item recently made. There are only a few known to exist. There is no evidence available to prove or disprove this piece

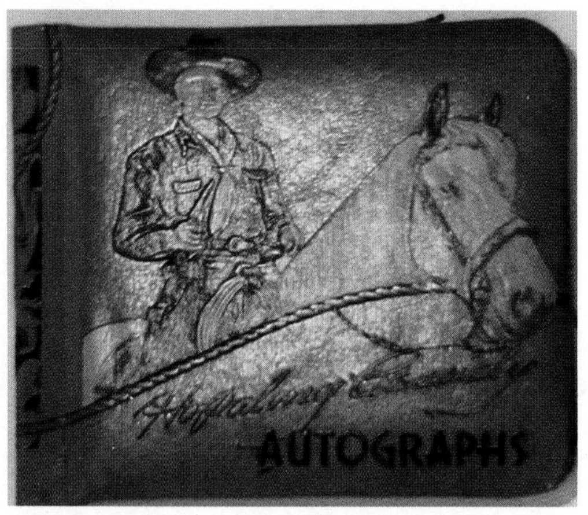

Early version of Hoppy autograph book was dark brown leather with Hoppy and Topper a little difficult to see. #1. $275 #2. $225 #3. $200

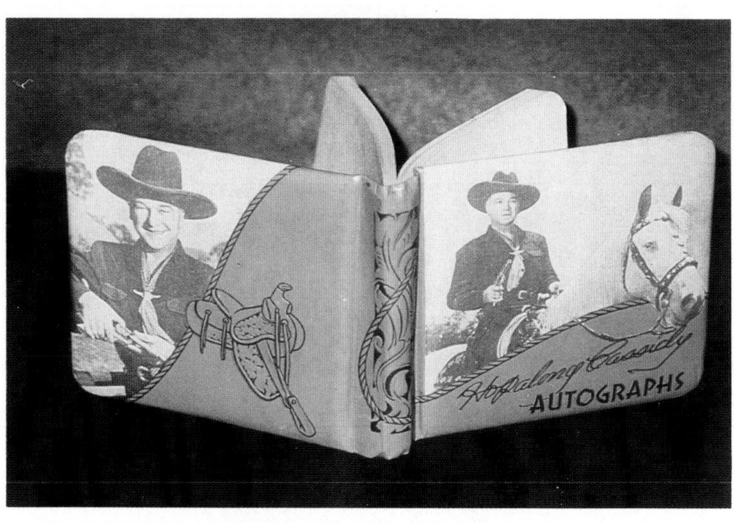

Later version of autograph book shows a marked improvement but is more difficult to find. #1. $300 #2. $250 #3. $225. From the Richard Stevens collection.

Hoppy die-cut cardboard picture frame came with Hoppy photo (also see "promotions") #1. $130 #2. $110 #3. $90

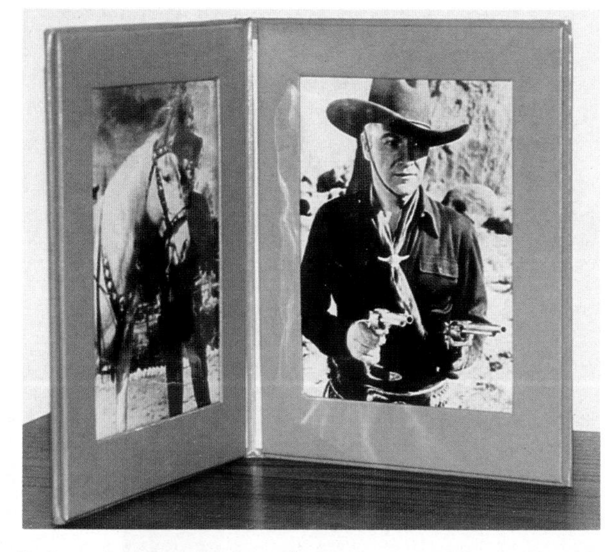

Deluxe leather Hoppy frame was made to match photo & scrapbook albums. Cover had graphics to match. #1. $170 #2. $140 #3. $110.

This three-section metal picture frame carried Hoppy's photo and Dana Andrews to help sales. While not a Hoppy item, its nice to have. Valued at $40. From the Dennis Smith collection.

There were two versions of the photo album/scrap book sets with the rarest being the least expensive (above). Using the same graphics as several of the school pencil cases (see "school items" chapter) which also shows Hoppy & Topper within a golden horseshoe. Due to its rarity, it carries a similar value as the more ornate.

Values of the above photo album and scrap book are: #1. $265 #2. $210 #3. $185. From the Jon & Charlie Cheek collection.

above photo of the deluxe photo album and scrap book clearly shows difference between the two versions. Material used was a finer grade erette with a string binding and embossed western designs. #1. $295 #2. #3. $240 (for either one). From the Dennis Smith collection.

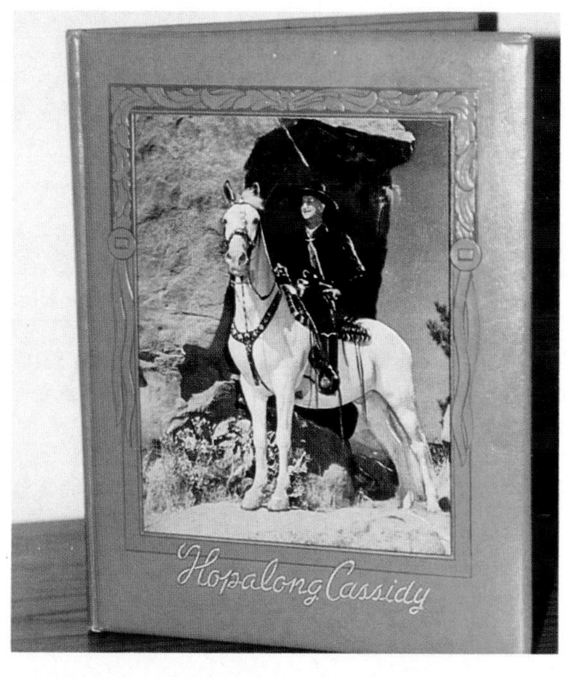

Cover photo of deluxe Hoppy picture frame shown on previous page.

HOPPY'S BOOKS

#1. condition: mint, showing no use #2. condition: excellent to near mint #3. condition: good to very good

"I'm writing because I can't help it" is a Clarence E. Mulford (1883-1956) quote on writing the many Hoppy stories over the years, beginning in 1907, from his home in Brooklyn, NY. The first eight "Bar-20" stories was published in Outing magazine. The stories were strung together to become Mulford's first hard cover book; "Bar-20." The original, and continuing "Hoppy" character in all of Mulford's works was a rough, gruff, he-man cowboy type. He was twenty three years old. He chewed tobacco, drank whenever he could, and fought with just about everybody. A far, far, cry from the Bill Boyd version. His second book, "Hopalong Cassidy" was published in 1910 to rave reviews. The Argosy All-Story Magazine (shown below) began printing "Hoppy" with the December 15, 1923 issue titled: Hopalong Cassidy Returns I: The Snakes." The Hopalong Cassidy's Pal" story, was published on May 2, 1925 with many in-between.

Argosy All-Story Weekly magazine started the Hoppy stories in 1923. the above is the first story issue (L) and the Argosy to the right is a 1925 version. Both are very rare. #1. $125 #2. $100 #3/ $75 (left mag) and $30 less per condition for others. From the Mike Pellow collection.

Note

Many early Hoppy books came in publisher sets (above and left photos) Needless to say, First Editions are very valuable. If you think you may have a first edition of a Mulford hard cover book, you are advised to take it to an antique book specialist to have it verified. The book values listed in this chapter do not reflect first edition values.

Different publishers used different graphics and jackets to attract readers. Note the two different styles on "Hopalong Cassidy Takes Cards." Most all hard cover Hoppy books came with colorful jackets with the exception of published sets that were shown on the previous page. Another graphics change is seen in "The Coming of Hopalong Cassidy" shown below. There were many British (UK) made Hoppy books published since the 1900's which some consider more valuable.

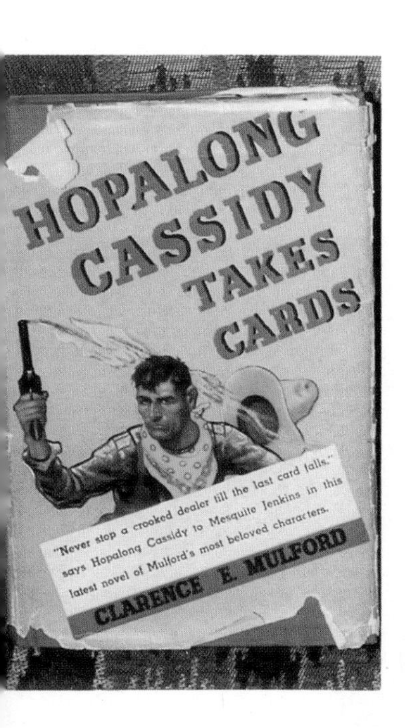

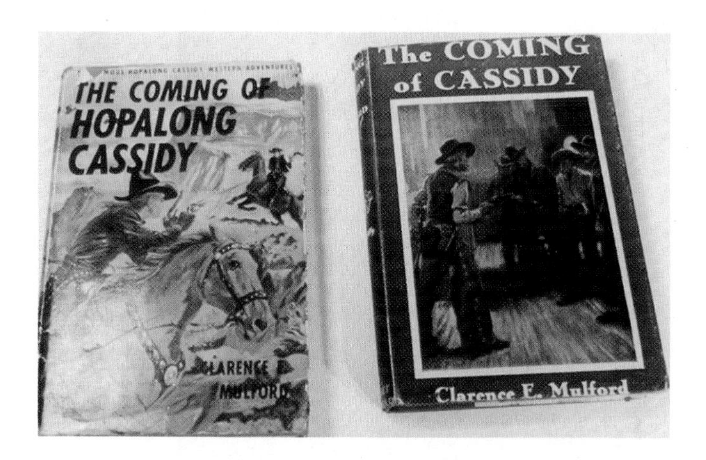

The field of book collecting is very specialized as is that of comic books. While most Hoppy hard cover books written by Mr. Mulford have a general value of $25 to $40 each, first editions and signed first editions are worth substantially more.

Hoppy books came in all sizes and shapes; from pocke soft-cover to "Western" reader and hard cover. You wil note that all were not written by Clarence E. Mulford. Th four shown below (1950-1952) were written by an "un-known" author named "Tex" Burns. The books shown to the left, are in #1 and #2 condition, and the most valuabl of all Hoppy books ever published (with the exception o first or special issues) They were the first four books eve written by Louis L'Amour, the great American writer.

These mint and near mint "Tex" Burns books are from the Pellow/Hoffman collection and have near mint jackets. They are valued between $300 and $450 each.

Published by Bantam Books, Inc., the Hoppy books are back in the saddle with the current release of all four "Tex" Burns books under the author's real name. The fact that Mr. L'Amour wrote the books over fifty years ago, just came to light when his son released this information four years ago. Bantam has been publishing one book a year for the past four years. They are also available in soft cover from major book stores. You may be interested to note that the first book re-published; "Trail to Seven Pines" spent six weeks on the New York best sellers list.

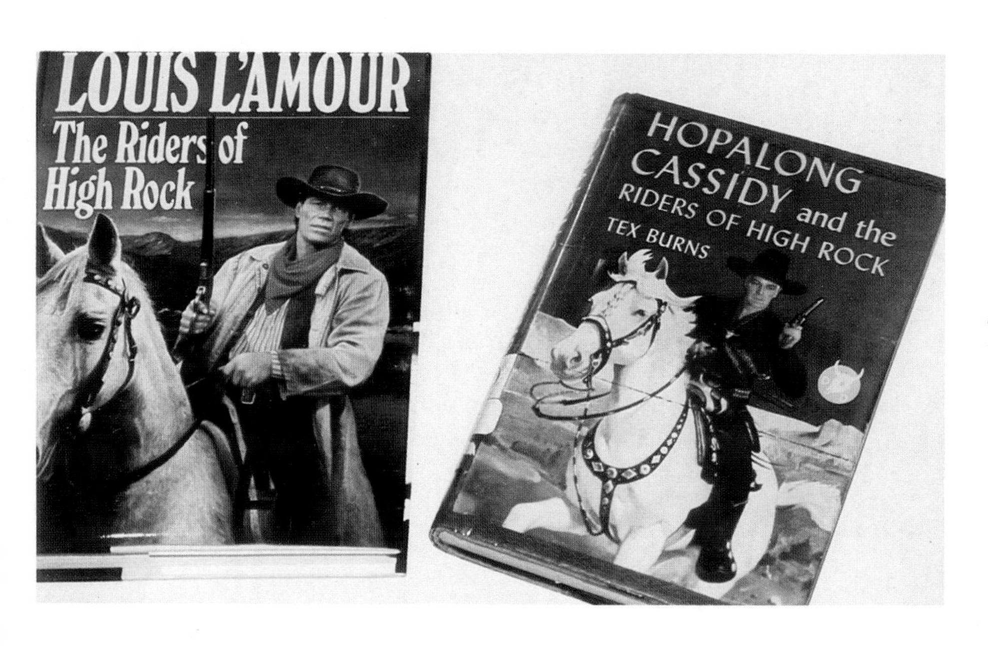

The two books (L) are the same title, but were published forty years apart. The "Tex" Burns version shows our Hoppy on the jacket, the 1995 version is under the author's real name.

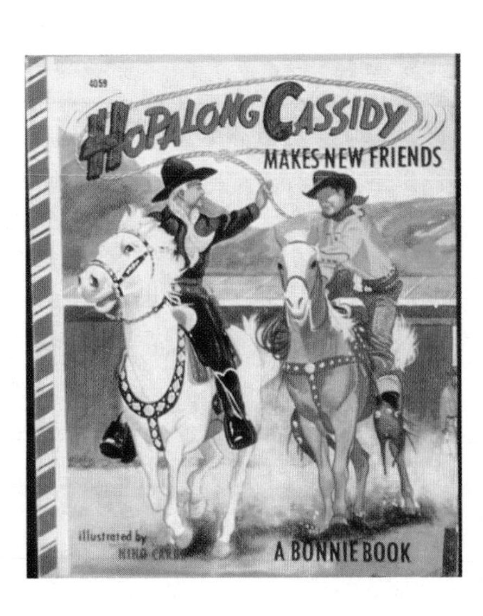

Bill Boyd, recognizing that he had become a childrens' hero, had a wide selection of books designed and written for his audience - six to twelve year old children. Produced in the 1950's, some were straight readers, some had "pop-up" scenes, and some were "TV viewers" where scenes actually moved. Books of this sort are surprisingly available at reasonable prices; from $75 for a #1. "TV" book or "pop-up" book and $55 for a plain reader. The large "pop-up" at bottom of page is an English version. From The Jon Cheek collection.

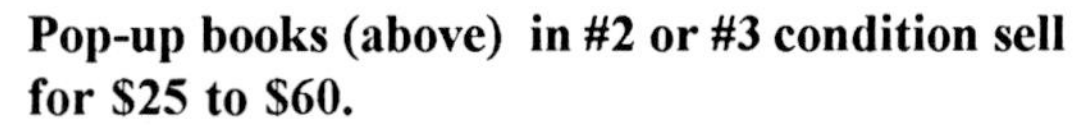

Pop-up books (above) in #2 or #3 condition sell for $25 to $60.

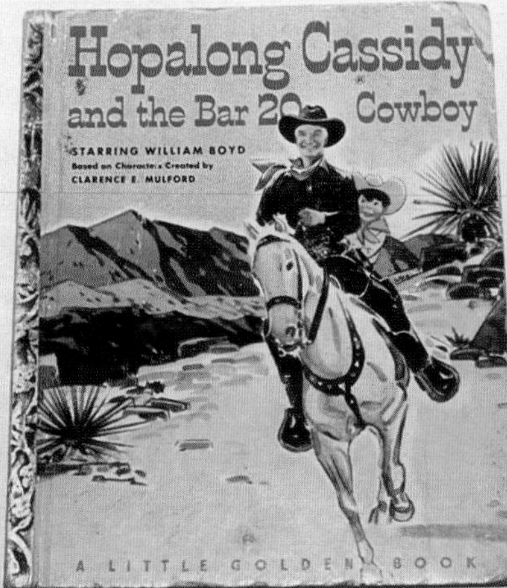

Golden Books (R) are "readers" and sell for $25 - $55.

Rare English "jumping" book: #1. $130 #2. $100 #3. $85

The two Bonnie Books shown above are different versions of the same story; "Young Friend Danny." The left book is a plain reader, the one on the right is a "TV" viewer with moving scenes. Interestingly, the "Danny" reader shown is quite rare and valued at the same price as the "TV" viewer: #1. $75 #2. $60 #3. $50. The "Lucky at Copper Gulch" book (L) is a large version "TV" viewer and is valued the same as the large "Double X Ranch" which is a pop-up book: #1. $140 #2. $120 #3. $110. The "Hoppy & Lucky" book is a large reader only: #1. $110 #2. $100 #3. $80.

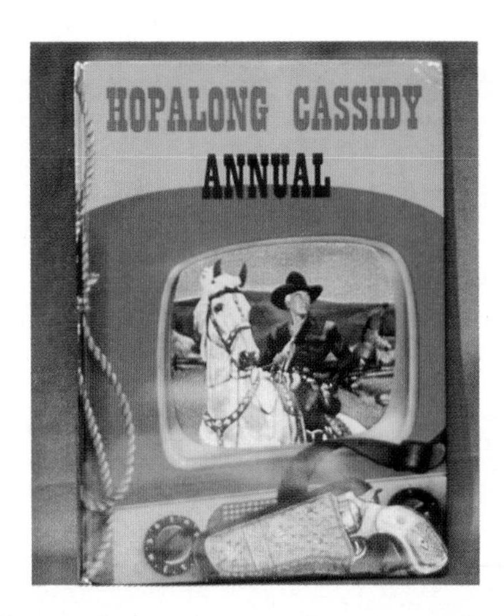

While the Cole Bros. circus program is not exactly a book per se, I felt it should be listed here, rather than in "promotions." Hoppy owned a goodly part of the Cole Bros. circus and often appeared without notice (I know, that's where I met him). The Hoppy cover for Cole Bros. circus is very rare: #1. $225 #2. $200 #3. $175. From the Jan & Bill Hoffman collection.

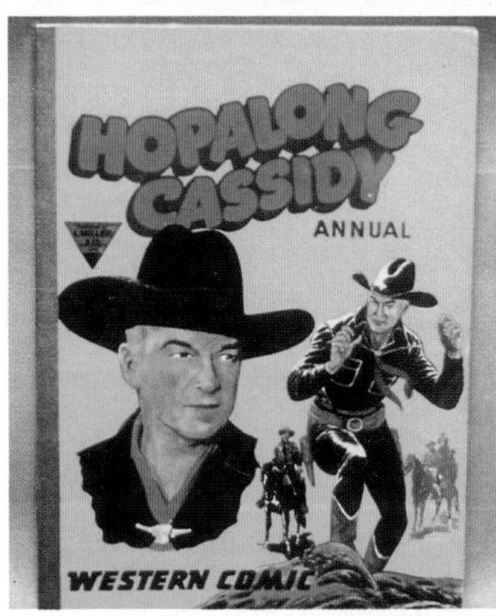

The Annual above, is a Hoppy western comic hard cover from England. It has a 30% higher value than "standard" England annuals. From the Frank Smith collection.

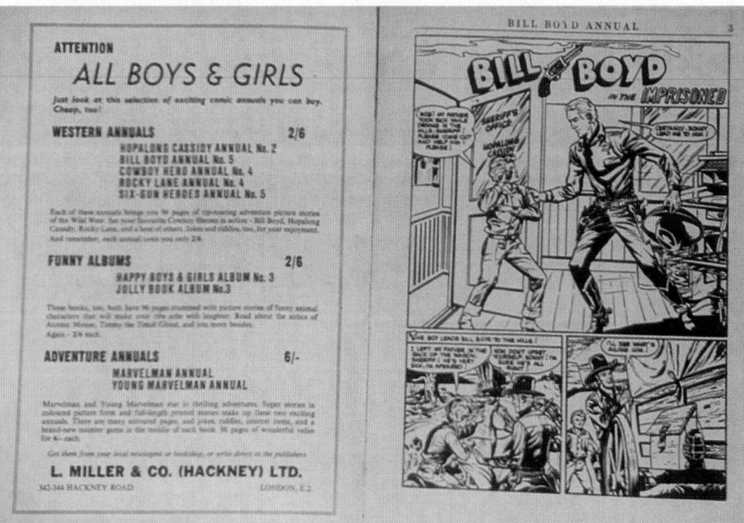

The UK loved Hoppy nearly as much as we did. He are several of L.Miller LTD published Hoppy bool #1, #2, #3, as well as the "Annual." Most had gre graphics. #1. $125 #2. $110 #3. $100. From the Jon Charlie Cheek collection.

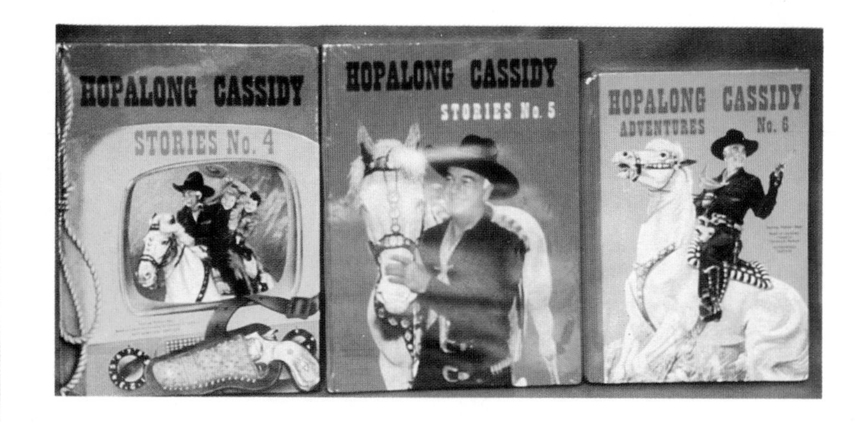

The above UK Hoppy books indicate there were at least six different volumes written in addition to the "Annuals" which came out once a year. From the Jon & Charlie Cheek collection.

Shown on the left are a combination reader-comic book, and in some cases a coloring book too! They are about 4x4" and very collectible. I think there are 12 books in the complete set: #1.$45 #2. $30 #3. $20. (coloring books have similar values)

The two display versions below are from Ted Hake's Americana auctions. Thanks Ted.

HOPALONG CASSIDY Trouble Shooter A COLORING BOOK Starring William Boyd — WILLIAM BOYD and Little Tex, STAR OF Hopalong Cassidy

THE BAR 20 NEWS

The Official William Boyd Fan Club Publication

HONORARY PRESIDENT..........................William Boyd
8901 Wilshire Blvd.
Beverly Hills, Calif.

ACTIVE PRESIDENT..........................Joan Breyer
R. D. 13, Box 665
Akron 19, Ohio

VICE-PRESIDENT..........................Dorothy Reinhart
R. D. #6, Lydius St.
Schenectady, New York

SECRETARY..........................Barbara Wicks
15 Clayton Street
Schenectady, New York

JOURNAL EDITOR..........................Dorothy Reinhart
R. D. #6, Lydius St.
Schenectady, New York

HONORARY MEMBERS

Grace Boyd	Ron Hagerthy	Joan Vohs
Robert Stabler	Bing Crosby	Joan Evans
Madoline Mahoney	Robert Mitchum	Ralph David Parrow

ARE:

istered with Movie Magazine
istered with Movie Fan Magazine
istered with Movie Stars Parade Magazine

1. No. 1

Pictured above, is the first issue of the "Bar-20 News which was the official Hoppy fan club publication. Th first issue shows a list of honorary members whic include a few noteworthy listings: Bing Crosby an Robert Mitchum. The Valentine issue (lower left) wa published in February, 1954. They are very collectible, you can find them! #1. $75 #2. $60 #3. $50

HOPALONG VISITS CREATOR in Maine and gets an awed welcome from author's grandson, Bruce Perkins, 8. Mulford is warming to Boyd these days.

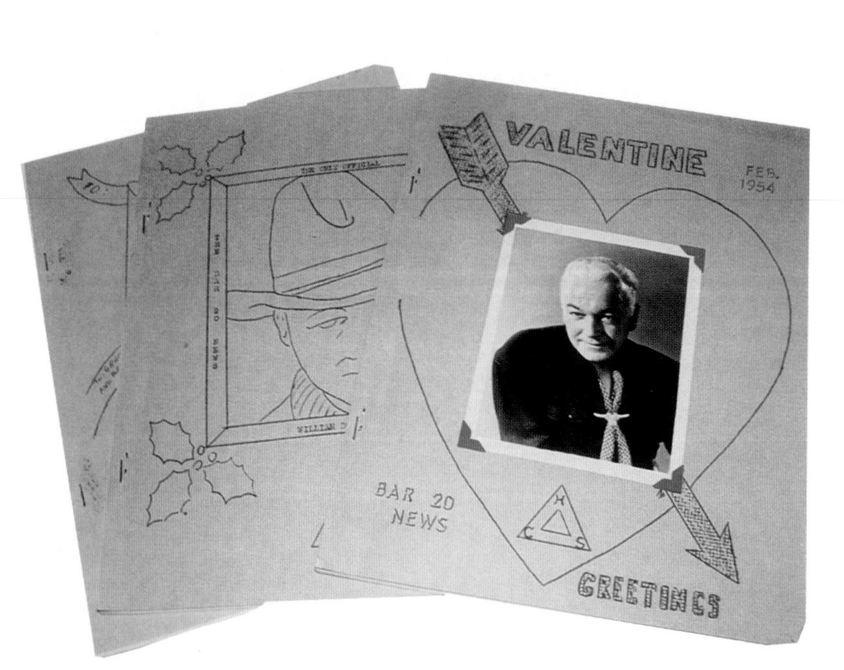

The photo shown above was taken in 1949 when B went to Fryberg, Maine to negotiate the remaini "rights" to the Hoppy name. Bruce Perkins, Mulford grandson, is the lad next to Bill. Hoppy broug young Bruce a personal Hoppy outfit. Bill broug Mulford the oil painting of "Hoppy" shown on t cover of this book.

BIKES & TRIKES

#1. condition: mint, showing no use #2. condition: excellent to near mint #3. condition: good to very good

Owning a Hoppy bike or trike always made you feel special, whether you were four years old and could only handle a trike (velocipede) or ten, and rode a twenty-inch two wheeler . . . or are forty and a collector of the "Cadillac" of 1950's bicycles and trikes... The Hoppy Rollfast! Rare to find and expensive to buy . . . they are worth finding even in the worst condition imaginable. We are proud to bring together for the first time anywhere, all the bikes and trikes made by Rollfast that bore the Hoppy name and unique design. Don't be too shocked when you see the values of these little beauties. They cost over a weeks pay in the 1950's and haven't gotten any cheaper over the years. RIDE 'EM COWBOY!

Unique Hoppy bicycle store sign is in some cases, more rare than the bikes themselves! This nearly three-foot long colorful paper sign is a treasure in itself. Investment value is in the $1,200 area. From the Jon & Charlie Cheek collection. The Hoppy Rollfast insignia (L) was mounted on the front frame member of all the bikes.

The trike (R) is a 16" version similar (but not in the same condition) as the photo (L) in the bike ad. This trike sold for $800 in "restorable" condition. A restored photo of this bike is on the next page.

The above photos are before and after restoration of the same 12" trike. Thought by many to be the rarest of all Hoppy bikes/trikes. Shown on the left in original restorable condition (purchased at $1,400). Four months of painstaking, detailed work resulted in a wonderful restoration down to the smallest detail. The current value of a restored 12" trike is between $4,000 and $4,500 depending on restoration exactness. A mint, original 12" is worth over $6,000. (with original tool kit mounted on back of seat - not shown here).

Detail photo showing some key elements necessary for an acceptable restoration. The paint is four coats of acrylic enamel, color sanded and hand-rubbed to a very high points luster. Chrome was triple plated, decals were reproduced, wheel spokes were cad triple plated. Note: original back wheel tires for this 12" trike are nearly impossible to find.

This is the restored 16" trike shown on the previous page. Some difference! A professional restoration would cost $1,200 bringing the cost of this restored trike to $2,000, which relates to these values: #1. $3,000 #2. $2,500 #3. $2,200. In original condition these values would represent a 40% increase. From the Lee & Sharon Mitchell collection

What, no stirrups?

This well-groomed bike, being apple-eyed by the official Hopalong Cassidy (Bill Boyd) and the bike's manufacturer, is more royalty-producing evidence of TV's part in the current western craze among U.S. spratlings. After nursing the mania for several months with Hopalong movies shown on TV, last spring Bill Boyd licensed twenty-odd manufacturers to make Hopalong shirts, jeans, boots, guns, etc. The results were stunning: Boyd's department-store appearances often drew thirty to fifty thousand youngsters; and some $5 million worth of Hopalong items sold by Christmas yielded Hopalong Cassidy Enterprises about 5 per cent royalty, which Boyd shares with Clarence Mulford, creator of the limping cowboy. H. C. Enterprises forecasts 1950 sales of an improbable $50 million; but if Hopalong, the kids, and TV can all take it, who is to say?

The plain looking Hoppy bike pictured above, is an unrestored 16" "sidewalk cruiser" version that is complete except it is missing the one-gun holster set that was attached to the top cross bar. In good original condition (as shown) it is valued at $1,600. Restored condition would be: $2,800 and mint, original, $3,500. From the Steve Castelli collection. A note to potential bike restorer's - the seat is the key. If you find a Hoppy bike with the original seat in good condition, it is worth restoring. To date, the special seat material for the Hoppy bike is not available.

ews article with Bill Boyd and president of Rollfast icycles admiring what looks to be the first 20" full dress oy's bike off the production line. Bike sizes by the way, are easurements of the wheel/tire size: a 12" trike has a 12" ont tire, a 16" bike, 20," 24," 26" sizes are taken from re dimensions. From the Gene Douglass collection.

The Bicycle Journal magazine featured the Hoppy bike on the cover of the May, 1950 issue. The bike, while very expensive,was an immediate hit! A copy of the magazine is worth $125 to collectors' today.

Three issues of the Bicycle Journal make great claims about the "all new" Hoppy bike line. Bicycle Journal magazines can be found for $60 to $125 each depending on condition. From the Jon & Charlie Cheek collection.

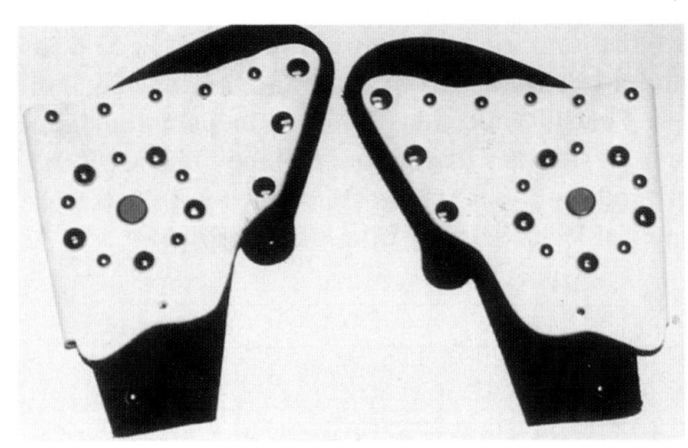

The above, are reproduced holsters for the boys'/girls' 20," and 24" bikes. They are very nicely done and available for under $100 a pair.

Photo of the unusual chain- guard and Hoppy decal on the 16" bicycle. Not much identified the bike as a "Hoppy" except for the small chain-guard decal and the holstered Schmidt gun. (not shown) From the Steve Castelli collection.

Bike pictured on left is a 20" girl's in original condition, including tires, holsters and fringe on back rack. Overall condition is between a #2 and #3. (guns were added) Value of this bicycle is $3,800. Note: the boys' bikes are always worth more than the girls.' There are fewer around in recognizable condition.

ove girl's bike is an older 24" restored version that remains in very good dition. Girls' bikes maintain a lower value that boys' bikes principally ause they were better cared for and seldom stripped. The above bike in #2. dition is valued at $3,500 without the set of Schmidt cap guns. The George hmidt, Co. made Hoppy holster gun sets, and except for two special guns, all re used in the Hoppy bikes, including "Buck'n Bronc" and those marked opalong Cassidy."

Full size theatre poster offers a free Hoppy bike give-away every Friday. Unframed poster is valued at $225. Several Hoppy contests also gave bikes as main prizes.

0" boy's bike was restored to "full dress" condition cluding saddle bags, hand-grip streamers, chrome axle aps and leather fringe on back fender support. Notice that e ornate chain-guard is a little unusual for this model. This ike was offered for sale for $6,000 three years ago (1993) nd has been sold at a confidential price. From the Corky eigh collection.

This is the rare 26" boys' Hoppy bike made in the mid-1950's. There are substantial differences between this model and the smaller sizes. Notice that there are no holsters, but a chrome "U" bar on the tank would accept special holsters if wanted. A fully restored boys' bike is valued: #1. $4,500 #2. $3,800 #3. $2,600. If the bike is in "original" condition, add 40% to the "restored" values. From the Charles Ringhel collection.

HOPPY

The bicycle to the right is the 26" version, not nearly as "dressy" as smaller sizes. Notice the chrome spring fork suspension on the front, and the sweep of the cross-bar tank. Both the boys' and girls' 26" version boasted a tank horn. Note the unique black & white original pedals. Bike is in original #3. condition and valued at $3,500. From the John Hirsch collection.

The 26" boys' & girls' bikes came with a very distinctive black & white pedal with a "Hoppy" strap as shown above. These pedals were not used on other sizes. They are sometimes available from classic bicycle collectors and are worth $500 per set.

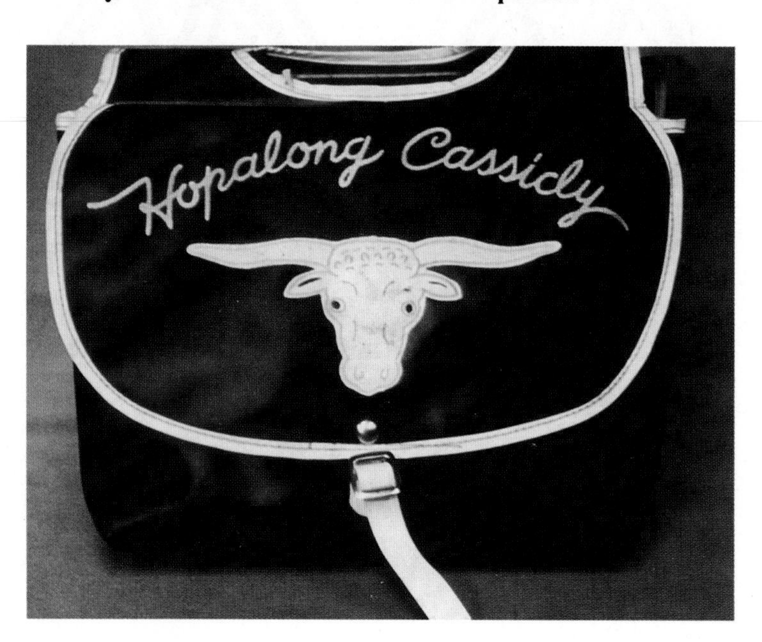

There were several bike "accessories" including the Hoppy horn and a variety of bike saddle bags. Collectors today prize original Hoppy saddle bags like the one shown: #1. $850 #2. $750 #3. $600. From the Jon & Charlie Cheek collection.

Haley Ellis, dressed in traditional Hoppy garb, is riding a 12" Hoppy "velocipede." Children quickly out-grew this small trike. Photo from Phil Ellis.

Dressed in an 1950's era Hoppy girl's outfit, four year old Haley Ellis (granddaughter of Phil Ellis) holds the older, traditional Hoppy bike saddlebags. These very rare bags are valued at: #1. $1,100 #2. $975 #3. $850. From the Phil Ellis collection.

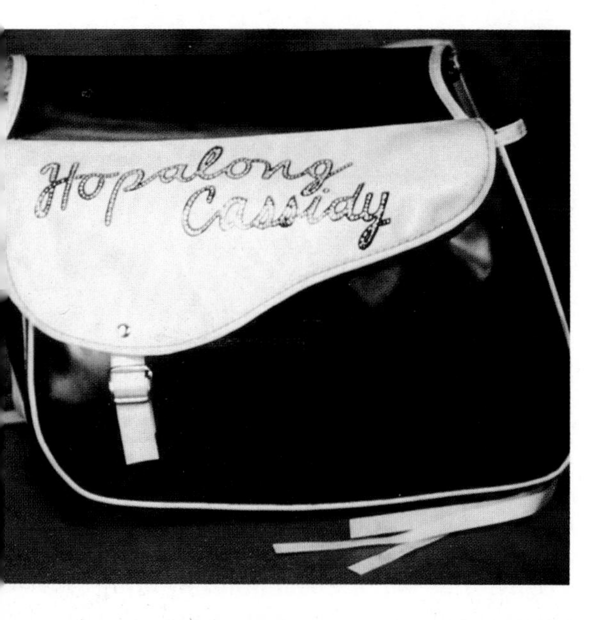

versions of Hoppy saddle bags are hard to find ıding the two-tone design above; #1.$850 #2. $750 $600. There are phoney saddle bags that some try to as original. Some crooks have even installed the ·oduction Hoppy conch to make the bag look real. thing they haven't been able to do is duplicate the py name. So if it doesn't say "Hoppy" on the bag, ıces are its a phoney!

Girls' 26" bike in original #2. condition is valued at $3,800. Original condition values are: #1. $4,400 #2. $3,800 #3. $3,000. Restored bikes would bring 30% less. From the Charles Ringhel collection.

This original tool kit was available and came with both the 12" and 16" trike "velocipedes." While an original tool kit in #1 or #2 condition is worth between $550 - $650, they are being reproduced for a more reasonable $65. From the Jon & Charlie Cheek collection.

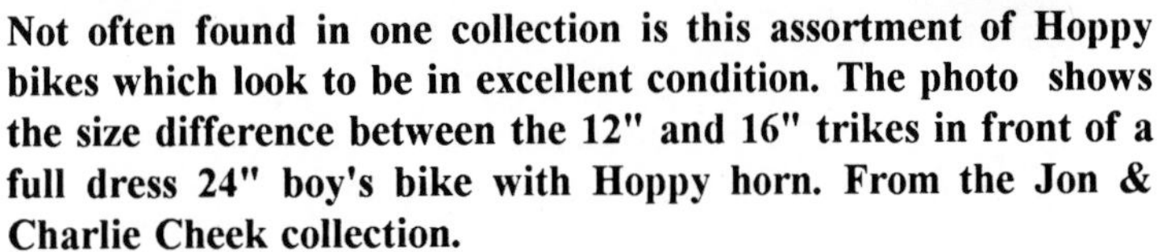

Not often found in one collection is this assortment of Hoppy bikes which look to be in excellent condition. The photo shows the size difference between the 12" and 16" trikes in front of a full dress 24" boy's bike with Hoppy horn. From the Jon & Charlie Cheek collection.

Seeing is believing! Pictured here is the one of a kind Hoppy Harley from California (where else?). It is clearly a "fantasy" item and never was produced, but should have been. It is the most beautiful Art Deco piece of 40's and 50's nostalgia that has been my pleasure to have ever seen. The frame is from a 1949 Schwinn bike, the 3.5 HP engine is a genuine Whizzer from the same era. Does it run? You betcha! The owner did a little peddling and engaged the clutch and it literally roared down the street!

This little black beauty is proudly owned by John Kennedy who has a hobby of building things that go fast. John, who is in his early 50's was a dyed-in-the-wool "Hoppy's kid" when young and never forgot the Man. John is not a Hoppy collector, nor is he a Hoppy Fan. He did this project mainly out of respect for Bill Boyd and what he represented to America's youth. Would he sell it you ask? "Not right yet" would be his reply. If he did, it would probably bring $10,000 from the glassy-eyed collector who wrote this book!

CAMERAS PINS & BADGES

#1. condition: mint, showing no use #2. condition: excellent to near mint #3. condition: good to very good

There were only two types of Hoppy cameras made, and both are in demand by collectors. The Hoppy box camera is an all metal "Brownie" type that takes 120 film, has a top strap and a front metal plate with the images of Hoppy & Topper. The only accessory item was a special flash attachment, sold separately. The camera box is a heavy cardboard and is quite colorful. #1. $550 #2. $475 #3. $350 (without box deduct $250.) The metal flash attachment 'pinned' into the side of the camera: #1. $375 #2. $300 #3. $250. (deduct $150 without box). (Early box cameras did not have pin-holes for flash attachment).

he photo to the right shows another etail of the box camera flash and on the ır right is the small Hoppy camera. his camera had a plastic body and fixed ns and took 35mm film. The camera as not as popular as the box version. he camera had a metal winding knob nd a round metal plate over the lens ont with the Hopalong Cassidy enorsement. #1. $425 #2. $350 #3. $300. leduct $200 without box). Earlier verons of this camera came in a much lainer box which is shown on the followg page.

Hoppy 'field glasses' or binoculars, were very well made and quite useful. The 'barrels' were metal with plastic eyepiece and glass lenses. There were two different versions made, the black (L) and the silver & red (next page). #1. $475 #2. $340 #3. $300 (deduct $200 without box)

The Hoppy camera display (R) shows a small early version of the Hoppy 35mm camera with an almost generic box.

Hoppy field glasses (above) show the different versions available. Note the silver with red eyepiece glasses (bottom left) and the oldest version in the center. Some glasses came with one decal, some with two. The most unusual decal graphic is the single decal bust of Hoppy on the top left. The silver & red glasses are quite rare and collectors pay $100 more for them than the black. The single bust version would rate the same value in my opinion. From the Jon & Charlie Cheek collection.

There were literally hundreds of different Hoppy pins produced in the 1950's. The three shown above were special 'premium' pins that were attached to a ribbon which contained a western charm. Note that the pin itself is the same. 'Premium' pins seem to have the same value: #1. $125 #2. $85 #3. $65. Authentic pins alone are: #1. $45 #2. $30 #3. $25 each.

Rare glasses & case (L) features silver & red binoculars and generic leather case. An investment value item, it may be worth over $1,000 in #1 condition. Jon Cheek collection

Display of three different pins (red green, blue) used as 'premium' pins. Collectors value both red and blue pins $5 to $10 more than the green.

e above two pins are from newspaper motions and are generally valued at $75 $125. The fold-over badges (right photo, tom row) are premium items from Burs Cookies (there were 12 to the set) They y in value from $30 to $45 each. The nt badges (center row) were made from stic or metal and bore Hoppy's name, ge or photo. They range in value from to $125. From the Jon & Charlie eek collection.

hown above are the Savings Club badges (L) and a wide selection of premium nd promotion pins by row. The larger photo pins are valued at $75 (top row) vith the exception of the two white promo pins which are "Daily" $65. and Boston" which is $85. Photo pins on the 2nd. row are $50 to $65 each. The third ow contains 'standard' photo pins and promo pins valued at $40 to $55. The next ow contains yellow, dairy promotion pins which are quite hard to find. They are alued at $50 to $65 while the row of small red 'Hoppy head' pins on the bottom ow are very rare, they will also sell for $50 to $65 each. The Savings Club pins vill be detailed on the following page. From the Jon & Charlie Cheek collection.

The glassine envelope (above) contains a 3" white Hoppy savings club badge that is a reproduction item. It is selling for $20 to $25. The two lower badges are original and shown for size.

Detail photo of Bread promo Hoppy pin with bent tab. Valued at $40.

The Andy Clyde (California Carlson) pin is a nice collector find. They are valued at $45 each. From the Mike Forthun collection.

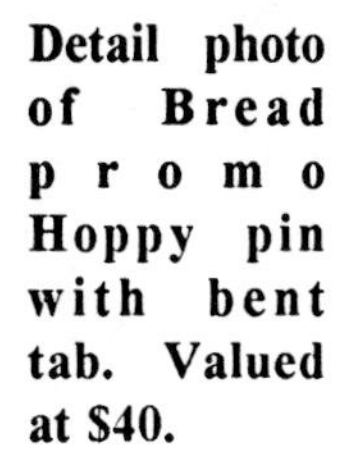

Authentic Hoppy Savings Club pins are both rare and valuable assets. Made from tin-litho, the smaller pins were given to savers depending on amount of money deposited or saved: 'Tenderfoot,' 'Wrangler,' 'Bulldogger,' 'Bronc Buster,' were awarded for lower amounts and are valued at: $20 to $25. 'Trail Boss' has a higher value of $35 and the small 'Straw Boss' pin (left photo- white star on silver background) is $350. Note in the photo above, this pin is much larger than the more common pins. It is valued at: $250 (the smaller version is much more rare). The gold on gold 'Foreman' pin has been selling for $500. The large white 3" pin (top of photo on left) was worn by bank tellers only and is quite rare. It has maintained a value of: $125. From the Jon & Charlie Cheek collection. The complete savings set in the top photo that has the original pins, promo cards, envelopes and letters is valued at $1,000.

Above is the complete set of 12 Post cereals tab badges. You can see that only a few can be easily identified with Hoppy's name or image. In mint condition, with unbent tabs they are worth an average of $45 each. From the Bill Hoffman collection.

Detail photo of Post tab badges, which were free premium items in many Post cereals. Also shown is tab bread promotion badge.

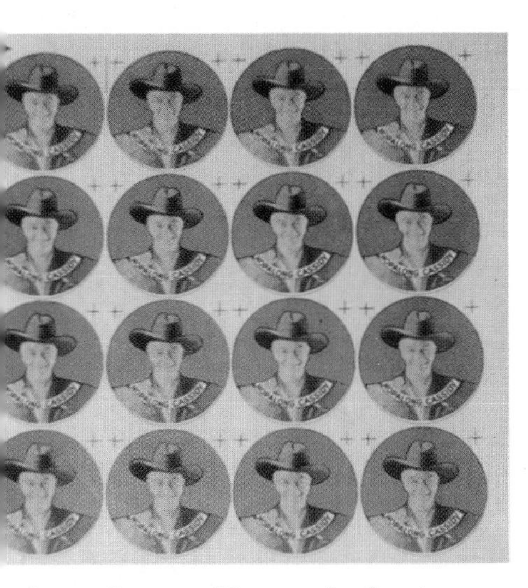

sheet of green Hoppy pin fronts was to produce the original celluloid pins. It be a one of a kind collector's piece. le nearly impossible to value, it may g $300 at an auction. From the Mike hun collection.

The above detail photos are of promotion dairy and bread products endorsed by Hoppy. They are celluloid pins (red bread pins are celluloid - yellow dairy pins are tin litho) and show a wide variety of sponsors. Yellow dairy pins are: #1. $65 #2. $55 #3. $50 The red bread endorsement pins are: #1. $70 #2. $60 #3. $55.

Mike Pellow sent in this fine photo of a display of Savings Club pins along with a gold-capped Hoppy wallet. Please note the size of the 'Foreman' pin to the silver 'Straw Boss' pin. In the complete set on the previous page, they are both the same size. One Savings Club item rarely seen is the "penny-coin" given by banks to new members. See "Miscellaneous" chapter for a photo of this rare piece.

While this etched "Hoppy" boot-pin seems real enough, it is a phoney as well as the card. Do not pay more than $5. for it if you feel you must buy it.

This Hoppy pin is from the 1991 Lone Pine Hoppy Film Festival in California. It is very striking and well made, and a good value at $25.

Detail photo of embossed six-point Hoppy badges. These items originally came on a card (see photo below). On the card they are $75 - without card the value is $ $45.

Detail of the photo-badge mounted on store display card (R). These badges are made in England but there are plenty around the US. $85. in #1. condition.

An excellent store display piece of 12 badg (made in England) a few of these cards are in th country and are valued at $1,200 (which is n much more than the value of the badges)

Embossed Hoppy image badge on card is shown with solid brass 'Sheriff' badge (L) and color photo badge.

Hoppy gun & holster charm (R) is a rare find. Gun can be removed from vinyl holster. Item is valued at $140. From the Jon & Charlie Cheek collection.

Solid brass badge in the photo on the left is valued at $75. The six-point color image badge is valued at $110. Both in #1. condition.

Display of card mounted charms, badges and special Hoppy pins are shown here, with values and other details found in the 'Jewelry' chapter.

CLOTHING
BELTS & WALLETS

#1. condition: mint, showing no use #2. condition: excellent to near mint #3. condition: good to very good

This chapter contains general Hoppy clothes and accessories. Hoppy outfits, both girls' and boys', will be found in the "Guns & Outfits" chapter.

Hoppy "winter wear" includes this plaid lined, soft fabric jacket with spaced fabric fringe. Jacket front has two slash pockets and Hoppy & Topper patch over left breast. This zipper-jacket is quite rare: #1. $475. #2. $400 #3. $350. From the Porter Albin collection.

Winter fashion would not be complete without Hoppy ear muffs. Shown above, are three different colored sets; blue, black and red. Each side has a smiling Hoppy image. #1. $450 #2. $375 #3. $300 (deduct $200 if no box). From the Jon & Charlie Cheek collection.

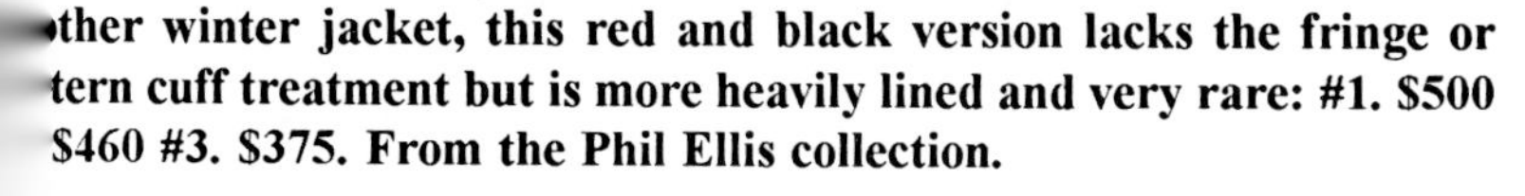

ther winter jacket, this red and black version lacks the fringe or tern cuff treatment but is more heavily lined and very rare: #1. $500 $460 #3. $375. From the Phil Ellis collection.

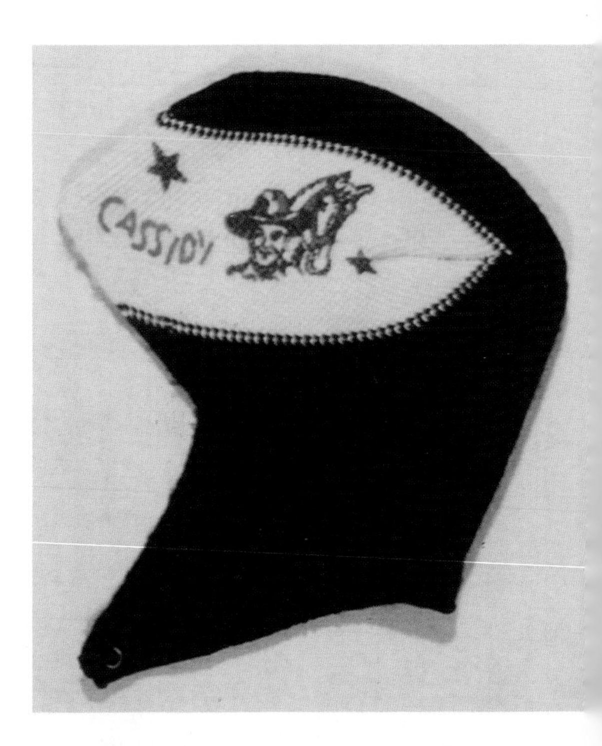

Similar in design to the red & black jacket on the previous page, this all fabric version has fringe and plaid lining. #1. $500 #2. $460 #3. $375. From the Ron Pieczkowski collection. The jacket below is a denim type from Blue Bell, and has Hoppy image steel buttons & snaps. The graphic on back was only used on a few denim jackets. #1. $385 #2. $320 #3. $ 280.

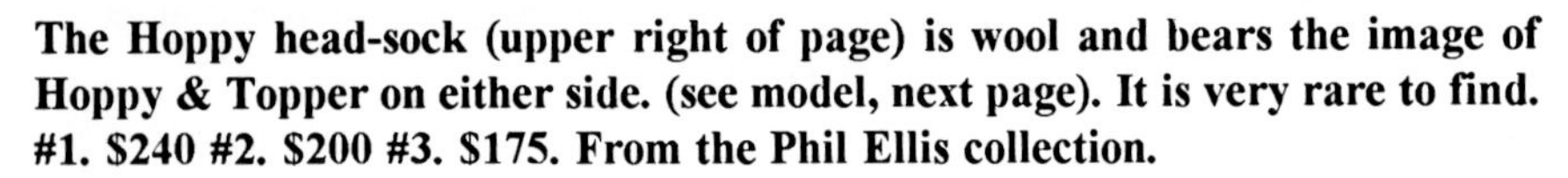

The Hoppy head-sock (upper right of page) is wool and bears the image of Hoppy & Topper on either side. (see model, next page). It is very rare to find. #1. $240 #2. $200 #3. $175. From the Phil Ellis collection.

Hoppy T-shirt box (R) came with a variety of shirts. Each shirt had a colorful image of Hoppy and Topper. #1. $450 #2. $400 #3. $350. Shirts alone are worth $100-$135. From the Jon & Charlie Cheek collection

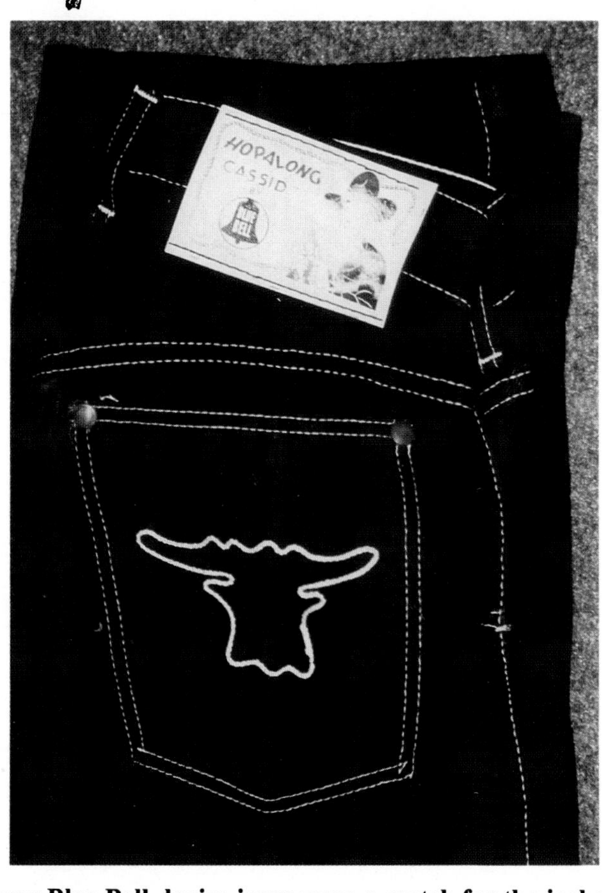

ppy Blue Bell denim jeans were a match for the jacket on previous page. They also had Hoppy buttons. #1. $240 #2. 00 #3. $175.

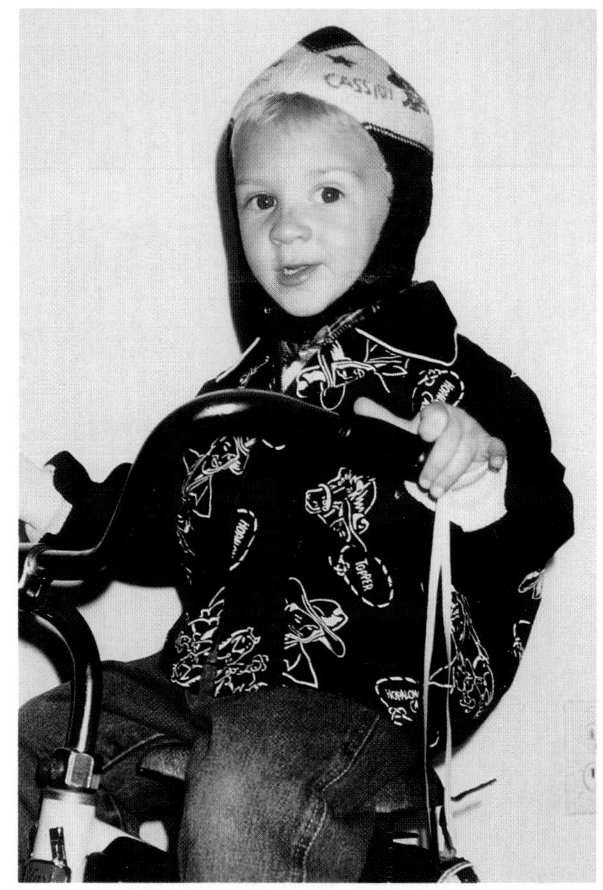

Master Cody Ellis (grandson of Phil Ellis) models the Hoppy head sock and black Hoppy shirt-jacket while riding a Hoppy trike. Shirt-jacket: #1. $260 #2. $225 #3. $200.

ther version of a Hoppy sweat shirt. Similar graphics were l on T-shirts as well. Sweat shirts: #1. $175 #2. $130 #3. $100

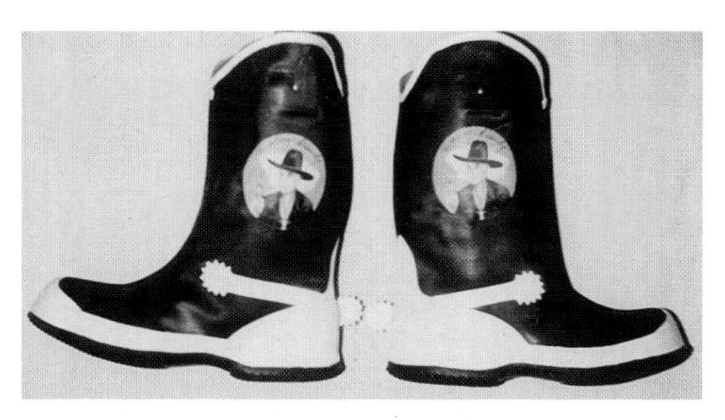

Rubber Hoppy slip-on boots are a nice winter item. Notice rubber spurs and color Hoppy image on each. #1. $850 #2. $700 #3. $600. (deduct $400. without box) From the Phil Ellis collection.

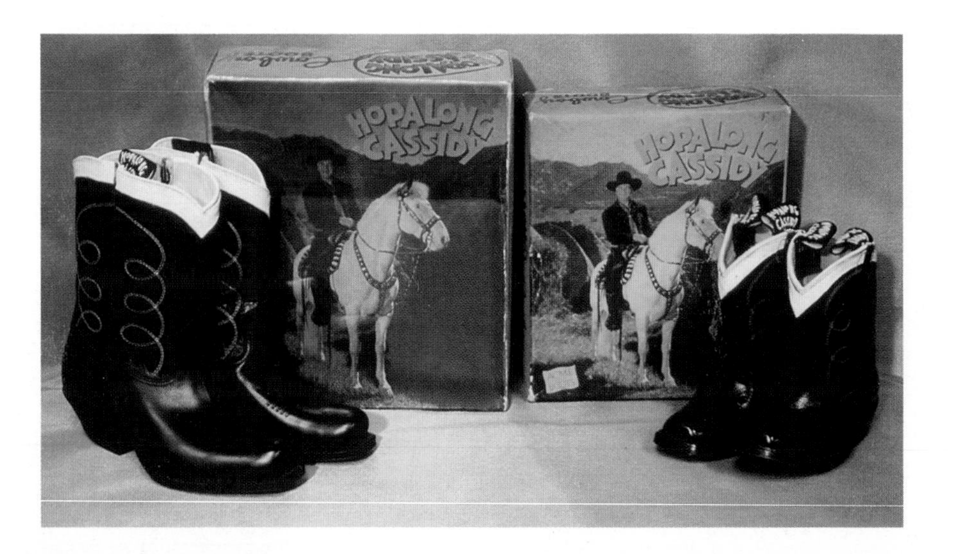

Two versions of the Acme Hoppy leather cowboy boots are shown in black and brown. There were several different designs. The only way you can tell a Hoppy Acme from others is by the elastic pull-tabs on either side, which are marked accordingly. The above boot sets and boxes are from the Jon & Charlie Cheek collection, the brown (L) is from Steve Axelson. #1. $600 #2. $525 #3. $450 (deduct $250 if no box)

Two versions of the popular Hoppy T-shirts show very different graphic designs. T-shirts also came in a variety of colors. #1. $135 #2. $100 #3. $75. From the Mike Merryman collection.

The Hoppy cardigan (button front) is perhaps the rarest of the Hoppy sweaters. It also has a different design than pullovers. #1. $345 #2. $300 #3. $260.

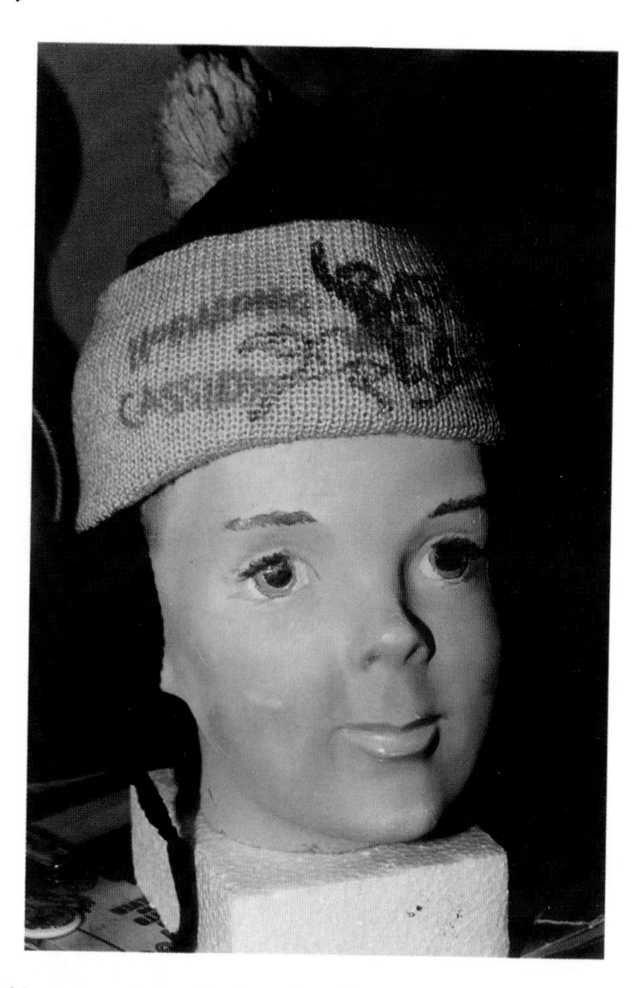

Above manikin displays the Hoppy wool cap with ear protectors. Hoppy can be seen riding Topper across the front. #1. $300 #2. $260 #3. $195.

Photo from Brian Beirne collection

Blue pullover long sleeve Barclay sweater shows image of Hoppy on front and Topper on back. Sweaters came in blue, brown, tan and grey. Sweaters came with the Barclay's Hoppy sticker (L) #1. $ 285 #2. $235 #3. $180 (add $35 with Barclay's sticker) From the Steve Axelson collection.

The above photo shows the back of the rare Hoppy cardigan sweater shown on a previous page. Notice the difference in the Hoppy image and name placement. From the Ted Hake Americana auction.

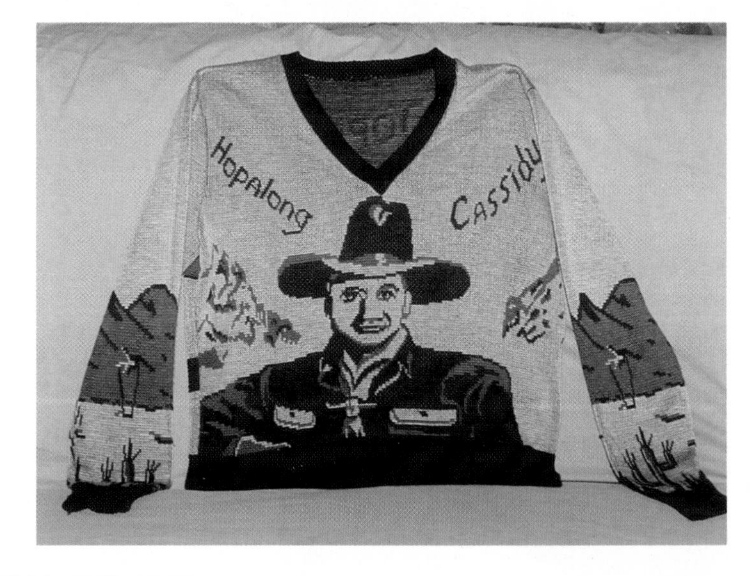

The Hoppy sweater from the Mike Merryman collection (above) is called a "v" neck pullover and is the most common style available. The short-sleeve sweaters however, are crew neck and came with two different graphic styles. The one shown (upper left) is a black and red two color with a wider neck band than the (lower left) one color version. To my knowledge, both carry similar values: #1. $300 #2. $265 #3. $200. From the Porter Albin collection.

Note: there are reproduction sweaters with similar design. Some with reproduction price tags.

The Hoppy sweater shown on the right is from a 1953 Wards catalog and shows a crew neck sweater with completely different graphics and name placement. To my knowledge, it was a prototype graphic that never was a production piece. According to the catalog, it cost $3.98 and came in black (?) brown and navy colors. It had Topper pictured on the back.

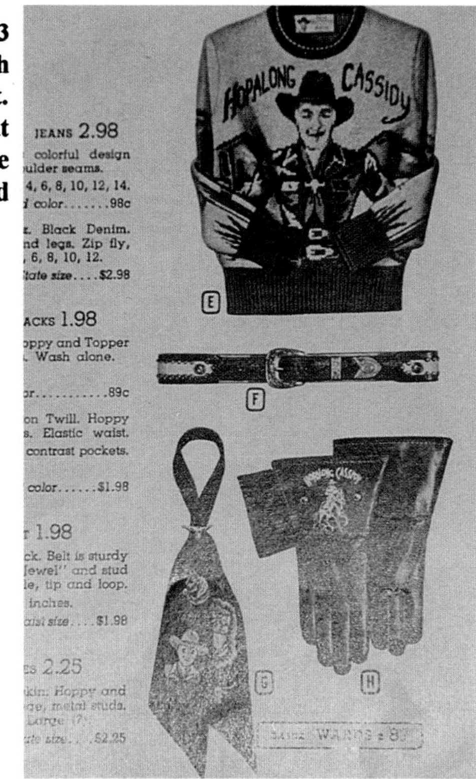

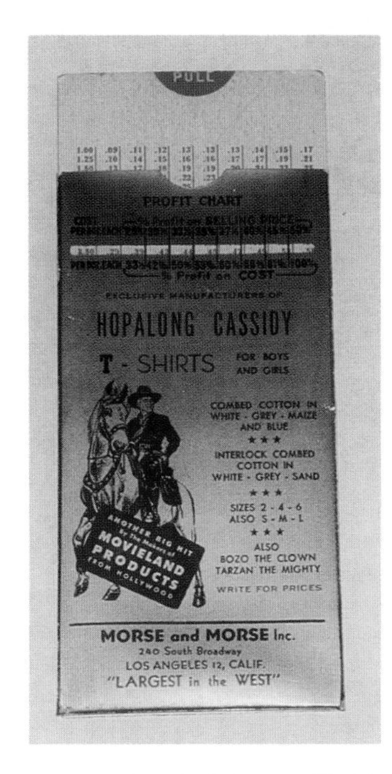

A promotional Hoppy T-shirt profit chart calculator (above) was sent to many stores to show the profit available for carrying Hoppy shirts. This unique promotional item is valued at $75 -$100. From the Brian Beirne collection.

ppy boy's red & white striped socks in ginal bag is a wonderfully rare find. I ld classify this as an investment item with alue of $350 to $450. From the Jon and rlie Cheek collection.

Color ad for Hoppy socks (below left) and slipper socks showing the red & white version for sale at 39 cents a pair.

Any collector would welcome this Hoppy socks box into their collection even though someone has written on this near mint store box in grease pencil. Box alone is worth between $250 and $400 depending on condition. From the Sharon Delaney collection.

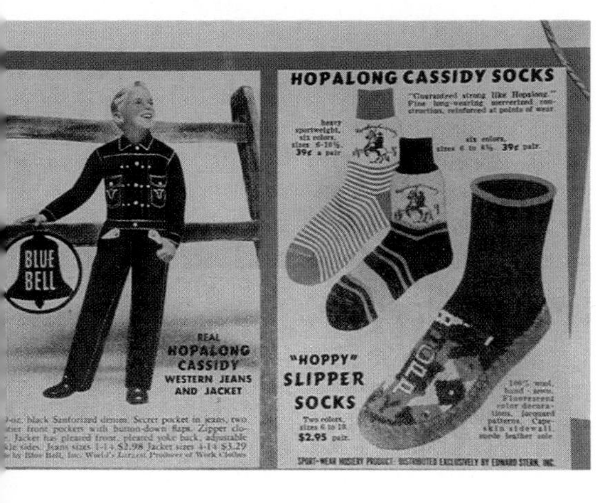

Colorful Hoppy sports shirt for kids displayed color western scenes as well as Hoppy & Topper. Shirt had elastic arm openings and waist. #1. $210 #2. $175 #3. $135. From the Mike Merryman collection.

From the Wards catalog, children models display Hoppy wear. Boy at right is wearing a Hoppy sweat shirt which carried a 98 cent price in 1952. The same sweat shirt today, is worth over $200.

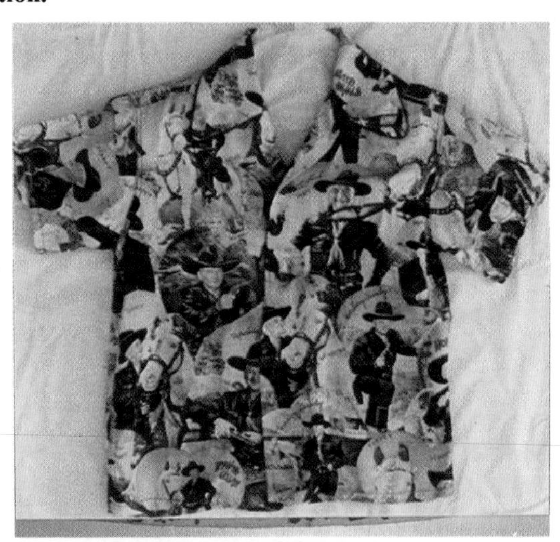

This blue Hoppy graphic short sleeve shirt carries multi action scenes of Hoppy & Topper. It is quite rare. #1. $220 #2. $185 #3. $150. From the Ron Pieczkowski collection.

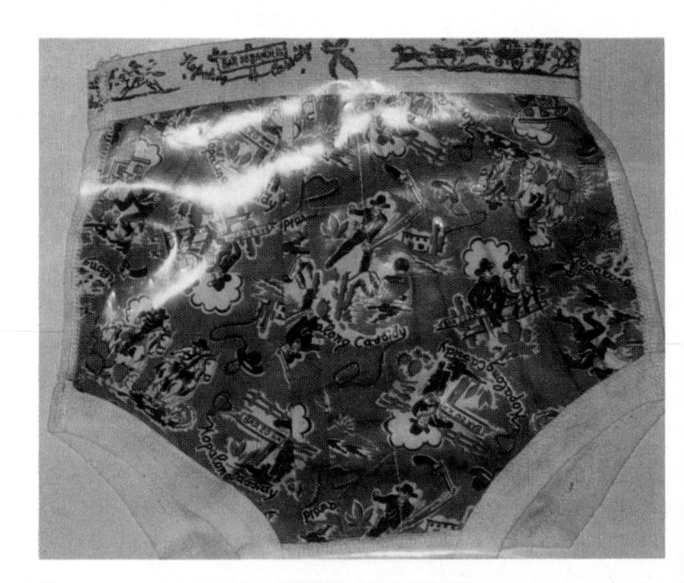

There were two types of Hoppy undershorts made; (jockey type and boxer shorts) both types are very hard to find. #1. $250 #2. $200 #3. $165. From the Phil Ellis collection.

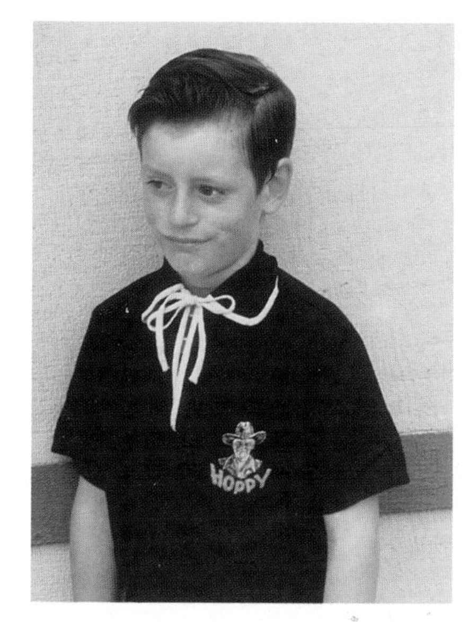

The charming model on the right is Kristia Abramson, who is modeling a very ornate Hoppy fringed shirt with cuff and shoulder area reflective garnish. It is a very rare clothing piece. #1. $275 #2. $235 #3. $200. Her brother, Ian Abramson (L) does not seem to be very pleased to be sporting the popular Hoppy short sleeve slip-over western shirt. If he knew that it was worth $150 in #1. condition, he may have been a lot more interested. Our thanks to John Abramson for the son and daughter model photos.

This attractive two-tone western shirt (above) is typical of the quality and design of Hoppy clothing. #1. $165 #2. $120 #3. $85.

A very rare and controversial clothing item is the Hoppy overalls. The pair on the left bear a Wards label inside, and is thought to be a special Wards only product. #1. $375 #2. $320 #3. $ 280. From the Bill Larzelere collection.

The Hoppy jewel-fringed, clip-on bow tie shown above is a nice addition to any Hoppy collection. #1. $140 #2. $100 #3. $85. From the Phil Ellis collection.

The two pair of Hoppy elastic waist shorts shown above are very difficult to find these days, as are the Hoppy swimming trunks, which could not be found even for this book. The shorts are: #1. $275 #2. $235 #3. $ 200.

The "standard" Hoppy necktie shown above came in a variety of designs and colors. They are hard to find, but are still a good value. There also is a Hoppy clip-on necktie with similar images. #1. $110 #2. $85 #3. $50 (standard and clip-on neckties)

Red, Hoppy "western" clip-on tie is another variation of clothing accessories offered. #1. $135 #2. $100 #3. $85

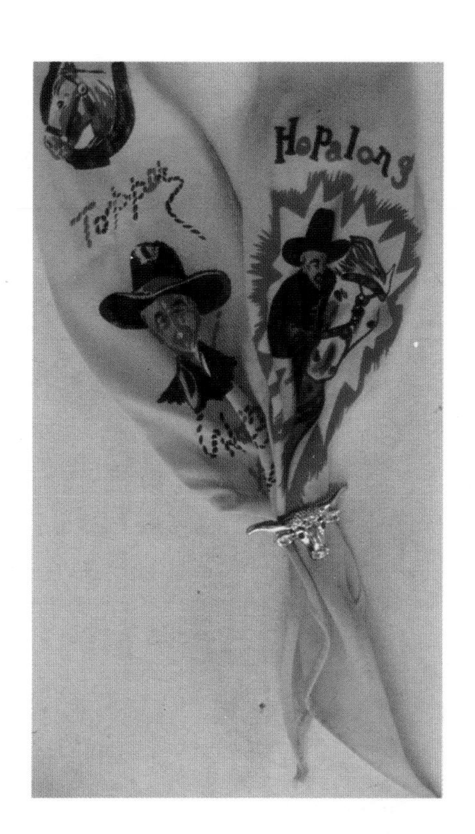

Above yellow, rayon graphic neckerchief and steer-head slider is typical of the many versions produced for Hoppy.

From the Ted Hake collection

on and Charlie Cheek were kind enough to send this reat photo of their Hoppy neckerchief (western scarf) ollection. Both rayon and cotton versions are valued at: 1. $135 #2. $100 #3. $75. (steer head not included)

Note unique steer-head slider

Formal attire silk (rayon) fringed scarf was worn on special occasions. #1. $265 #2. $225 #3. $185. From the Phil Ellis collection.

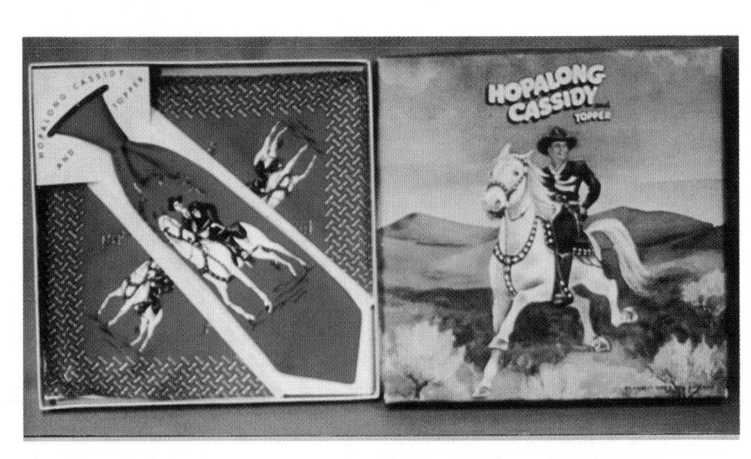

Clip-on necktie (rayon) and matching handkerchief boxed set is a prized collectors piece. #1. $600 #2. $550 #3. $400. From the Jon and Charlie Cheek collection.

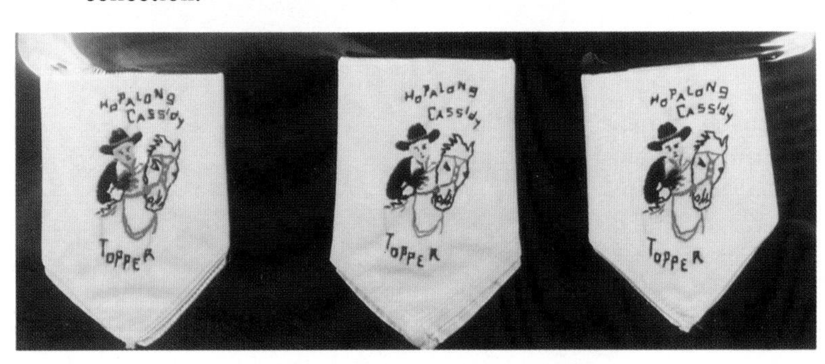

Monogramed Hoppy handkerchiefs came in several styles and graphics. A nice collectors find. #1. $75 #2. $60 #3. $45. (each) From the Jon and Charlie Cheek collection.

Girls could "accessorize" with a Hoppy bow from Burlington Mills, for their hair. Bow came attached to display card. #1. $130 #2. $100 #3. $75. (deduct $ without card)

Rip-off handkerchiefs made today are poor quality for the $20 - $35 price.

View of rayon handkerchief that came with boxed set pictured at top of page.

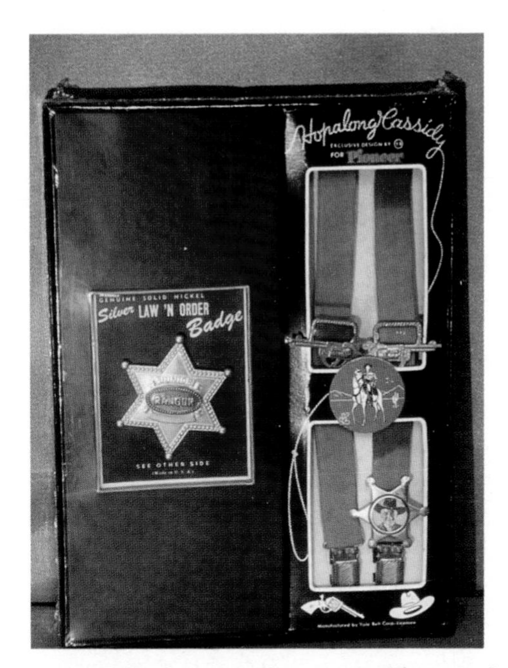

The first boxed suspender set that I've seen, this may be a very early version of the Hoppy suspender sets to follow. Made by the Pioneer Company. Plain brown suspenders had gun mounted "adjusters," A six-point badge w/Hoppy image, a special pin and a solid nickel badge on card. #1. $530 #2. $480 #3. $430. From the Jon and Charlie Cheek collection.

Suspenders on card, is the most common way to find these great items. Brown, plain suspenders have gun "adjusters" and six-point Hoppy pin. Clasps have changed to resemble steer head. #1. $ 400 #2. $325 #3. $270. (Deduct $150 if no card.)

ique die-cut card contains striped suspenders with er head clasps. Set has no pin or badge and no gun ljusters." May have been last version made. #1. '5 #2. $400 #3. $350. Deduct $250 without card. m the Brian Beirne collection.

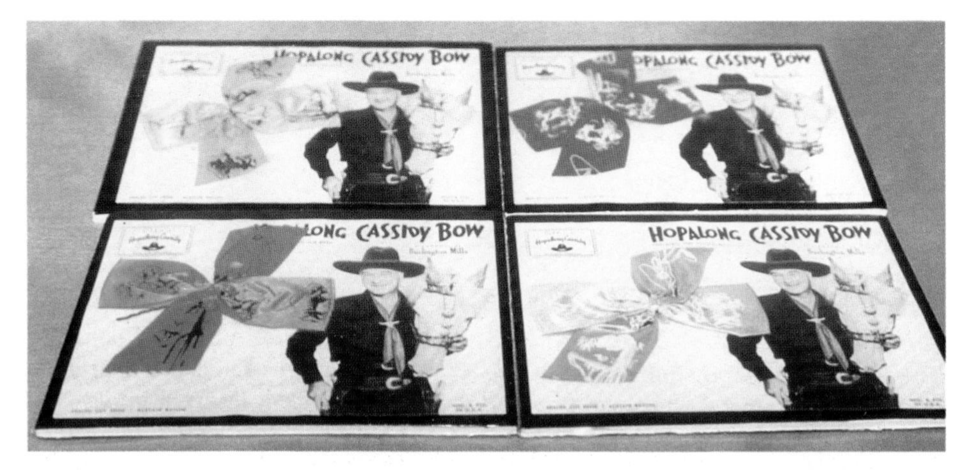

Display of different color Hoppy girls' hair bows. From the Jon & Charlie Cheek collection. Valued at $135 on card.

*another version of die-cut card suspenders will be found at the end of this chapter.

Ornate Hoppy belt (above) is displayed to show metal "Hoppy" attached to leather. A tooled leather belt in similar condition without the display card is: #1. $110 #2. $85 #3. $60.

Loose Hoppy plastic belts (below) are more common than the leather and are obviously cheaper: #1. $95 #2. $60 #3. $45. (Add $100 if card mounted)

The "Trophy" Hoppy belt came in several designs (note abo samples) and was a very popular accessory item. Sold as "switch-a-buckle", it is rare to find them in unused conditio #1. $345 #2. $300 #3. $260. (Deduct $125 without card). Th bottom belt is from the Jon & Charlie Cheek collection.

The above wallet is quite unique due mainly to the metal studs and jewels. Hoppy wallets came in several variations as exhibited in the next few pages. #1. $245 #2. $200 #3. $175 (deduct $100 if no box). from the Charlie Cheek collection.

The gun/holster belt is a popular collector item due to its design. The silv colored, vinyl coated belt had a small metal gun attached to the belt tip whi when buckeled, inserted into a vinyl holster. #1. $385 #2. $340 #3. $300. (Dedu $125 without card) From the Bill Larzelere collection.

Hoppy leather wallet (left) and box by Pioneer Company. Wallet has zipper opening and front and back embossed panels. #1. $245 #2. $200 #3. $175 (Deduct $100 if no box). From the Ron Pieczowski collection.

A different design of the Hoppy leather wallet with zipper closure. Same value as embossed wallet. From the Jon & Charlie Cheek collection.

Below: a detailed view of the "Hopalong Cassidy" embossment.

Very ornate, plastic gold-capped Hoppy wallet (above) came with a gold good luck coin instead of normal silver version. Note metal sawtooth edge design.

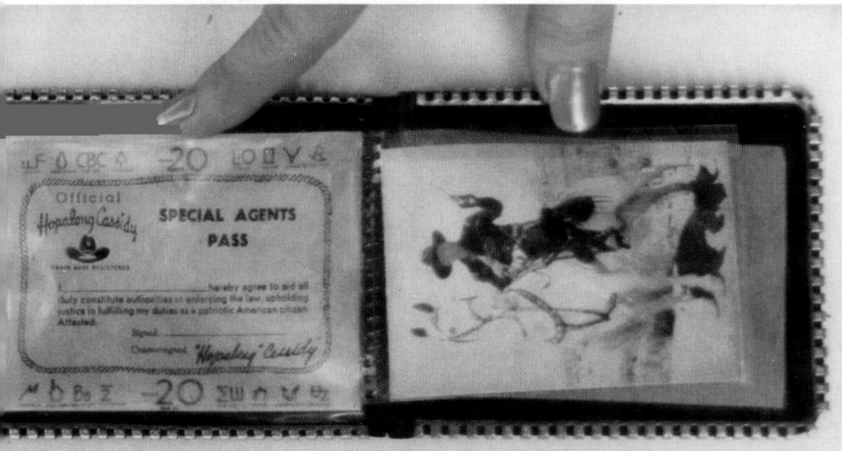

Interior of gold-capped wallet contains, in addition to the gold good luck coin, a photo of Hoppy as well as a "Special Agents Pass." which was an I.D. card. Also made by the Pioneer Company. #1. $275 #2. $230 #3. $200. (Deduct $100 if no box). From the Bill Larzelere collection.

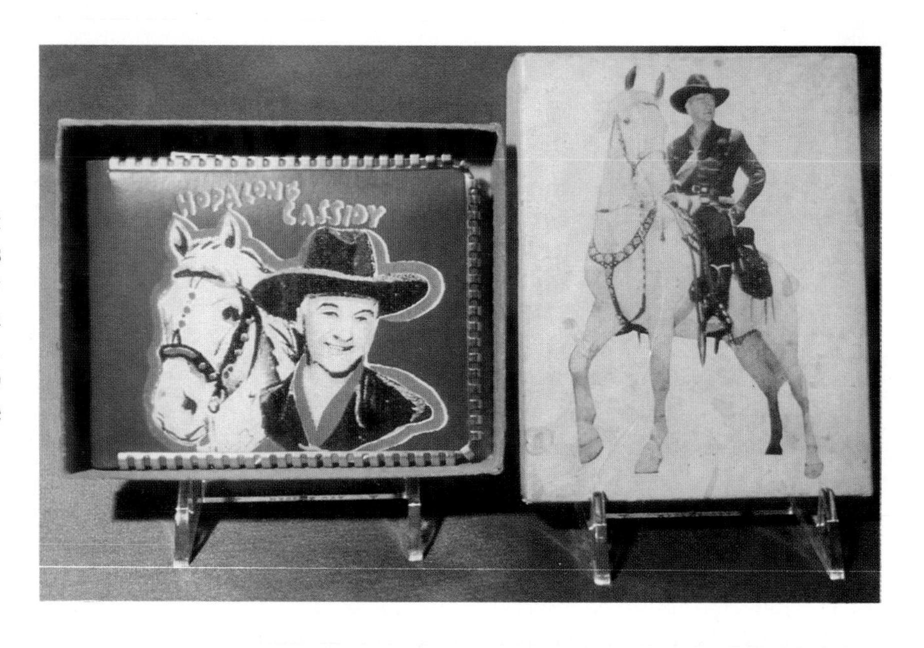

Folding, black leather Pioneer wallet with saw-tooth edge in original box. This is perhaps the most common Hoppy graphic used. Wallet contains good luck coin, "Agent" pass and Hoppy photo. #1. $245 #2. $200 #3. $175. (Deduct $100 if no box) From the Jon & Charlie Cheek collection.

Display of two similar leather wallets to the above boxed version. Note that these two wallets have zipper closures. Same values as listed above. From the Jon & Charlie Cheek collection. Note the slight image variation between the two.

Savings Club wallet is similar to one found on previous page with the exception of the "Honor Member Savings Club" decal. This wallet is an excellent collectors' find. #1. $400 #2. $325 #3. $280. (deduct $100 if no box). From the Jon & Charlie Cheek collection.

Hoppy riding Topper wallet designs came in both zipper and folding types shown on right. Both wallets were leather, and contained a good luck coin, "Agent" pass and a photo. Note edging design on folding wallet on right. Values are similar to the other wallets listed on this page. From the Jon & Charlie Cheek collection.

additional different design leather ets (R) are both zipper closure. All er wallets were offered in either n or black. Values are similar to r designs with similar construction contents: #1. $245 #2. $200 #3. $175 uct $100 without box). From the Jon harlie Cheek collection.

Two versions of the Hoppy plastic folding wallet with similar graphic to "gold-capped" wallet on previous page. Plastic wallets are rarer than the leather. #1. $250 #2. $210 #3. #185. From the Jon & Charlie Cheek collection.

other variation of Hoppy wallets (R) d a leather insert and colorful water cal placed within the saw-tooth edging. e wallet to the right is another version the "gold-capped" wallet mentioned rlier. The decal wallet is valued the me as the plastic wallets above. From e Jon & Charlie Cheek collection.

Perhaps the most distinctive and expensive of the Hoppy wallets is this soft, pliable, folding wallet made from lamb skin. Trimmed with a braided cord and featuring a metal steer head on one side, and a metal embossed "Hopalong Cassidy" plate on the other, it was a very subtle and adult-type wallet. #1. $325 #2. $290 #3. $265. (Deduct $100 if no box). From the Bill Larzelere collection.

Reverse side of lamb skin wallet

Another version of the leather, zippered wallet with a unique blue background. Mint wallet as shown in box must contain Hoppy coin and "Agent" card along with Hoppy photo. #1. $245. #2. $200 #3. $175 (deduct $100 without box)

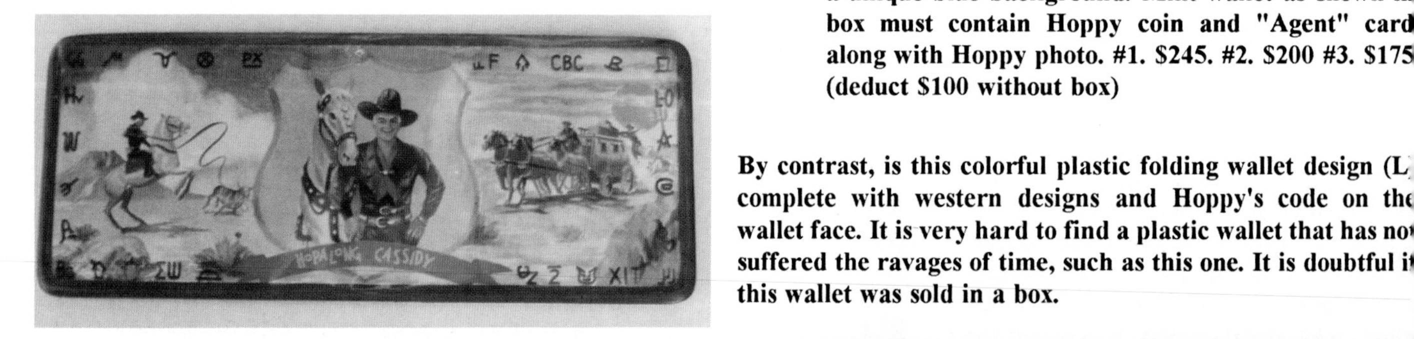

By contrast, is this colorful plastic folding wallet design (L) complete with western designs and Hoppy's code on the wallet face. It is very hard to find a plastic wallet that has not suffered the ravages of time, such as this one. It is doubtful if this wallet was sold in a box.

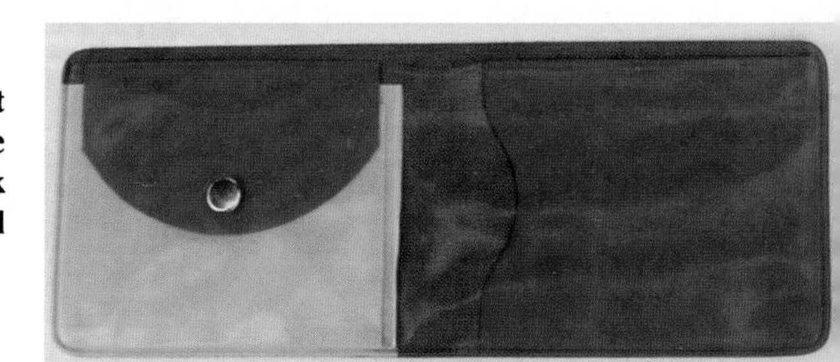

While the wallet's interior is quite garish, it is as functional as any, including a change purse, which contained the Hoppy good luck coin. #1. $160 #2. $100 #3. $65. From the Bill Larzelere collection.

LATE ARRIVALS

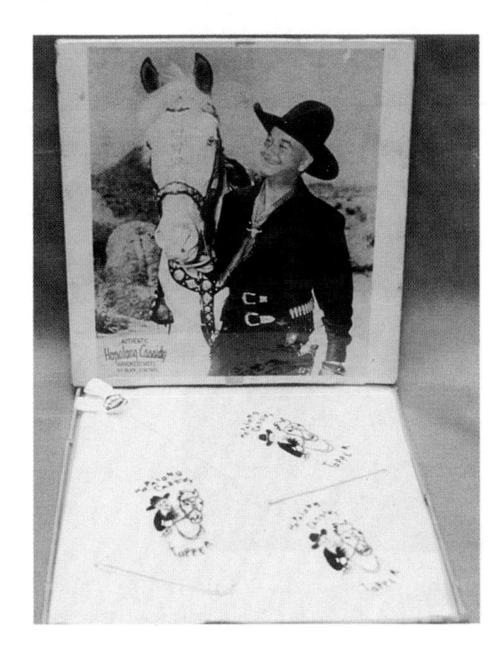

lection of Hoppy Hanks in original box. Linen ndkerchiefs each bore a stitched Hoppy mono-am of sorts. #1. $350 #2. $275 #3. $225. (deduct 50 without box). Individual handkerchief in #1 or condition for $30-$45 each. From the Jon & arlie Cheek collection.

Very colorful and rare black and yellow Rayon scarf was for formal youngster occasions. #1. $275 #2. $225 #3. $175 There is no known box for this really neat Hoppy item. From the Jon & Charlie Cheek collection.

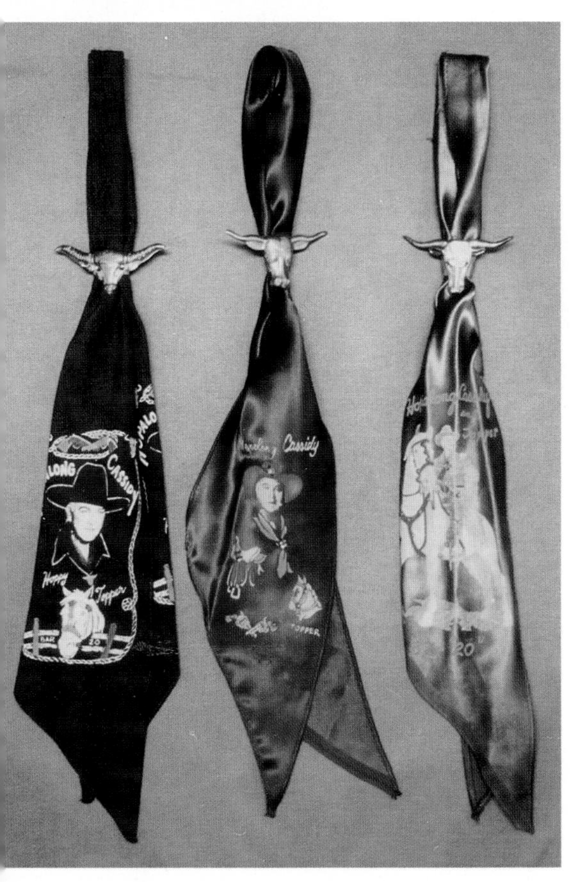

The red Hoppy hat (above) is a rare item that should be in "Outfits" chapter. Alas, there was no room. #1. $300 #2. $260 #3. $200. Note that it is a "Deputy" hat. From the Jon Cheek spread.

Detail photo of additional Hoppy satin ties and sliders. Each is valued at $135 in #1. From Jon & Charlie Cheek.

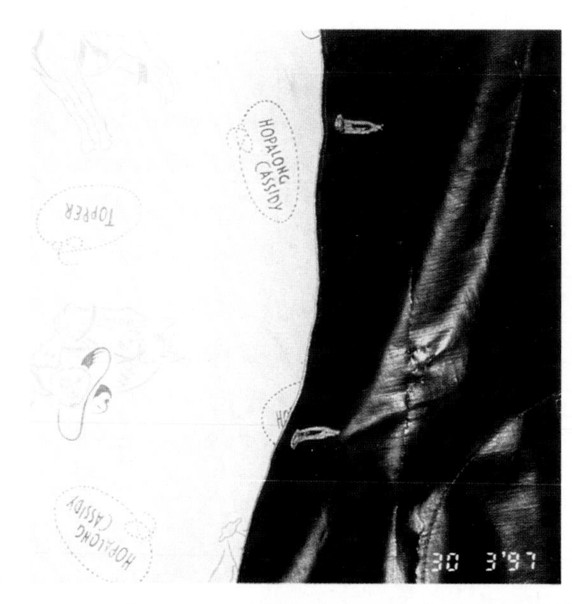

Perhaps one of the rarest clothing items of all, is this Hoppy raincoat or "slicker." The rain outfit included a rain hat (not shown) the raincoat and the rubber Hoppy boots. This is certainly an "investment value" item with a value estimate of: #1. $1,200 #2. $1,000 #3. $800. The proud owner declined to have his name printed.

This blue tee shirt may not have come packaged as shown but is a good example of the quality of the many tee shirt variations. #1.$145 #2. $100 #3. $75. From the Frank Smith collection.

Store display sign for Hoppy gloves. Cardboard sign was counter-top display. #1. $350 #2. $300 #3. $250. From Jon & Charlie Cheek.

Die-cut suspender package (upper right) is similar but different from one showed earlier in this chapter. #1. $325 #2. $300 #3. $275. From the Jon & Charlie Cheek collection.

hich is more unusual, the box or the shirt? Little known but I will venture a value of $275 for each #1. condition. From the Frank Smith collection.

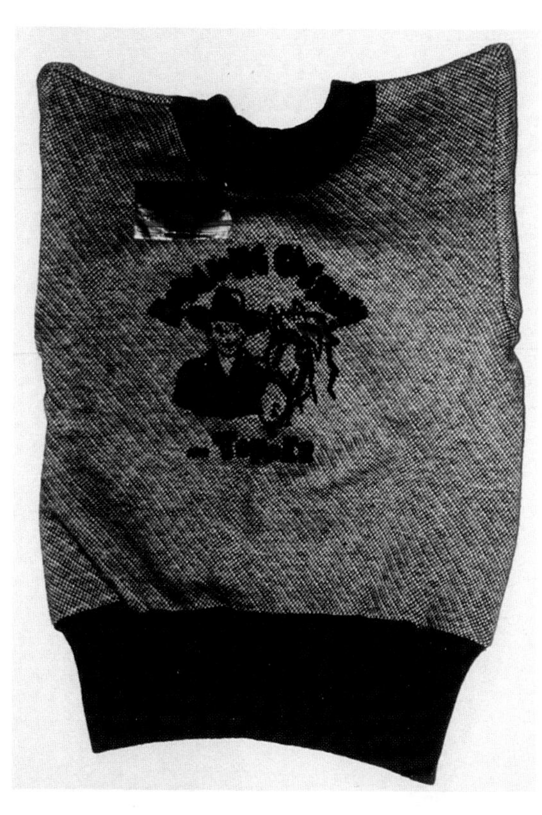

Another head-scratcher is this sweater. While it has a Flagg manufacturing label on the front, there is no collar brand label. The sweater is definitely era material, so it may be real. #1. $300 #2. $250 #3.$200.

is Merry Christmas Hoppy socks package uld make a nice addition to any collection. e empty package alone is valued at $150 and uld be $350 if it had a pair of socks. from e Frank Smith collection.

If I didn't wait an extra month to publish this book you would not have seen this sweater-shirt and the sweaters on the following page. To make it more interesting, the above is a salesman's sample from Barclay with an attached lot card (not visible). An investment value item with a estimated value of $550 in #1. condition.

This crew-neck red sweater may also qualify for one of a kind status. Also a salesman's sample from Barclay. #1. $500+. According to the lot card this is model HC24 that came in green, brown, black and navy. How many have you seen?

This sweater came in the original cellophane package with a Barclay's printed photo. Note similarity to sweater design. #1. $475 #2. $425 #3. $375. Deduct $150 without package and printed photo.

Another salesman's sample of the cardigan sweater. Note lot card and button card. #1. $450 #2. $400.

Another unusual design, note that Hoppy's hands on his guns, also piping around neck. This is another salesman's sample valued at $475+

COLORING & CRAFTS

#1. condition: mint, showing no use #2. condition: excellent to near mint #3. condition: good to very good

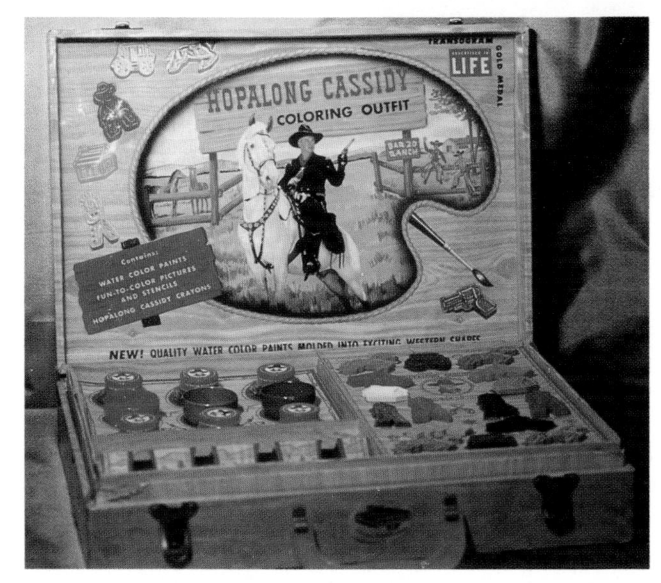

Ioppy coloring sets came in a variety of sizes, the largest nd most rare is the one shown above. Fashioned as an rtist's briefcase containing several trays of paints, crayons and ubject sheets, it is an excellent collectors' find. The glass jars hown are Hoppy poster paints which are sometimes found selling or over $25 each. #1. $950 #2. $800 #3. $650. From the Jon & harlie Cheek collection.

All of the Hoppy coloring outfits were made by Transogram, and had similar box covers. The gun and Indian figures shown in the set were actually "brick" water colors. Some sets had cowboy stencils. #1. $400 #2. $275 #3. $225.

While the crayon pack is missing from this set (top area) the set is NM #2. condition. A smaller set than shown on the upper right, it has a cowboy pallet and more water color shapes. #1. $375 #2. $250 #3. $200.

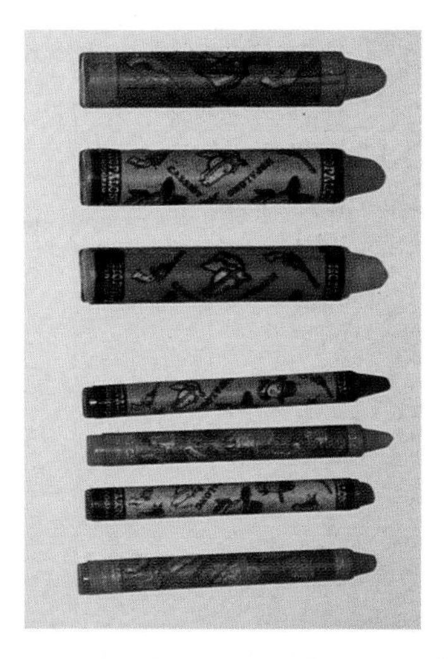

Hoppy crayons came in two sizes, regular and jumbo as shown above. Unused "regular" crayons have been selling for $3-5 each, jumbos $5-8.

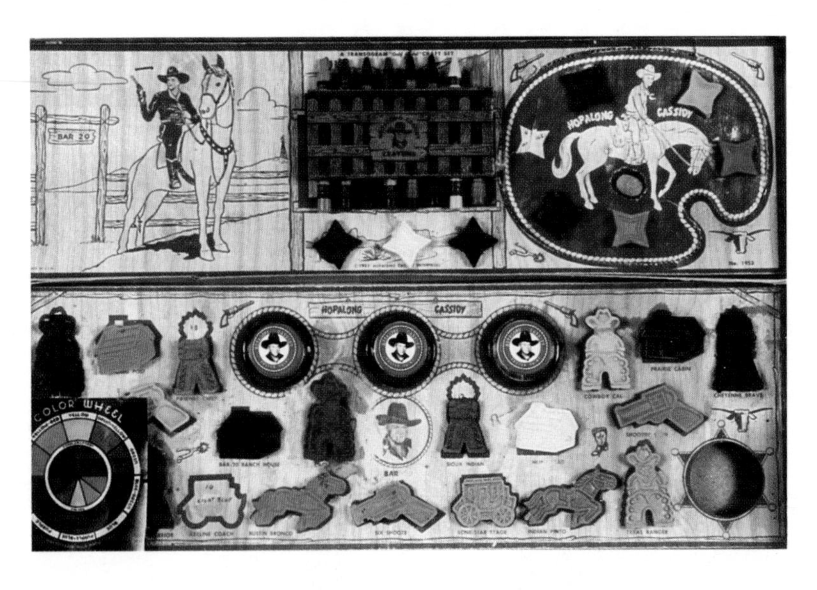

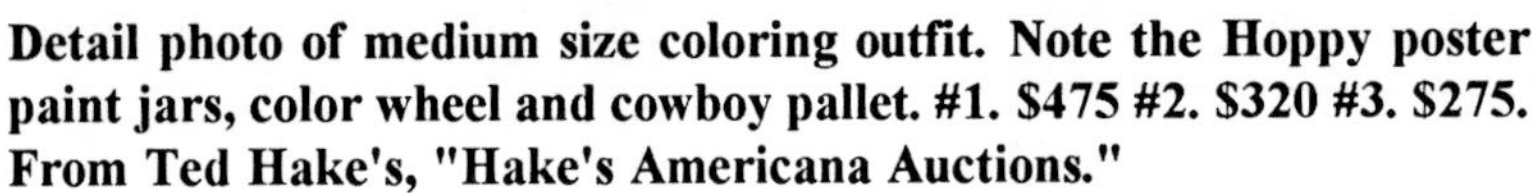

Detail photo of medium size coloring outfit. Note the Hoppy poster paint jars, color wheel and cowboy pallet. #1. $475 #2. $320 #3. $275. From Ted Hake's, "Hake's Americana Auctions."

Close-up sample o Hoppy poster paint ja with Hoppy bust o screw-on lid. Hopp jars have been sellin between $20-$30.

The Hoppy woodburning set (above) while not an uncommon item to find, is almost impossible to get in unused condition as shown. Set contains burning tool, wood plaques, water colors & brush, burner holder & tips and foil papers to "burnish" certain areas. #1. $650 #2. $500 #3. $425.

Hoppy crayon stencil sets carried both regular & jumbo crayons. The one shown is the smaller set. #1. $350 #2. $275 #3. $250.

If you are looking for the "slate" set it is in the "School Supplies" chapter..

Large crayon & stencil set had more cra ons and wooden plaques similar to tho found in the woodburning set. Very collec ible in any condition. #1. $400 #2. $325 # $275.

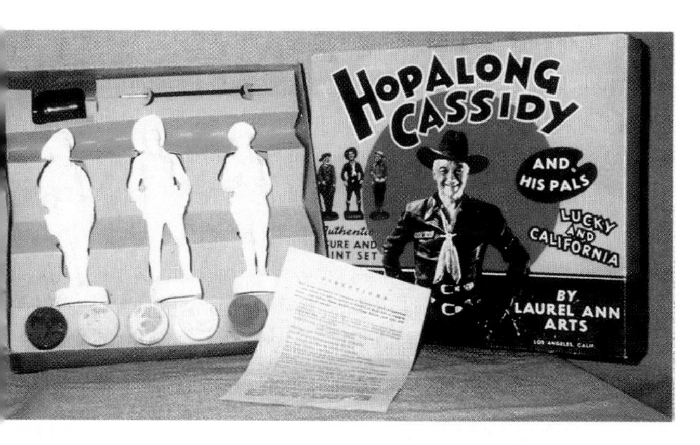

Hoppy plaster paint set was made by Laurel Ann Arts, in Los Angeles, CA. The other two figures in the set are: ucky" (Rand Brooks) and "California" (Andy Clyde). A t set (above) is a very rare find. #1. $1,250 #2. $950 #3. 0. (individual statues from the set are valued at $50 each 1 all three valued at $200) The Hoppy statue is $100. m the Phil Ellis collection.

Perhaps one of the most "fun" Hoppy crafts was the plaster statue painting set. The light-weight, detailed, plaster forms insured the fact that many would not survive. The above painted set belonged to the author of this book for many, many years.

The Hoppy puzzle on the left is a wood picture puzzle with a cardboard color picture of Hoppy for framing. #1. $165 #2. 100 #3. $75. From the Porter Albin collection.

Large Hoppy picture puzzle and assembly tray by Whitman Publishing. Also has extra picture for framing. #1. $145 #2. $100 #3. $60

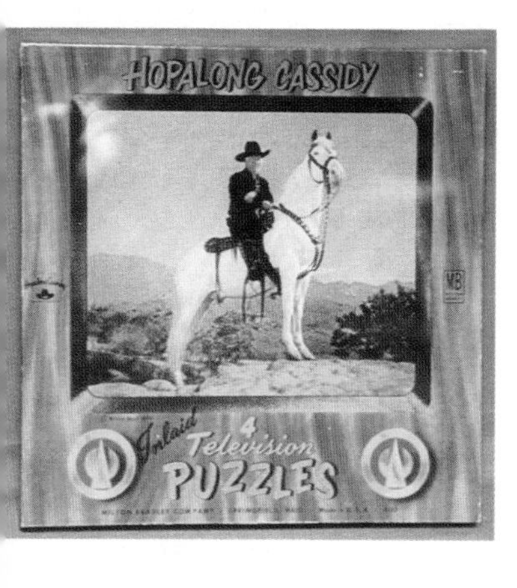

Puzzle set to the far left contains 4 "television" puzzles and is more common than the puzzle set containing 3 "film" puzzles. Both sets maintain similar values: #1. $165 #2. $100 #3. $75.

Two similar Hoppy puzzle sleeves may have different puzzles and different access areas as shown above. Both were made by Milton Bradley, but note that the smaller puzzle has the "approved" Hoppy seal. (Sizes of puzzles shown are not in perspective.) Values on both puzzle types are: #1. $145 32. $100 #3. $60

Punch-out sample from book on left.

Hoppy punch-out book (above) is a very difficult collector's quest to find. You could punch-out cardboard pieces and fold tabs to make pieces stand. It had a great deal of play value, and very few exist in any condition. A rare Hoppy collectible. #1. $195 #2. $145 #3. $100.

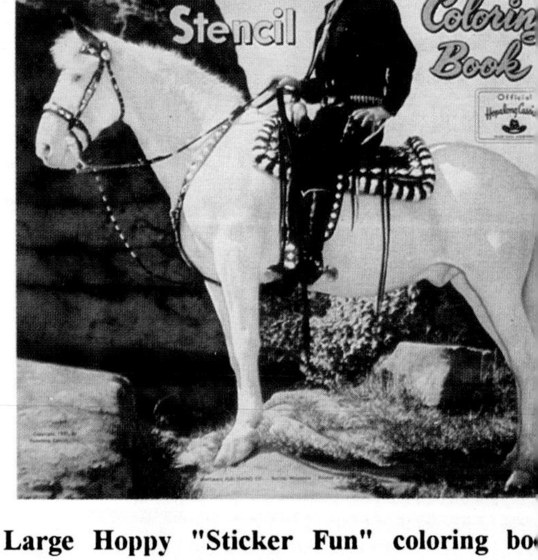

Large Hoppy "Sticker Fun" coloring bo contained color "sticker" pieces as well western scenes to color. A very in-demand ite #1. $170 #2. $140 #3. $95.

loring book on right a rare "Funtime oks" edition and tains cut-out sec-ns. Graphics are o different than st Hoppy books. #1. 50 #2. $125 #3. $100. om the Brian Beirne lection.

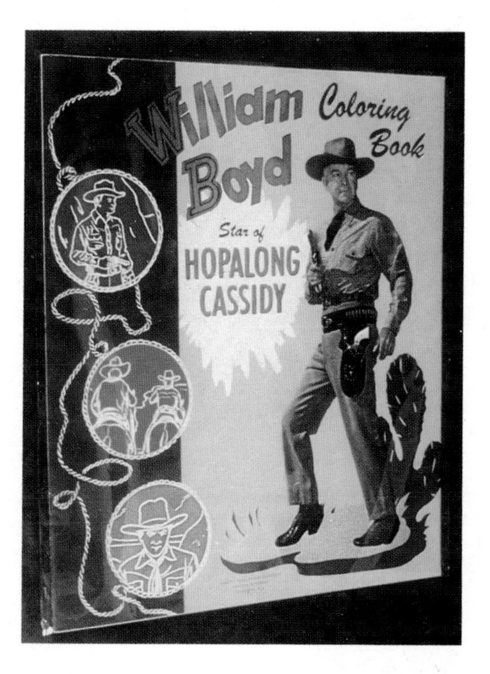

While Abbott Publishing and Samuel Lowe, Co. produced many Hoppy coloring ooks, other publishers included Golden Books, Funtime, Etc. The books shown on is page all maintain similar values: #1. $125 #2. $100 #3. $75.

The Hoppy coloring book (r) is a rare "jumbo" 88 page book made by Golden, Co. Considering that some of the"large"Hoppy books were only 10 pages, a "jumbo" is quite unique: #1. $150 #2. $125 #3. $100

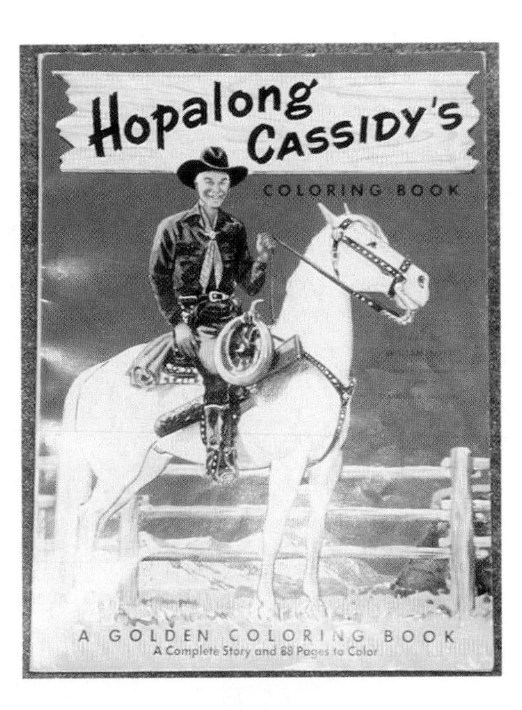

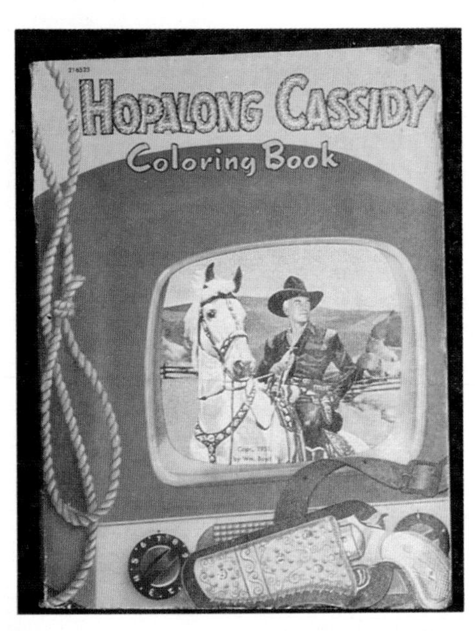

The above book is another "jumbo" Hoppy "TV" coloring book with a similar value to the Golden Book.

The above Hoppy book is similar to the large retail versions with only 10 pages. This book was a free promotion by Acrobat Shoes and given away when visiting their shoe stores. It had excellent garphics and cover colors. #1. $175 #2. $150 #3, $130

A different variation on the large size Hoppy coloring book with 10 pages. #1. $125 #2. $100 #3. $75

This "large" coloring book is from Samuel Lowe Company, and offered 32 pages to color instead of ten. #1. $125 #2. $100 #3. $75.

It should be noted that conditions and values relating to coloring books assume the books have not been used. If the books have been used, a value deduction of up to 50% is warranted.

This Hoppy book is also a "large" size with the same photo used for the cover of the "Acrobat" Shoes promo book. #1. $125 #2. $100 #3. $75.

Another "large" version of a Hoppy coloring book: #1. $125 #2. $100 #3. $75. From the Porter Albin collection.

Super large Hoppy coloring book from Abbott Press has, in my estimation, one of the prettiest graphic covers of all the Hoppy books. It too, has 10 very large pages to color. #1. $140 #2. $120 #3. $100.

COMICS & CARDS

#1. condition: mint, showing no use #2. condition: excellent to near mint #3. condition: good to very good

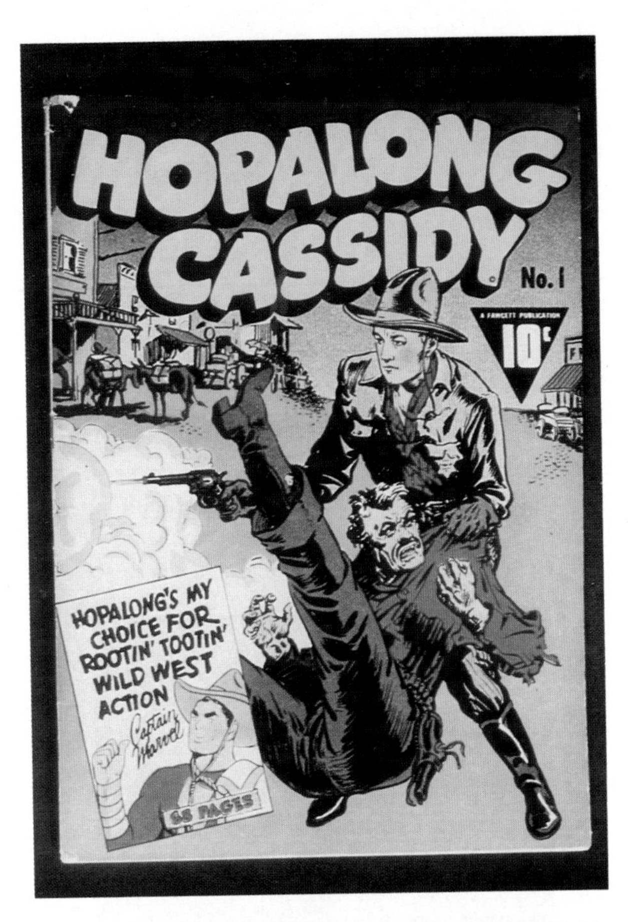

Hoppy comics were first published by Fawcett Publishing in 1943 (above is #1 issue) then they stopped for several years only to start again in 1948. The comic "rights" were sold to "DC" Comics in the 1950's. At a recent auction a #1. Hoppy (1943) comic sold for over $1,400 and all other Hoppy comics have had a value surge. From the John Mlachnick collection. Photo by Catherine Gibson.

Hoppy comics are an important part of every collection. Many paper collectors specialize in them. In order to be complete, collectors must find all the comics that featured Hoppy: "Six-Gun Heroes," "Bill Boyd," "Hopalong Cassidy," and "Real Westerns." For current comic book values refer to Overstreet Comic Book Price guide, available at most book stores.

From the Richard Stevens collection

Comic books containing Hoppy are so specialized (as well as other comic book characters) that it would be difficult to assess reasonable market values in this book. There are many Hoppy comics available in #2. and #3. conditions for $20 to $35. Is there more value in buying a "Bill Boyd" over a "Hopalong Cassidy?" Frankly, I don't know. I do know that if the issue number is under #10 and you can afford it, it's a good deal!

Assortment of various comics carrying Hoppy stories.

Several versions of the Bill Boyd comic.

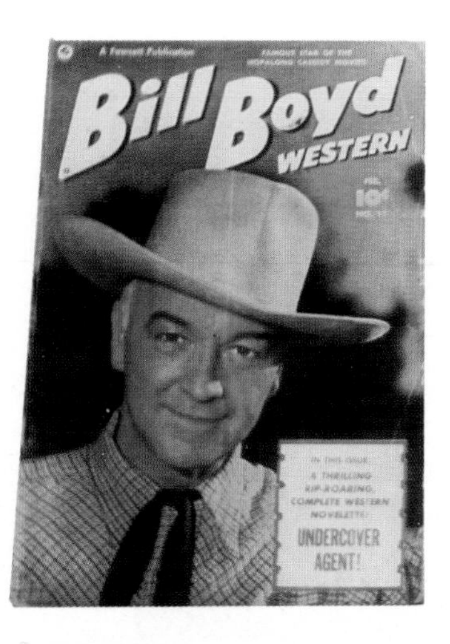

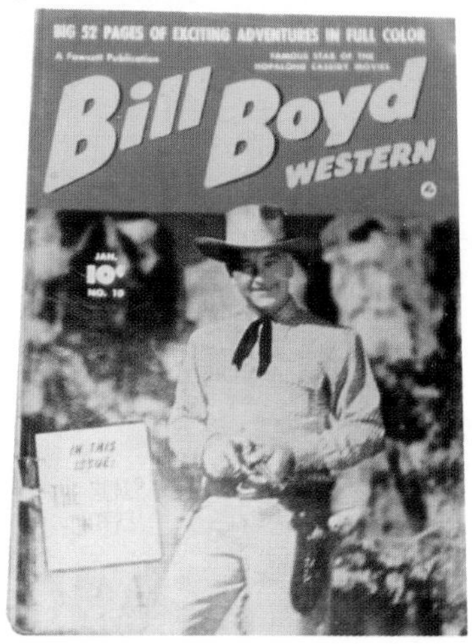

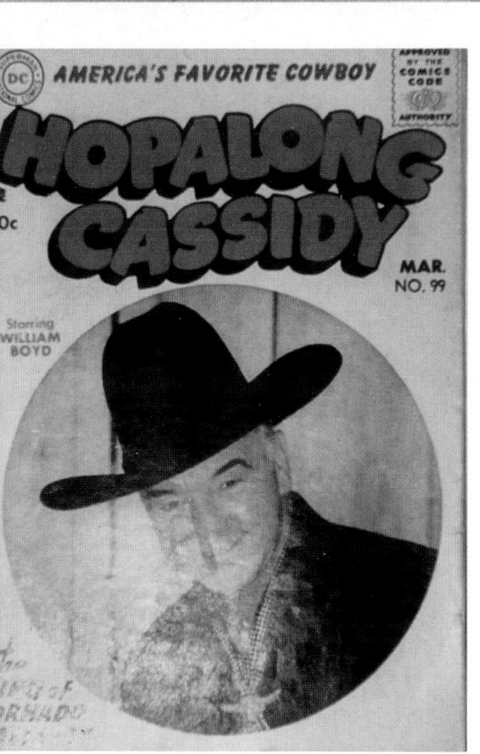

ld for changeover to "DC" comics and oto of issue #99 (above). #1. $55 #2. $40 #3. 0. From the Brian Beirne collection.

Not to be outdone, the British had hard-cover comic annuals: #1. $200 #2. $165 #3. $120. From the Jon & Charlie Cheek collection.

Bill Boyd comics are similar in value to "Hopalong Cassidy:" #1. $40 #2. $30 #3. $20. If the issue number is #5-10 add 20% if it is #1-5 add another 20%

Hoppy was marketed under many varieties of comics, from books to comic strips to special promotion comics like the Bond Bread comics shown above, and to the right. #1. $140 #2. $110 #3. $85 (without labels -- see "Ads & Promotions" chapter) The Philadelphia Sunday Bulletin newspaper (above right) had a "Fun Book" of comics which often featured Hoppy on the front page. #1. $125 #2. $85 #3. $60.

If you happen to find a color or b&w comic strip signed by Dan Spiegle, you can add $75 to the value. Dan signed very few comic strips.

A Hoppy color comic strip (above) under the newspaper banner is a nice collector find. #1. $55 #2. $45 #3. $30.

and Sunday comic strips can be nicely displayed (above) if s are limited. Unlike original comic book art (R) there is no n comic strip original art that was saved by King Features, Inc. vas the Hoppy comic strip distributor. The eight panel uncolored al comic book art (R) is one of the few original art Hoppy pieces n to exist. It may have an investment value in excess of $1,000. the Bill Hoffman collection.

The above assortment of 4x6" Hoppy cards are the British version of trading cards (they are actually post cards) and are quite neat to have. They are generally found in #1. or #2. condition selling for $25 to $35 each. From the Mike Forthun collection.

te popular in the 1950's was the "mini" comic (4x4") which featured many popular charac- . The Hoppy "mini" set (above) was in many s a combination comic book - coloring book n stated on the cover. (See Hoppy's Books ter). There are 12 to the set. #1. $45 #2. $30 #3. From the Jon & Charlie Cheek collection.

Cowboy Trio card set (R) are 4x6" color post cards of Hoppy, Roy and Gene. Cards are attached to each other with a perforated edge. A #1. condition set is valued at $60. From the Mike Forthun collection.

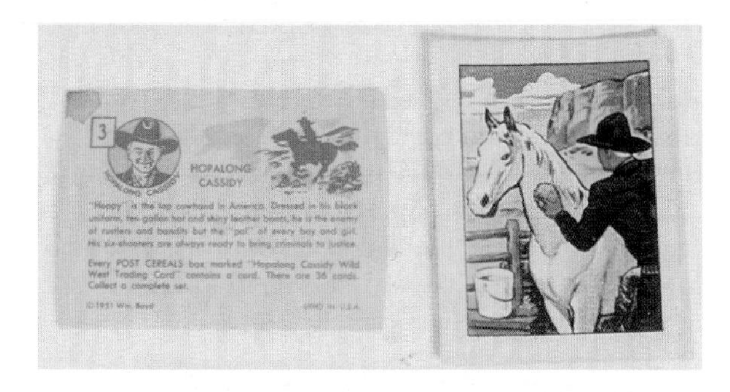

Sample of Post Cereals Hoppy card (front and back) were exciting for kids to collect. Collectors now collect them for $8 to $12 each.

Another source for Hoppy cards were found in penny arcades of the 1950's where cards were dispensed by machine. Generally inexpensive duo-tone cards were offered in shades of blue or brown. The Hoppy cards shown above are "arcade" cards which often had Hoppy's side-kicks as well as himself. Cards are valued at $10 to $15. From the Richard Stevens collection.

Post Cereals offered free Hoppy trading cards in every box. (see promotions and food endorsement chapters) There were 36 cards to the set. In addition to trading cards, Post Cereals also offered special Hoppy badges. Trading cards are: #1. $12 #2. $10 #3. $8. each.

Topps chewing gum offered Hoppy duo-tone action scenes from Hoppy films in each pack of one cent and five cent gum. (see food endorsement chapter) Each set (24) is based on a particular Hoppy film. Card values: #1. $14 #2. $11 #3. $9. (every 1,000th. card printed was a rare silver foil card. An added incentive for kids).

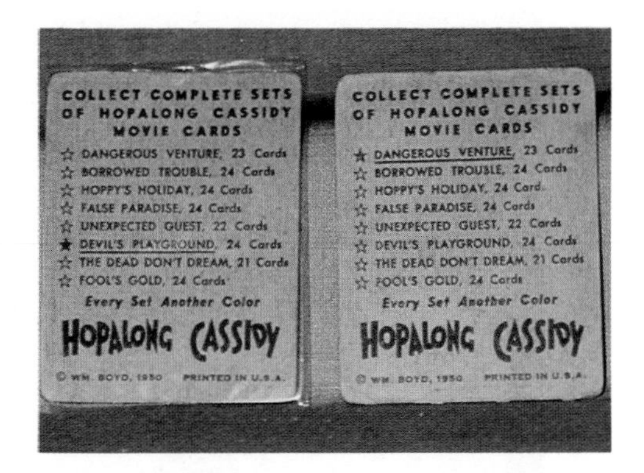

Hoppy color movie cards were the last to be produced as a gum card. They were little different than the duo-tone cards and were artificially colored (above right). They were produced in limited quantities and prized by some collectors. #1. $18 #2. $14 #3. $12. From the Phil Ellis collection.

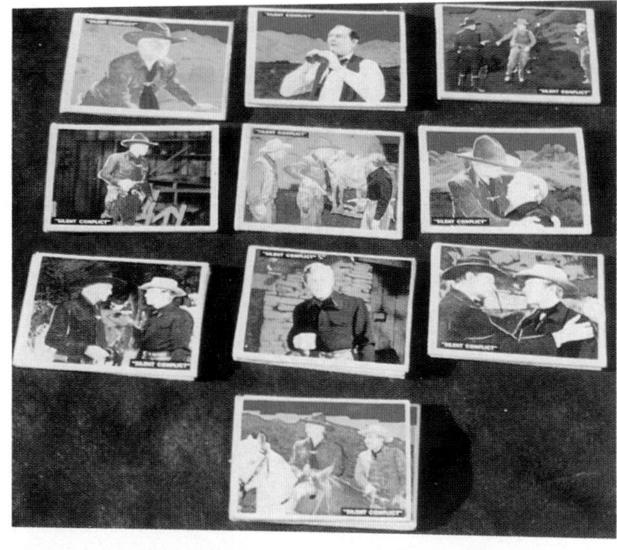

Display of later edition Hoppy color trading cards from the Phil Ellis collection.

Rare Hoppy "foil" gum cards. Each 1,000th. card was printed this way and randomly placed in gum wrappers. From the Ted Hake, Hake's Americana auction.

There were eight cards to the "foil" card set, any of which is difficult to find. #1. $240 #2. $180 #3. $145. From the Mike Pellow collection.

Cards on the left are from Hopalong Cassidy cookies. (Burry's) There was one in every box. #1. $24 #2. $20 #3. $16 From the Jon & Charlie Cheek collection.

Framed assortment of Hoppy cards make a nice display piece to hang on wall.

Perhaps the prettiest "character" cards on the market, then or now, the Hoppy greeting cards designed by Buzza Cardozo are always impressive. Surprisingly, there are quite a few still available at reasonable collector prices. This part of the "cards" chapter will show you some of the most interesting.

The "Howdy" card came with a Hoppy green pin which was easily detached. The card is quite rare with the mounted pin. #1. $95 #2. $70 #3. $55. (pin alone is valued at $35.)

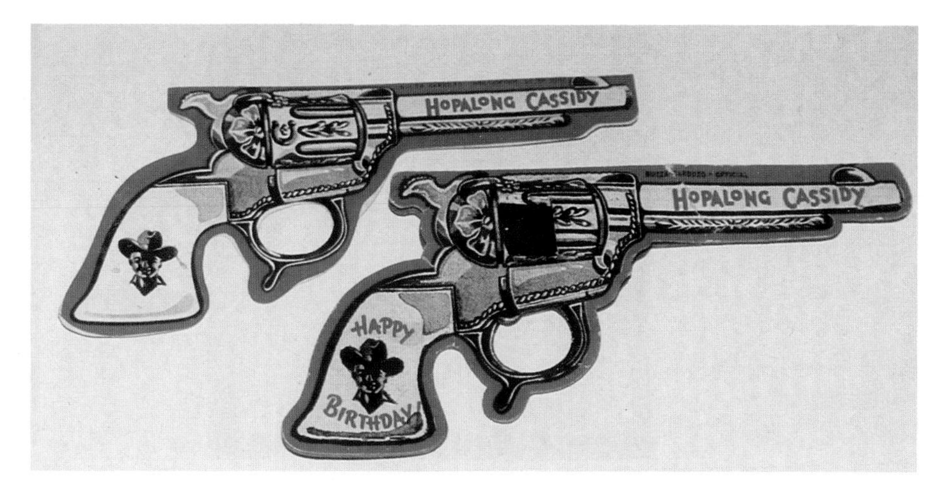

There were two "gun cards" made. The top card was for any occasion, the bottom, a birthday card, had a "clicker" inside. #1. $55 #2. $40 #3. $30. The "clicker" birthday card has an added value of $25 per condition.

py action card. Open card to make e's legs move and rider's arms move. $100 #2. $80 #3. $65. From the Mike hun collection.

Large "wagon wheel" card. Four action Hoppy scenes are shown by turning wheel. #1. $110 #2. $90 #3. $75

me card has "spinner" (upper right) and en card opens, reveals a game board. #1. $90 $70 #3. $50

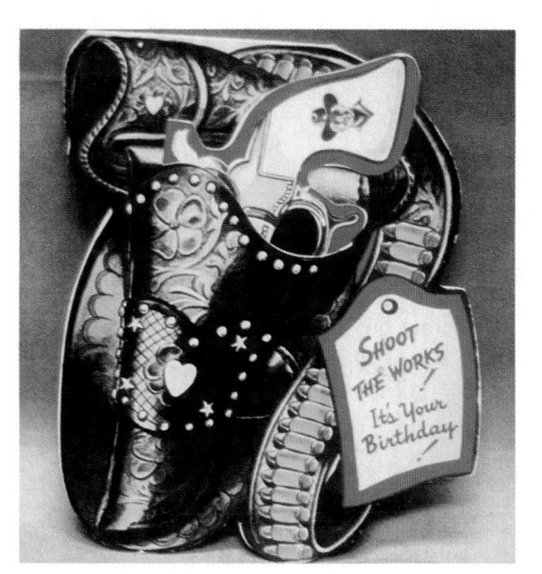

One of the hardest cards to find is "Shoot the Works." Card contained a removable paper gun (see top of page) which was often lost or destroyed: #1. $135 #2. $120 #3. $100. From the Jon & Charlie Cheek collection.

"Hello" friendship card has lead gun charm on cover. #1. $85 #2. $60 #3. $50

Rarest Hoppy card is the "gum" card. When opened you find a stick of gum.

Hoppy balloon card (L) had either a red or blue balloon with Hoppy's image.

The gum stick is a wrapped penny Topps, with trading card (mayb a foil card). #1. $325 #2. $275 #3. $225. Without gum card is $30

While the balloon card was a nice gift to a boy or girl in the 50's, today's collectors prize it even more: #1. $240 #2. $200 #3. $175. Many collectors feel this card is harder to find than the gum card.

Rare HC Valentine card is hard to find. Card has rubber band across heart. #1. $125 #2. $100 #3. $80. (deduct $10 if rubber band is missing). From the Mike Forthun collection.

ppy pop-out card cover

Birthday party invitation card (and envelope) was a kids version of RSVP. #1. $55 #2. $40 #3. $30

out card (inside) was a neat sur- for kids. #1. $85 #2. $70 #3. $60

Inside of Birthday party invitation card.

xpanding rope birthday card cover.

Most all Buzza Cardoza designed Hoppy cards held a surprise of some sort. On the rope card, they used a white string on card cover and graphics inside. #1. $90 #2. $75 #2. $65

Stated age Birthday cards had plastic number on cover (up to 12) and revolving scene wheel to turn. A very difficult card to find. #1. $125 #2. $100 #3. $80 (deduct $30 if plastic number is missing).

Silver spur Hoppy card is one of the largest made. Card had a photo of Hoppy inside which was viewed through die-cut hole in cover (knot hole). #1. $100 #2. $80 #3. $70. From the Mike Forthun collection.

Shootin' Straight card is noteworthy because there is a lead boot on cover. A highly collectible card. #1. $85 #2. $70 #3. $50 (deduct $40 of boot is missing)

Pop-up Birthday card with ranch scene. #1. $70 #2. $55 #3. $40

Boys "horse apple" card showing same scene as girls. Either one: #1. $75 #2. $60 #3. $45. From the Mike Forthun collection.

Hoppy "horse apple" cards were often confused with each other. The boy/girl images were almost identical. From the Mike Forthun collection

Hoppy & Santa card was very popular. #1. $95 #2. $75 #3. $60

Hoppy & Topper card. #1. $95 #2. $75 #3. $60.

Merry Christmas gun card is quite unusual for the occasion. Note: top of gun is die-cut #1. $95 #2. $75 #3. $60. From the Mike Forthun collection.

Hoppy Christmas cards are popular with collectors because there are so few of them. Most are very traditional. #1. $95 #2. $75 #3. $60.

Very colorful Christmas card with kids in Hoppy garb. Simple card with superior graphics. #1. $95 #2. $75 #3. $60. From the John Abramson collection.

FOOD ADS AND PROMO'S

#1. condition: mint, showing no use #2. condition: excellent to near mint #3. condition: good to very good

As food endorsements was one of Hoppy's main avenues of advertising, and Hoppy paper "collectabilia" is becoming so very popular, it is only natural that this important aspect has its own category. Paper and promotion values will be given when known. If a collector is at all interested in Hoppy endorsement items - they should be quite excited about this chapter.

Shown in "endorsements" this photo of the Bond Bread factory is a natural place to begin the ads and promo section. It was, after all, Hoppy's favorite!

Most collectors are familiar with "Spun Honey" paper coasters, but not many have seen the "Spun Honey" recipes on a coaster-size fold out. #1. $30 #2. $20 #3. $15. from the Mike Merryman collection.

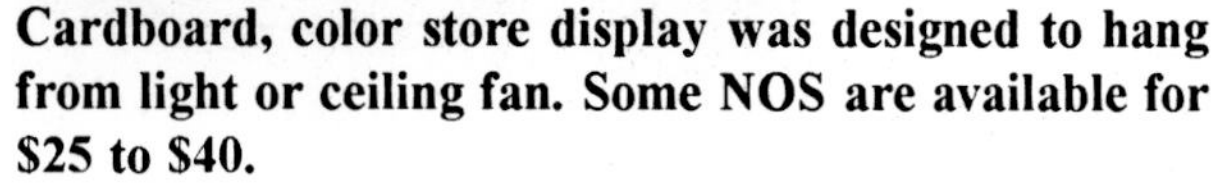

Cardboard, color store display was designed to hang from light or ceiling fan. Some NOS are available for $25 to $40.

Section of the in-store Hoppy paper sign for Bond Bread. Sign is 4'x3' and very colorful. Surprisingly, there are quite a few remaining: #1. $250 #2. $200 #3. $150.

Bond Bread Hoppy end-label mounting page has places to mount 16 special Hoppy action labels. #1. $175 #2. $140 #3. $120 (without labels)

mo Bond Bread color comic with label mounting pages. #1. $140 #2. 0 #3. $85. (no labels). Hoppy labels (R) have been going for $12 to each.

Bond Bread Hoppy label ads directed toward kids - reminding them to collect all 32 different end-labels. Ads are a nice find for $40 to $55 each. From the Richard Stevens collection.

Hoppy color end-label as shown in Bond Bread ad (L). Fro the Ted Hake collection.

Two different Bond Bread end label designs. The circular pattern is said to be th most currnet. From the Ted Hake collection

36" cardboard grocery store display sign is one of many styles used, and still available. #1. $225 #2. $185 #3. $140. Sign is also reproduced in tin (endorsements) and sells for $15 to $30.

.0" color Bond Bread Hoppy photo is lorsed "Good Luck from Hoppy" on top ht. #1.$35 #2. $25 #3. $15. From the hard Stevens collection.

School book covers may be reproduced - there are a lot available. Prices are a modest $15 - $20.

promotion paper hat is a recent new Bond Bread discovery item. It seems to be genune. #1. $65 #2. $50 #3. $30

There were several versions of the bread label hang-up albums including the ones shown: "Hoppy Captures the Bank Robbers" - Hoppy Captures the Rustlers" and last but not least, "Hoppy Captures the Stagecoach Bandits" As earlier stated the hang up albums are hard to find and valued at: #1. $175. #2. $140 #3. $120 without labels.

Bond Bread color Hoppy trading cards are a nice collectors find. The next page will show a few of the various graphics that were found on the back. Cards have been selling for $15 - $20 each. From the Ted Hake - Hake's Americana collection.

Display of additional different Hoppy end-labels.

Hoppy store promotion sign had actual photo pasted on the cardboard. 18" in diameter #1. $150 #2. $120 #3. $100. The Brian Beirne collection.

WAYS OF THE WEST
MOST cowboys wear chaps over their pants when they're out on the range. It's the best way to protect legs from scratches when riding through the bush or herding cattle.

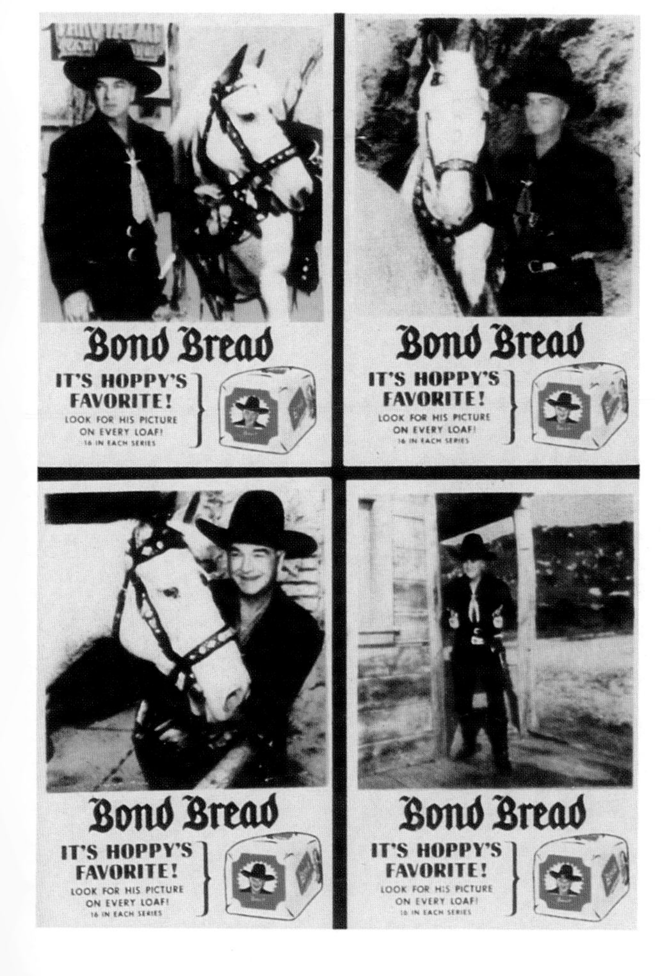

"Ways of the West" (upper left) is a sample graphic of the back of the color Hoppy Bond Bread trading cards pictured above. The cards pictured on the left are similar, but are not considered "trading cards," but advertising hand-outs. Values of these cards are around $20 in #1. condition. From the Ted Hake - Hake's Americana collection.

Speaking of Hoppy trading and collecting cards -- many collectors are understandibly confused about the number of different Hoppy trading cards out there. There are: chewing gum cards, the Post Cereal cards, the Bond Bread cards, the color British made cards, the Hoppy-Aid cards, Bond Bread advertising cards, Hopalong Cassidy Cookies cards (Burry's) and the Delicia brand ice cream cone cards. If you want to be complete however, you could add the Hoppy Bond Bread end labels too!

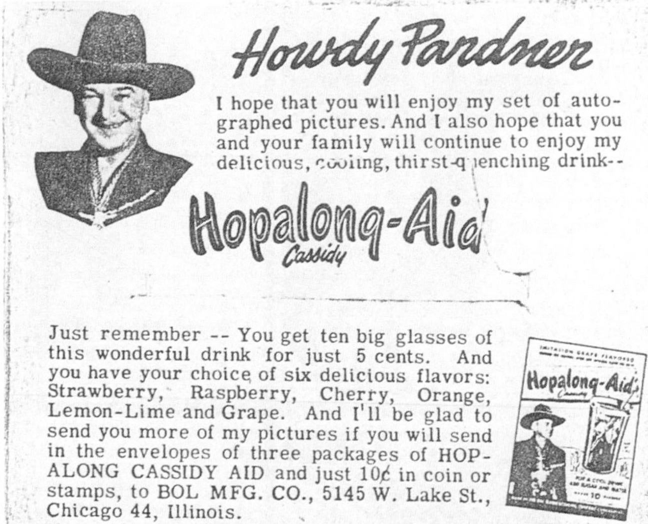

Howdy Pardner

I hope that you will enjoy my set of autographed pictures. And I also hope that you and your family will continue to enjoy my delicious, cooling, thirst-quenching drink--

Hopalong-Aid
Cassidy

Just remember -- You get ten big glasses of this wonderful drink for just 5 cents. And you have your choice of six delicious flavors: Strawberry, Raspberry, Cherry, Orange, Lemon-Lime and Grape. And I'll be glad to send you more of my pictures if you will send in the envelopes of three packages of HOP-ALONG CASSIDY AID and just 10¢ in coin or stamps, to BOL MFG. CO., 5145 W. Lake St., Chicago 44, Illinois.

One of the rarest Hoppy promotion sets that you could find would be the Hoppy-Aid mailer and card set shown. If you send in three Hopalong-Aid packages (Strawberry, Raspberry, Cherry, Orange, Lemon-Lime and Grape) along with ten cents -- you would get 12 cards sent to you in the packet shown.

The complete set is hard to value because it is so rare -- but my opinion is that $275 would not be unreasonable. From the Bill Hoffman - Mike Pellow collection.

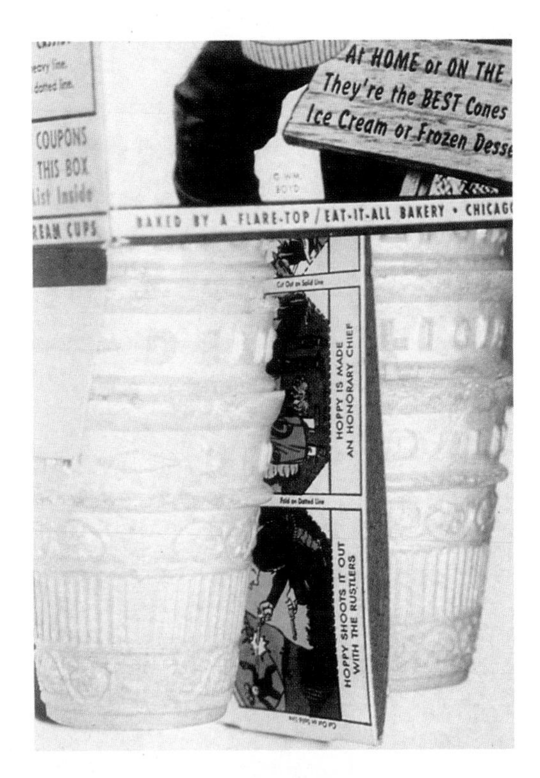

The above photo is a Delicia brand ice cream cone box complete with cones. You can see the cone dividers are actually cut-out color Hoppy trading cards with sub titles. It is not known how many cards there were, but it is assumed that each box had four. The reverse side of the divider strip had several Hoppy premiums that could be ordered. Intact cone dividing strips are worth $75.

ury's Farina cardboard h-out Hoppy rubber-band is in collector demand. Not remain due to its play . Card at far right has er bands and targets. #1. . #2. $200 #3. $165. From Mike Forthun collection.

There are many Spunny Spread 16x24" sepia-tone posters still around today for reasonable prices. #1. $55 #2. $35. From the Porter Albin collection.

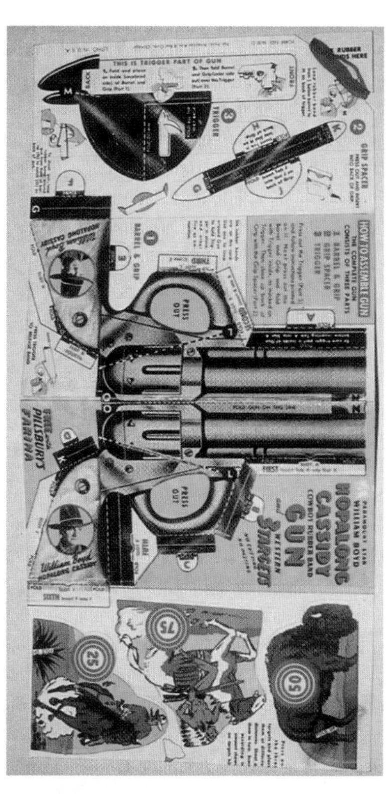

Pillsbury Farina cardboard rubber-band Hoppy gun with targets.

This is the first Hoppy ad for RC Cola that I have seen! Stranger yet, is that is was a part of a "Popsicle" premium folder (shown on next page).

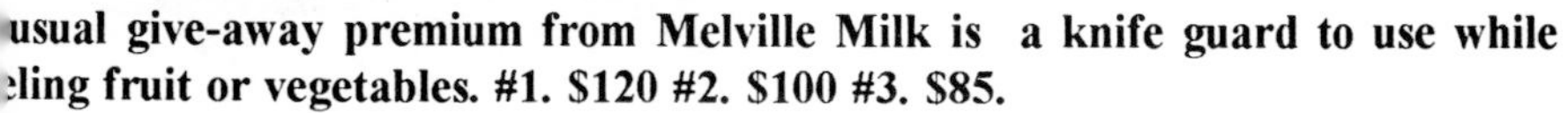

usual give-away premium from Melville Milk is a knife guard to use while eling fruit or vegetables. #1. $120 #2. $100 #3. $85.

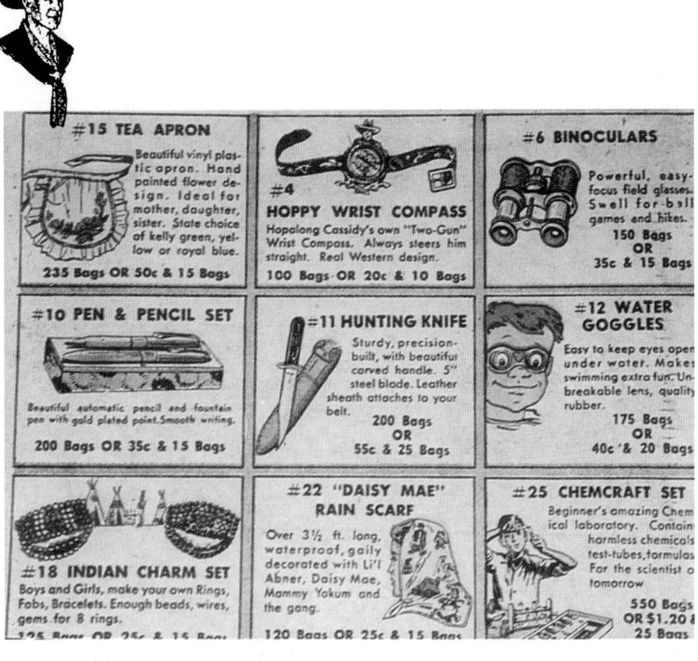

Notice the Hoppy wrist compass as a premium prize.

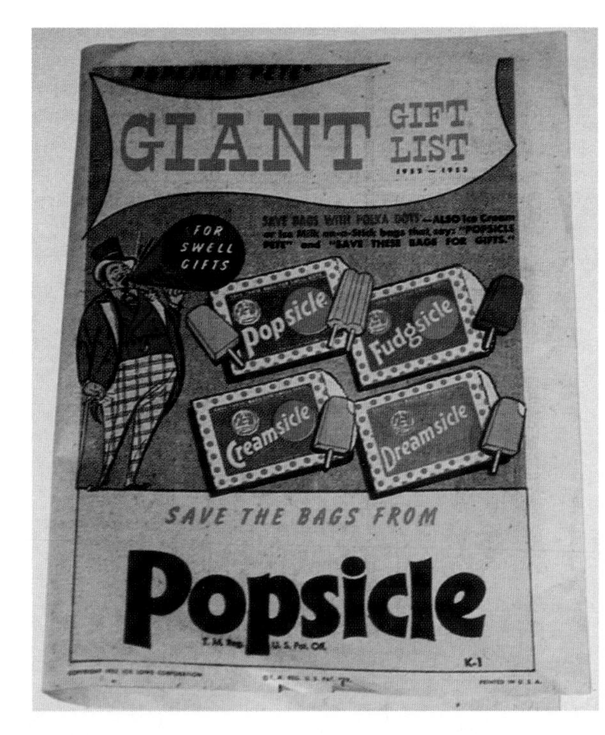

Save the wrappers from your "Popsicles" and get gifts (L) "Popsicle Gift List" also had a "RC & Quickie" comic strip -- at the end was the Hoppy RC ad. This folder would be worth $90 to most collectors. Among the premiums is a Hoppy wrist compass.

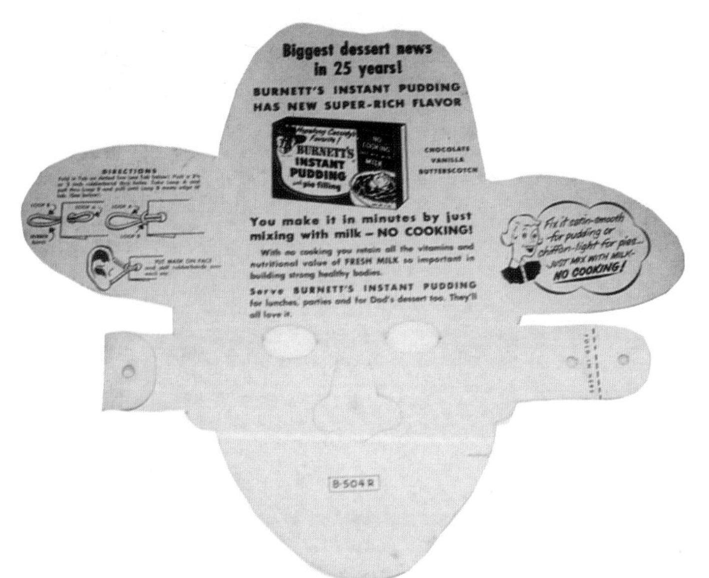

Shown on left is a Hoppy cardboard mask that was a premium item from Burnett's Pudding. Mask front is shown in the "Miscellaneous" chapter of the book. Mask had punch-out eyes and the Hoppy nose also opened: #1. $225 #2. $185 #3. $160. From the Gary Bondy, Jr. collection.

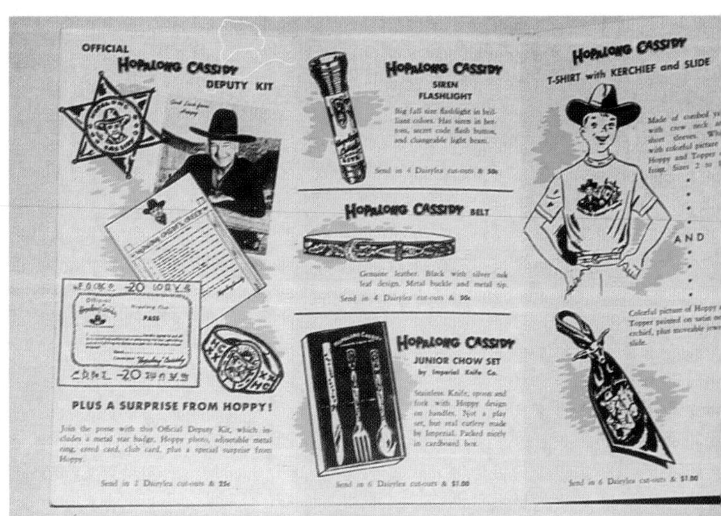

Dairylea "Deputy Kit" premium album: #1. $85 #2. $60 #3. $40 From the Mike Forthun collection.

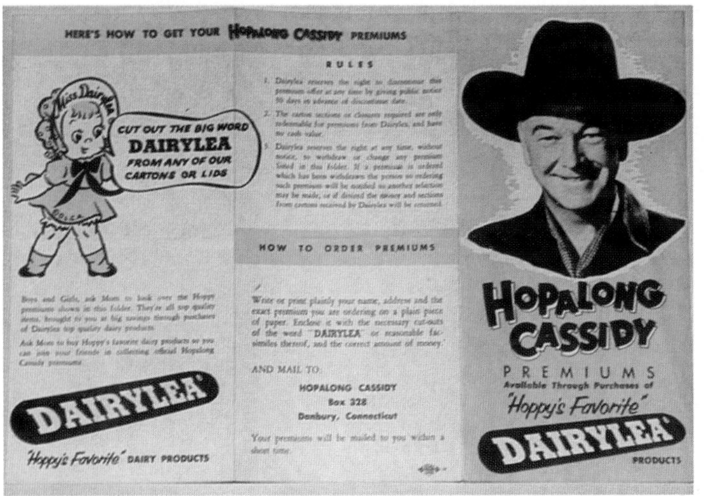

t to be outdone in the premiums market, Sunbeam bread erd a free "Ranch House Race" paper table game nplete with "spinner." #1. $175. #2. $140 #3. $100.

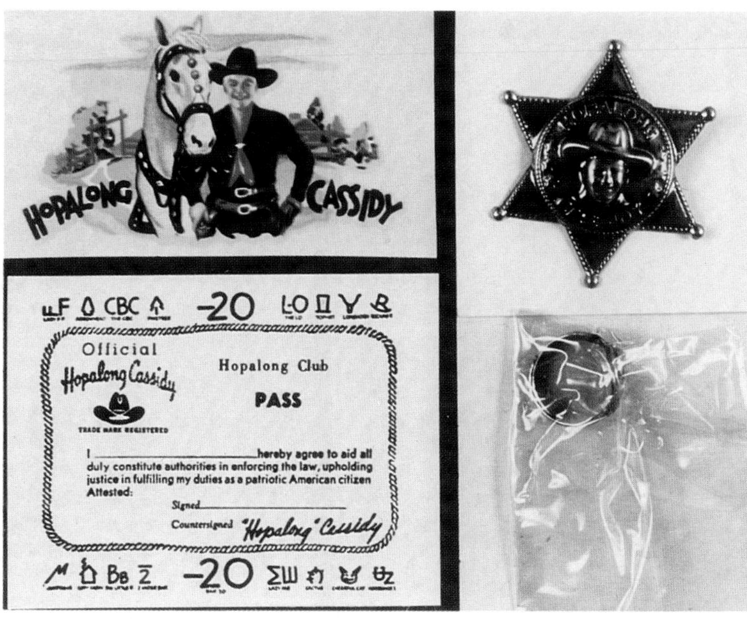

Hoppy Deputy Kits were popular sales tools for Dairylea and other dairies. The kit contained a "Hoppy Pass," a six-point badge and adjustable Hoppy metal ring, instructions, and color decal. #1. $300 #2. $250 #3. $200. From the Ted Hake collection.

cken of the Sea folder (R) was a store promo brochure for store agers. #1. $125 #2. $100 #3. $75. Tuna recipes (above) included ool lunches for the kids. #1.$60 #2. $45 #3. $30. The tuna pencil ever, is quite rare. #1. $100 #2. $80 #3. $60.

HOPALONG CASSIDY
GIFT PREMIUMS
Available through purchases of
"Hoppy's Favorite"
JO-MAR DAIRY PRODUCTS
JO-MAR DAIRIES COMPANY
SALINA, KANSAS
PRATT, KANSAS

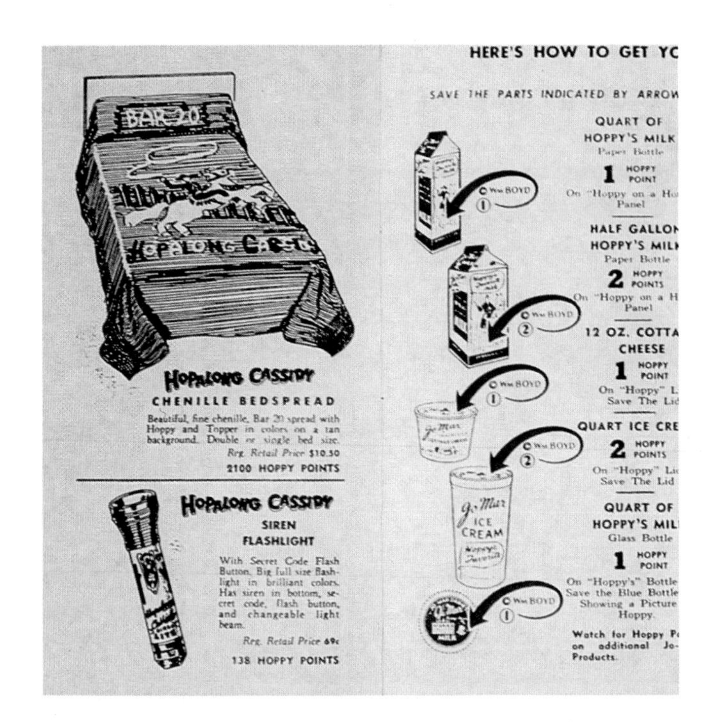

BAR 20
HOPALONG CASSIDY
CHENILLE BEDSPREAD
2100 HOPPY POINTS
HOPALONG CASSIDY
SIREN
FLASHLIGHT
With Secret Code Flash Button. Big full size flashlight in brilliant colors. Has siren in bottom, secret code, flash button, and changeable light beam.
Reg. Retail Price 69¢
138 HOPPY POINTS
QUARTER OF
HOPPY'S MILK
HALF GALLON
12 OZ. COTTA
CHEESE
QUART ICE CRE
QUART OF
HOPPY'S MIL
Glass Bottle
Jo-Mar
ICE
CREAM

Jo-Mar Dairies in Salina, Kansas, offered perhaps the highest dollar Hoppy premiums based on points for consuming their Hoppy products. This is the only listing I have been able to find that includes a pogo stick and the beadspread. Other Jo-Mar Dairy special promotions with Hoppy and Micky Mantle are also contained in this section.

The premium folder is worth: #1. $85 #2. $70 #3. $50.

HOPALONG CASSIDY
POGO STICK
Made of 1¼" steel tubing. Has rubber platform pedals, and molded rubber head of Topper on top. 50 inches long.
Reg. Retail Price $6.95
1390 HOPPY POINTS
HOPALONG CASSIDY
DELUXE WALLETS
Made of black calf plastic. Front is a bronze plate with colorful picture of Hoppy. Includes "top secret pocket" with lucky Hoppy coin.
Reg. Retail Price $1.15
230 HOPPY POINTS
HOPALONG CASSIDY
COWBOY HAT
Pure wool felt with genuine leather "Bar 20 Ranch" cord slide. Comes in small, medium, and large sizes.
Reg. Retail Price $1.95
390 HOPPY POINTS

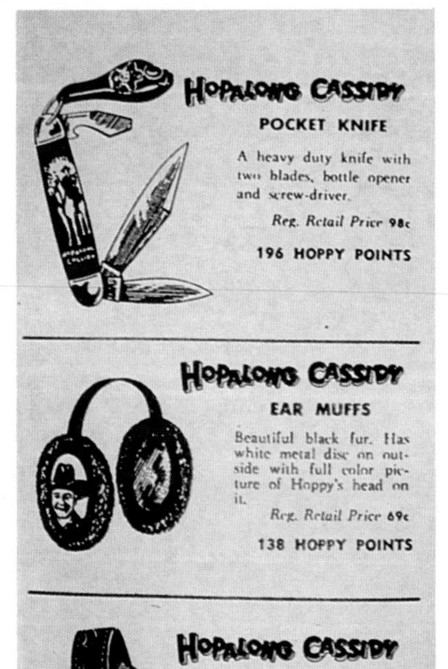

HOPALONG CASSIDY
POCKET KNIFE
A heavy duty knife with two blades, bottle opener and screw-driver.
Reg. Retail Price 98¢
196 HOPPY POINTS
HOPALONG CASSIDY
EAR MUFFS
Beautiful black fur. Has white metal disc on outside with full color picture of Hoppy's head on it.
Reg. Retail Price 69¢
138 HOPPY POINTS
HOPALONG CASSIDY
WRIST WATCH
Beautiful chrome case with stainless steel back. Black leather cowboy strap. Shockproof. Has gray dial with red hands and numbers. Has Hoppy's picture right on it.
Reg. Retail Price $6.95
1390 HOPPY POINTS

Grocery store hand-out cards that tell parents about the Hoppy TV show. #1. $30 #2. $20 #3. $15.

Guest Appearance card (store) had write-in area for special guest on the Hoppy TV show. #1. $150 #2. $125 #3. $100.

Store poster for "Snoboy Foods" informs Salt Lake viewers that Hoppy will be on channel 4 every Friday at 8:30PM. #1. $175 #2. $150 #3. $125

Full page magazine ad for Burnett's Pudding are readily available at $15 to $20.

Magazine ad for Post Cereals is quite common. Expect: $10 - $15.

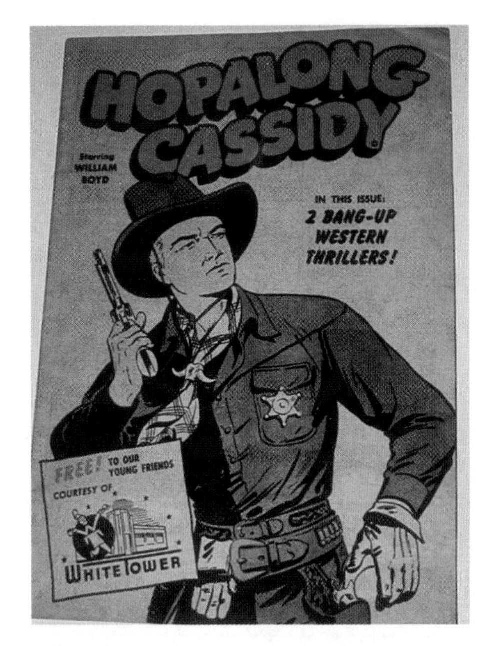

Special issue Hoppy color comic was just a few pages thick but a great promotion for White Tower hamburgers! very rare indeed: $150 #2. $130 #3. $100. from the Mike Forthun collection.

Rare Hoppy comic strip drawn by Dan Spiegle, included a "Blue Bonnet" ad underneath. #1. $80 #2. $70 #3. $50. From the Dennis Smith collection.

Hard to find "cereal pack" Hoppy ad shows him holding saddle. Great Hoppy image. Ad can be found in one of the 1950 issues of Look Magazine. Ad itself is valued at $20.

A great promotion find is this full page ad for Post Cereals promoting the free Hoppy trading cards inside each box. Ad is a difficult find but makes a great display piece: #1. $40 #2. $30 #3. $20.

A different Post Cereals ad featuring Hoppy and promoting the free Western Badges on Post Grape Nuts Flakes. This ad seems to be more common: #1. $25 #2. $15 #3. $10.

Cover of the Jo-Mar Dairies premium pack featuring Hoppy and Mickey Mantle. Item is very rare.

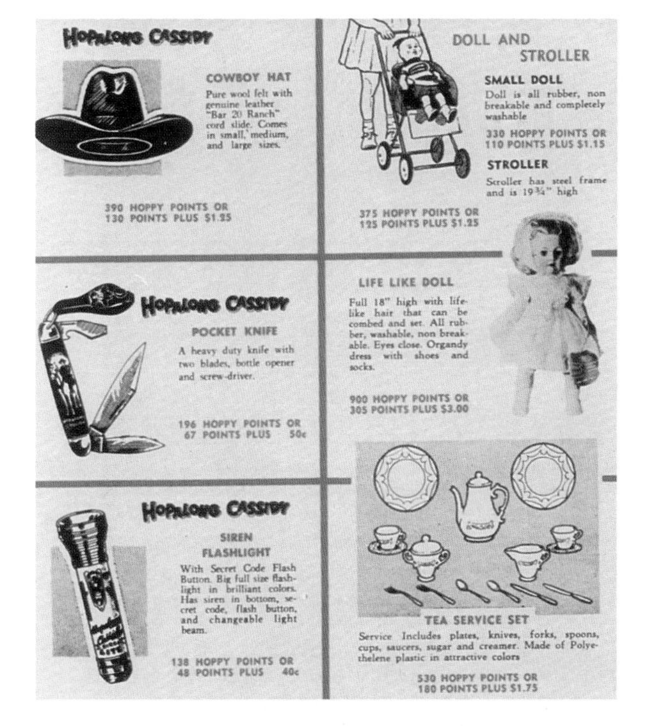

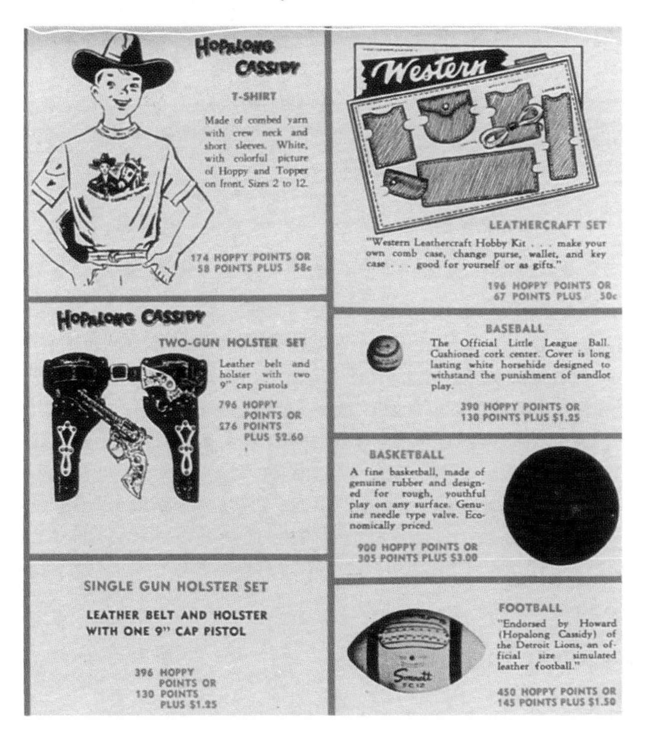

Jo-Mar put together a "sure fire" promotion program using two of the biggest 1950's heroes: Hoppy and Mickey Mantle. Inside pages show many of the great Hoppy items kids could have from cap gun sets to hats and tee shirts with Jo-Mar's "Hoppy Points." A demand item and very rare, the Jo-Mar premium brochure is: #1. $135 #2. $110 #3. $100. From the Ted Hake collection.

FOOD ENDORSEMENTS

#1. condition: mint, showing no use #2. condition: excellent to near mint #3. condition: good to very good

Hoppy endorsed literally hundreds of food companies and food items during his career, some of which bore his name as a product brand: Hopalong Cassidy Potato Chips, Chewing gum, "Hopalong" candy bars and the rare "Hopalong Cassidy" cookies. Some of the highest collector values are apparent in food endorsement items such as the Hoppy "Delicia" ice cream cone box that recently sold for over $1,200 (without cones) and a Hoppy cereal box wrapper that brought over $1,100, just to name a few. Limited to space, we will feature the most popular items as well as a few of the very rarest. I wanted to show you the 1936 Wheaties Hoppy box but wasn't able to get it. You will find however, the back panel to this rare item in the "cereals" section of this chapter. Vegetarians will no doubt smack their lips over the Hoppy Green Beans can, as will the rest of us. Remember, #1. values reflect mint - unused condition, #2. is excellent to near mint and #3. is good to very good.

WHAT TIME IS IT ANYWAY?

While endorsement items are usually coveted principally by paper collectors, I decided to put some very neat "hard products" here to attract the interest of everyone. "Food Endorsements" is a very big chapter covering almost unthinkable items. The store clocks displayed have mostly reached "Investment" value these days with starting values over $1,200 in #1 or #2 condition: Cloverlake (UL) $1,850, Royalcrest (above) $2,200, and Royalcrest All Star (L) $1,200

Cloverlake clock is from the Brian Beirne collection, The All Star is from the Jon & Charlie Cheek collection.

tail photo of rare irylea wall clock (R) wing Hoppy graphics. mplete clock (below) is unique square shape ve clock (won't run by elf) and the only one of kind that I've seen. vestment value is ,200. From the Brian irne collection.

The Cloverlake Dairy wall clock and ice cream selection marquee (above) is perhaps the rarest Hoppy clock anywhere. Investment value clock was reportedly offered for sale last year for $3,400. From the Sharon Delaney collection.

Linton Dairy clock (L) is identical to Royalcrest on the previous page. Values are also similar. From the Jon & Charlie Cheek collection.

You have no doubt collected a few, but walked past many samples of Producers Dairy Hoppy endorsement products thinking they are reproduction. They are not. Still called "Hoppy's Headquarters" Producers has used Hoppy on its products since 1950, and continue to do so today. The owners of Producers had a strong relationship with Bill and Grace Boyd, even to the point of naming their farm "Producers Bar-20" (below R). This recent article appeared in the Fresno paper about the Producers/ Hoppy relationship.

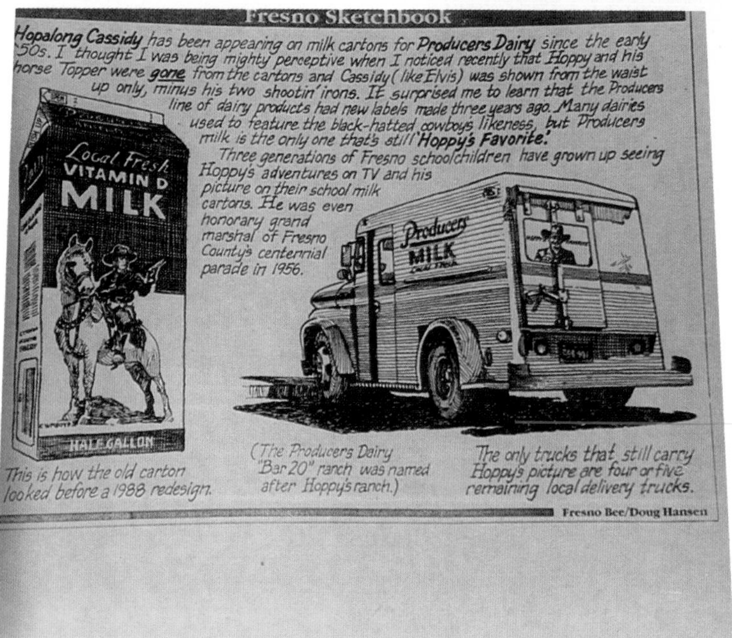

Fresno Sketchbook

Hopalong Cassidy has been appearing on milk cartons for Producers Dairy since the early '50s. I thought I was being mighty perceptive when I noticed recently that Hoppy and his horse Topper were gone from the cartons and Cassidy (like Elvis) was shown from the waist up only, minus his two shootin' irons. It surprised me to learn that the Producers line of dairy products had new labels made three years ago. Many dairies used to feature the black-hatted cowboy's likeness, but Producers milk is the only one that's still 'Hoppy's Favorite.'

Three generations of Fresno schoolchildren have grown up seeing Hoppy's adventures on TV and his picture on their school milk cartons. He was even honorary grand marshal of Fresno County's centennial parade in 1956.

Local Fresh VITAMIN D MILK HALF GALLON

Producers MILK

This is how the old carton looked before a 1988 redesign.

(The Producers Dairy "Bar 20" ranch was named after Hoppy's ranch.)

The only trucks that still carry Hoppy's picture are four or five remaining local delivery trucks.

Fresno Bee/Doug Hansen

While no longer used (or available) Producers had a fleet of home delivery trucks (L) with a bust of Hoppy on every one. The truck shown is a 1959 Ford, which was the last used for home delivery. Owned by Brian Beirne, "Mr. Rock & Roll" a disc jockey in Los Angeles (KERTH 101 FM). Brian who was always a Hoppy fan since birth, bought the truck and lovingly restored it to pristine condition. Its value? Somewhere in the area of $10,000!

e metal signs on this page are but a few used by ›ducers Dairy over their long history with Hoppy. ove is a 4'x7' building sign that probably has an estment value of $5,000. From the Phil Ellis collection. low is a large metal embossed 1950's milk carton sign ıt top) with a $1,200 value. From the Charles Ringhel lection. The 30' high metal sign (LR) still graces the ›ducers Dairy corporate offices in Fresno, California. It ıot for sale!

Chairman of Producers Dairy, Mr. Larry Shehadey (R) and son Richard Shehadey (L) who is now president, hold one of the few remaining metal truck-side signs from years ago. Current Producers products will not show Hoppy on Topper with guns drawn, older ones will. People have complained that a "gun drawn" image was not proper for milk containers. Most all of Producers products, from eggs to cottage cheese, and of course milk (even lo-fat) continues to bear Hoppy's image.

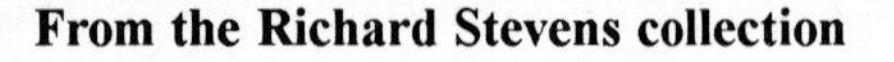

From the Richard Stevens collection

Producers products have been around since 195 and are very collectible. The sour cream co tainer with metal lid (UL) is: #1. $155 #2. $13 #3. $100. Old egg cartons are $45. new ones: $1 Boxes of butter (above) old version (Hoppy o Topper) is $35, new version: $10. Old versio of milk containers (Hoppy on Topper w/ gu drawn) is now $15 in #1. condition, new versions (as shown) bring $5. Thanks to Stev Axelson of Arizona for the neat photo of a pla of Producers butter.

Many dairies carried Hoppy on their bottles to promote health. Collectors try and find them to promote wealth. Hoppy graphics came in several colors: brown, black and red mostly, I will not include the small value separation that colors bring. The above photo shows all the bottle sizes (from L to R) of 1/2 pt., 1 pt., 1 Qt., 1/2 gallon. The photo (R) shows 1/2 gallon compared to rare 1 gallon milk. Notice the wire handle. 1/2 pt. #1. $75 #2. $60 #3. $50. Pint size: #1.$65 #2. $50 #3. $40. Quart: #1. $80 #2. $60 #3. $50 1/2 gal.: #1. $115 #2. $100 #3. $85. Gallon: $375 #2. $325 #3. $280.

The above photo shows two rare milk bottles: 1/2 gallon and gallon size. What we weren't able to show you was the Hoppy "creamer" bottles which had a bubble neck to catch the cream. Creamers (quarts) are worth: #1. $125 #2. $115 #3. $100.

Hoppy top wrappers (L) for bottles are quite rare to find. Expect to pay $25 -$35 for one in good shape. There are a variety of original Hoppy "pogs" (stoppers) from many dairies in different sizes. Expect to pay $15 for the quart size, and $20 to $25 for the 1/2 gallon. The Dairy bills (below) is a nice find for $20, in good shape.

Bills Payable Weekly

DAIRYMEN'S League

CO-OPERATIVE ASSOCIATION, INC.

DAIRYLEA Milk PRODUCTS

PHONE 34283 — 127 CLARK ST.

Route No. ____ Auburn, N. Y. ____ 19__

NAME ____ Acc't No. ____

ADDRESS ____

Period or Week Ending ____ 19__

Qts. Milk
Pts. Milk
Qts. Milk
Pts. Milk
Qts. Heavy Cream
½ Pts. Heavy Cream
½ Pts. Cream
Qts. Buttermilk
Cheese
Lbs. Butter

Weekly Amount Due
Previous Balance Due
Total Amount Due
Cash Received - Date
Balance

Routeman or Collector Sig. ____

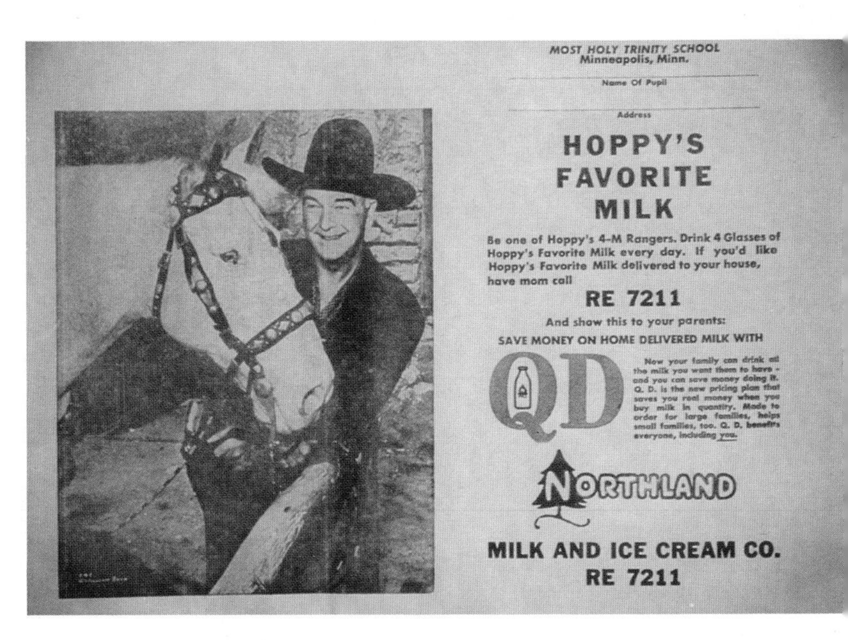

MOST HOLY TRINITY SCHOOL
Minneapolis, Minn.

Name Of Pupil

Address

HOPPY'S
FAVORITE
MILK

Be one of Hoppy's 4-M Rangers. Drink 4 Glasses of Hoppy's Favorite Milk every day. If you'd like Hoppy's Favorite Milk delivered to your house, have mom call

RE 7211

And show this to your parents:
SAVE MONEY ON HOME DELIVERED MILK WITH

QD

Now your family can drink all the milk you want them to have - and you can save money doing it. Q. D. is the new pricing plan that saves you real money when you buy milk in quantity. Made to order for large families, helps small families, too. Q. D. benefits everyone, including you.

NORTHLAND

MILK AND ICE CREAM CO.
RE 7211

From the Dennis Smith collection.

From the Dennis Smith collection.

Paper milk containers replaced bottles in the 1950's with the advent of the heavily waxed "flat top" (shown (R) and below). Earlier versions were generally two-color (see Dairylea) which then progressed to the more graphic "tent top" design we are familiar with today. The milk bills still came in a brown envelope (upper right) and were issued to schools as well as homes. The Northland Hoppy milk bill envelope shown is a good collector item for: $20 - $35. Flat-top containers (quarts) are: #1. $240 #2. $225 #3. $180.

It is very easy to tell a current "tent top" milk container from an older version simply by checking for the amount of wax that coats the container. The Leigh Valley container has much more wax than the Northland; therefore it is older. Generally, quart waxed "tent top" containers are: $180 in #2. condition. 1/2 gallon sizes are $215. Photos (left and above) are from the Jon & Charlie Cheek collection.

There are a lot of NOS (new old stock) O'Fallon Dairy qt. ice cream containers around keeping that value reasonable. Expect to pay $85 to $95 for a mint O'Fallon Qt. and lid.

A rare bulk Weber's gallon ice cream container surfaced that shows Hoppy both on the lid and container side: #1. $275 #2. $250 #3. $215. From the Jon & Charlie Cheek collection.

Single serving size ice cream lids remain while the small cups have pretty much vanished. Ice cream promotion pins (below) were give to customers who purchased. Pins today are $40 in #1. Ice cream lids with Hoppy on the outside or bottom are in demand items. Values range from $25 to $75 each, depending on size, picture and the dairy that made it.

Dairylea selection of 1 pt. flavors for a collectors sweet tooth. #1. $95 #2. $80 #3. $70. From the Jon & Charlie Cheek collection.

NOS (new old stock) promotion hangers (bottom) advertise "bulk style" Hoppy ice cream. Expect to pay $30 each.

Note: Ice cream lids date back to 1936 as promotion pieces for early Hoppy films. Look for the Paramount Studios name and the name of the film to be sure.

Ice cream aluminum foil chill bags (L) were offered by many dairies: #1. $40 #2. $30 #3. $20. TV ice cream box (UL) from Brown's Dairy is a nice collectors find: #1. $100 #2. $85 #3. $70. Ice cream cones are especially rare (above) and in demand by collectors. Investment value has one box selling at auction for $1,200 and others selling between $800 and $1,000. (both photos from the Jon & Charlie Cheek collection. (More ice cream cup photos on last pages of chapter).

A recent find of NOS Cloverlake ice cream boxes (LL) in a variety of flavors. These boxes are selling at $40 to $50 each. (From the Porter Albin collection.) Full color box of Puritan ice cream Qt. size (below) is a great find: #1. $85 #2. $70 #3. $60. (from the Bill Hoffman collection).

Cottage cheese lids of both paper and metal are good collectors items. The above assortment is from the Jon & Charlie Cheek collection. Metal lids are more ornate and have a higher collector value. Expect to pay $25 to $50 for paper lids and $65 to $85 for metal.

Nice cardboard container is a good find: #1. $120 #2. $90 #3. $70.

tail photo of two cottage cheese lids; left is metal, right is paper. The Country ub lid (#2) is $75, the Puritan (#2) is $60. The paper "large curd" lid (R) is $50 #2 condition.

Producers cottage cheese w/ metal lid.#1. $110 #2. $90 #3. $70

Assortment of cottage cheese containers with individual size Hoppy ice cream container in center. Ice cream container (no lid) in #2. is: $60 Dairylea cottage cheese (L) is: #1. $95 #2. $70 #3. $60. Lindale (R) is: #1. $95 #2. $70 #3. $60. both have lids. from the Jon & Charlie Cheek collection.

Yellow plastic "Hoppy Dinner milk" glass was also used as cottage cheese container for special promo's. Plastic glasses are: #1. $135 #2. $120 #3. $100. Lids (plastic) are: #1. $150 #2. $110 #3. $90

"Westren Series" glasses were sometimes used as food container for special promo's. Metal Dairylea lid fits perfectly. Glass: #1 $90 #2. $75 #3. $60. Lid: #1. $190 #2. $170 #3. $150. From the Jo & Charlie Cheek collection.

Display of different cottage cheese lids from the Jon & Charlie Cheek collection.

Rare 1/2 pint bottle from Sanida Dairy Erie PA looks to have a creamer top and has a paper Hoppy decal. #1. $175 #2 $140 #3. $100. From the Howard Reidinger collection.

There are so many samples of "Spun Honey" paper coasters around that many feel they are reproduction. I think they may be right. Mint coasters (L) show no ageing at all, but to make matters more complicated, someone is producing "Spun Honey" fantasy items such as the plastic nite light and plastic pencil sharpeners. There are original "Spun Honey" pieces however, including the recipes coaster shown above from the Mike Merryman collection. On the back of each is a printed recipe for using the product. This original piece is worth $40 while reproduced coasters are $5 and the nite lite is $10.

Barbara Ann Bread (Los Angeles) was also a Hoppy endorsement product. Shown (L) is a bakery roll of wrappers which sold at auction for $700 as well as a rare Barbara Ann strip of end-labels with Hoppy on each. The end-labels are from the Jon & Charlie Cheek collection. This strip of labels are not common because they were not saved like Bond bread end-labels. Investment value for this strip would be: $100.

Large cardboard store display Bond Bread sign came in black & white and this colored version: #1. $250 #2. $200 #3. $150. size is aprox: 36" wide and 30" high.

Store display bread loaf "dummies" came in a variety of shapes and sizes (above). Foam displays are being made from styrofoam and original wrappers. They are reasonably priced at around $70 each, but do not generally have end-labels.

Hoppy metal embossed sign (above) is a reproduction item selling for $10 to $15. Photo at left was taken at the Bond Bread factory as a news promotion when Hoppy first endorsed the product. All the drivers were dressed as Hoppy. Copies of the 11x14" photo are available for $40 in most areas.

Another sample of a store bread "dummy" loaf for sandwich bread (L) there are samples of wheat bread as well.

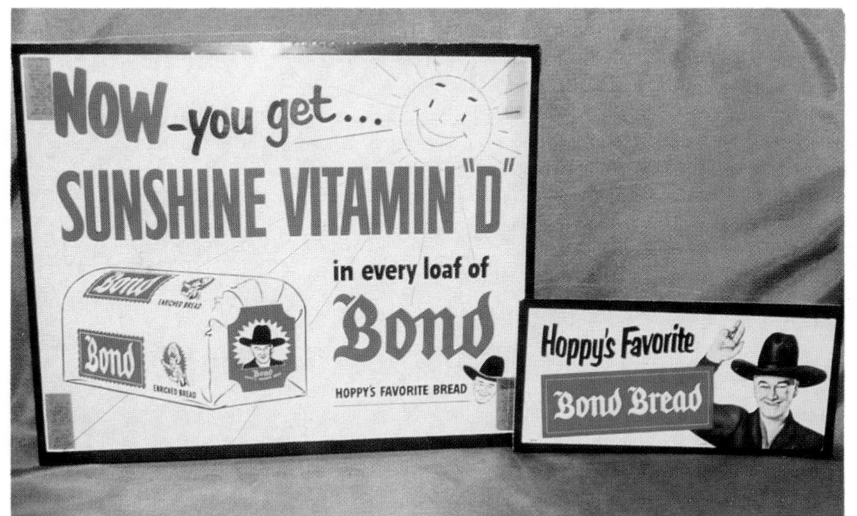

Store display ads promoting Bond Bread with vitamin "D" added (above) are quite rare as well as the smaller store sign seen to the right. The large sign was designed as a window mount (notice adhesive tape areas shown) but could be placed elsewhere. Sign is heavy paper. #1. (Investment value) $450. Smaller sign is also paper: #1 $175 #2. $150 #3. $125. From the Jon & Charlie Cheek collection.

Stroehmann's Bread Hoppy jig-saw premium puzzle (other items in "food promotions" chapter) Quite similar to the Hoppy game the company made. #1. $245 #2. $200 #3. $175. from the Jon & Charlie Cheek collection.

The fabled Hoppy Green Beans is shown here as a store display can that is sealed at both ends, but without contents. The proud owner of this can turned down $1,200 for it in my presence. An "investment value" item it is, without doubt. From the Frank Smith collection.

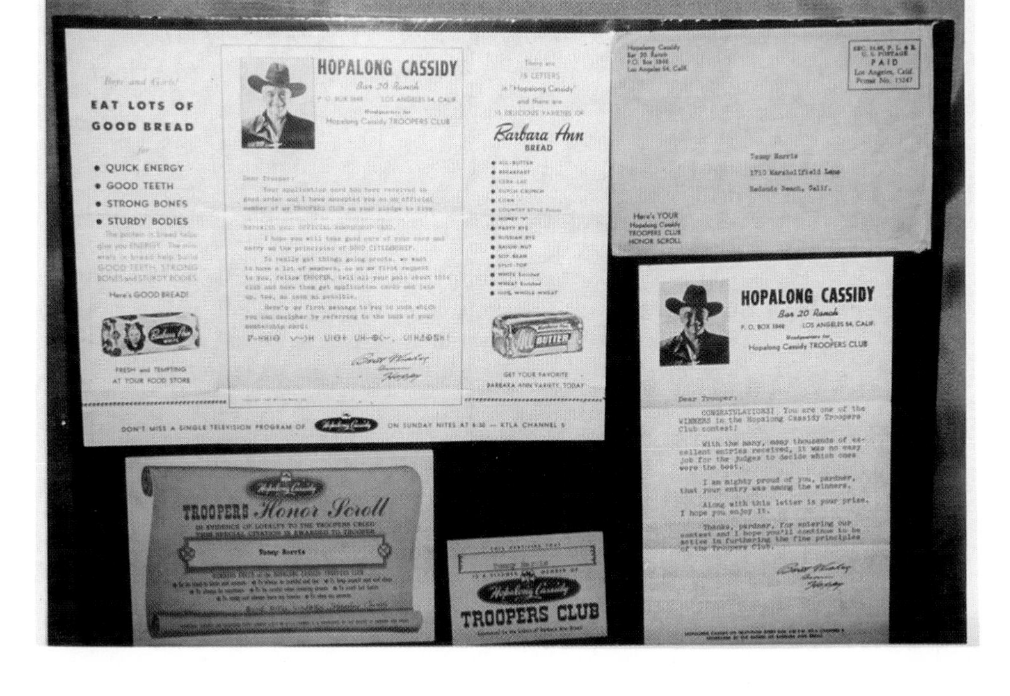

Rare Barbara Ann Bread "Troopers Club" promotion with "Honor Scroll" card and personal letters, mailing envelope. A very nice (and complete) set of endorsement related promotions. Complete set has investment value: $450. From the Jon & Charlie Cheek collection

White Star tuna can and recipe book. White Star soon became "Chicken of the Sea," which Hoppy also endorsed. White Star can (opened): #2. $325 #3. $275. Tuna recipes (L) show both White Star & "Chicken." Recipe books are: #1. $65 #2. $50 #3. $40. (From the Charlie Cheek collection). Colorful "Chicken" ad and recipe (L) is from the Brian Beirne collection and is worth $25. Large display of White Star recipes (R) is from the Ted Hake Americana Auctions.

"Chicken of the Sea" Hoppy tuna is harder to find than "White Star" which was the same company. "Chicken" values are $75 higher than the earlier version. If the can is sealed but empty (a store display can) it is easily valued at: #1. $600 #2. $550 #3. $475. From the Jon & Charlie Cheek collection.

Detail photo of inside of White Star recipe book (above) is from the Ted Hake Americana Auctions.

Another new potato chip find is this NOS 25 cent "family size" bag. There are just a few on the market for $300 to $350. From the Lee Mitchell collection.

Potato chip bags are a recent discovery in Hoppy food endorsements. A great many NOS 10 cent bags have been found from Kuehmann Foods. Prices seem to vary from $65 to $200 per bag, but I think will stabilize at around $60. From the Jon & Charlie Cheek collection.

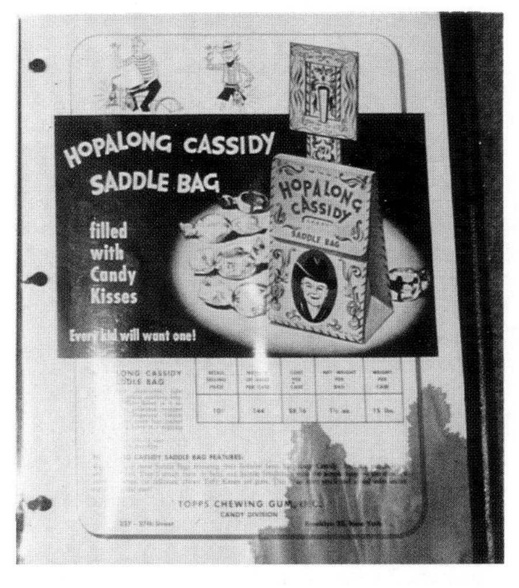

Salesmans' sample sheet for Hoppy saddlebag "candy kisses." Sheet indicates store prices and volumes. Complete "kisses" bags are rare and worth $150 each. Sales sheet is $ 75 in #1. and $60 in #2. Complete sales kit including new "kisses" bag is $450. From the Mike Forthun collection.

It is important to view the back of the Hoppy Green Bean can which shows a chuck wagon and offers a bean recipe. There are other reported Hoppy can foods that were made, and may still exist. keep your eye out for: Hoppy Collard Greens, Hoppy Peas, Hoppy Corn and Hoppy Peaches! Our thanks to Frank Smith for sharing this rare item with us.

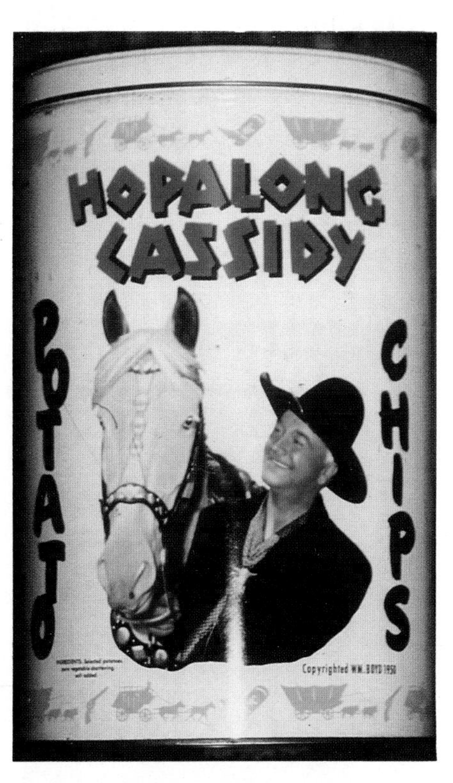

Large economy potato chip tin by the same company that makes the bags: #1. $375 #2. $330 #3. $280. (top should have "Bar-20" decal)

One of the most sought after Hoppy items is the famous (but hard to find) chocolate coconut candy bar (above). Pictured next to the bottom of a store candy box, the Hoppy bar or bar wrapper has an investment value of over $500. From the Jon & Charlie Cheek collection. The cardboard store display box (below) also shows the saddlebag "kisses" bag and the Hoppy party candy holder (see party & plates chapter).

Nearly as rare as the Hoppy candy bar, this store sign was a good point-of-purchase display piece near store candy displays: #1. $750 #2. $700 #3 $625. From the Brian Beirne collection.

There are more Hoppy store candy boxes around than candy bars or wrappers. Cardboard box had a die-cut lid that when opened, displayed Hoppy's hat and head. #1. $525 #2. $450 #3. $400. The small bag to the right is a saddlebag"candy kisses" bag without the top portion. Bags in this condition are worth $100.

Hopalong Cassidy Cookies were made by Burry's and are a great find today. Each box of cookies contained a free Hoppy badge and the back panel had several Hoppy cut-outs and action scenes. This is an "investment value" item with prices in the $300 - $500 range. If the package was sealed with contents, it would be even more. From the Jon & Charlie Cheek collection. More photos later in this chapter.

tail photo of peanut butter mug with original
ntents. Lid is scratched and faded, considered in #3
ndition.

Peanut butter was once contained in many of those colorful mugs we now collect (above) The two lidded mugs shown still contain original product: #1. $375 #2. $340 #3. $300. "Big Top" lids are" #1. $225 #2. $180 #3. $155. Special promo lid (R) for a photo of Hoppy is: #1. $250 #2. $225 #3. $200. From the Jon & Charlie Cheek collection.

rawberry Preserves 5" glass from Choice
ods, Inc. Glass w/ label is: $145. Glass w/
el & lid is $240. With contents: $350.
om the Jon & Charlie Cheek collection.

Rare unknown product glass seems to have "cloud" lunch box decal. Glass seems original but contents and maker are not known. #1. $300 #2. $230 #3. $200. Jon & Charlie Cheek collection.

Maryland Popcorn can unopened with contents:#1. $350 #2. $300 #3. $275. Empty or topless can deduct $100 in each condition.

Orange Marmalade glass from Choice Foods, Inc. Values similar to Strawberry version.

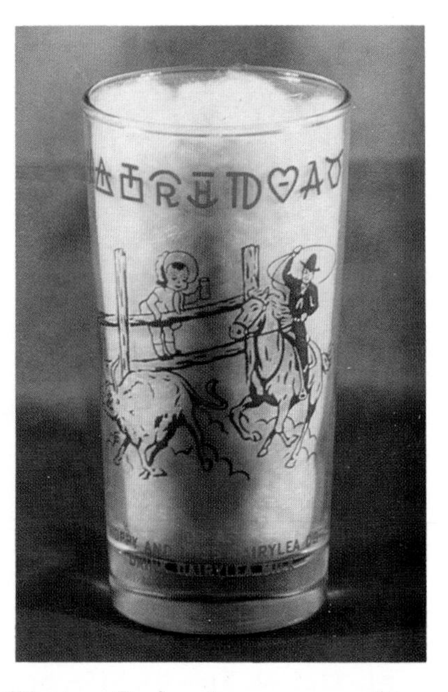

Western Series glasses were sold as a set and many were containers for cottage cheese (Dairylea). Set contained six different motifs. #1. $110 #2. $95 #3. $80.

Betsy Ross grape juice recipe book and product sheet is a nice endorsement find: #1. $100 #2. $75 #3. $60

Unusual Betsy Ross grape juice bottle (1 Pt.) is a nice find: #1. $175 #2. $150 #3. $125. From the Charlie Cheek collection.

Betsy Ross grape juice cans: #1. $175 #2. $140 #3. $100. If unopened with contents add $100. Betsy Ross juice bottle (above) remains unopened with original cap & contents. #1. $375 #2. $340 #3. $300

"Hoppy-Aid" drink mix came in several flavors (also see food promotions chapter) and is a great find: #1. $275 #2. $240 #3. $200 (add $100 if unopened with contents).

Display of nickel & Penny chewing gum wrappers and cards.

Penny chewing gum in original wrapper (R) with trading card inside: #1.$225 Gum wrapper only: $95. Nickle gum wrapper: $130. If unopened: $325. A Hoppy greeting card also contained a penny gum.

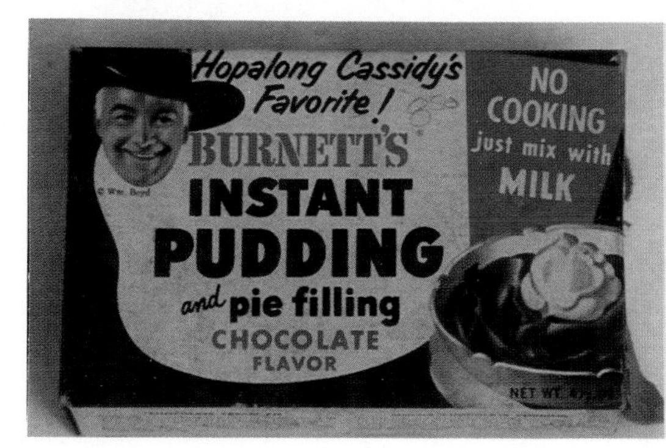

Burnett's pudding boxes are a great collectors find in any flavor: #1. $250 #2. $220 #3. $190. (unopened with contents add $100).

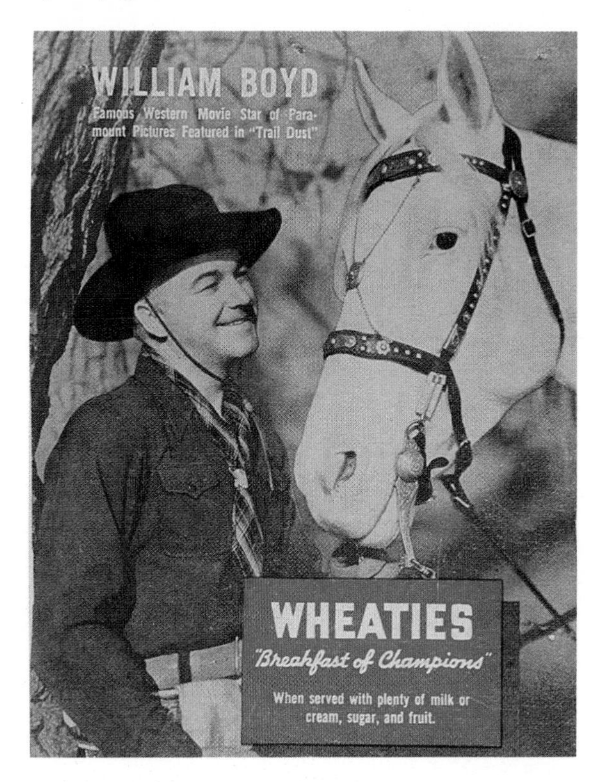

Item on right may not look like much but it is the back panel from a 1938 box of "Wheaties" cereal, and the first real Hoppy endorsement. There are a few complete boxes around today at an investment value of over $1,000. From the Brian Beirne collection.

Once free samples of Post's Wheat Meal in #1. condition will now bring $275 for this individual serving size box. If box still has contents, add $100. Hoppy endorsed many of the Post cereal products.

Photo of "family size" Post's 40% Bran Flakes along side of Wheat Meal sample box. Hoppy cereal boxes have recently increased in value: #1. $1,000 #2. $850 #3. $775. If box is unopened with cereal inside it would have an investment value of $1,400.

Post's Grape Nuts Flakes free Hoppy comic book (above) could have been listed in "promotions" or "comics" chapters, but ended-up here. If you bought the cereal during this promotion, you got a free comic book. Investment value: #1. $300. From the Brian Beirne collection.

Store delivery box for Hoppy chewing gum: #1. $275 #2. $225 #3. $175. From the Boyd Magers (Western Clippings) collection.

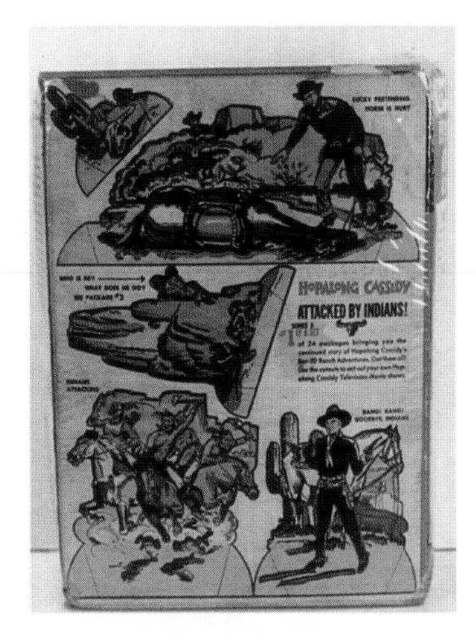

Back panel of Hopalong Cassidy Cookies. See next page for front cover graphics and values.

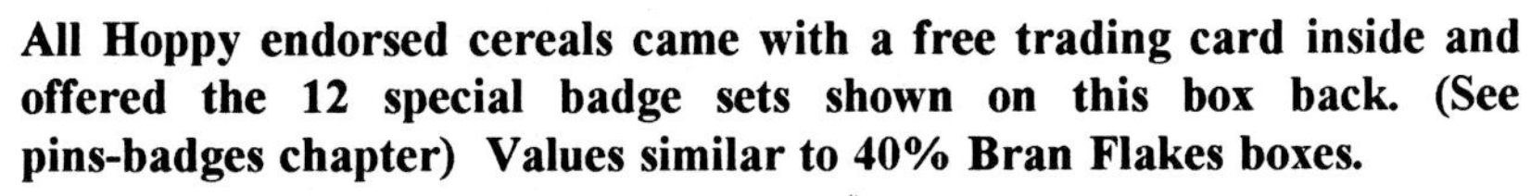

All Hoppy endorsed cereals came with a free trading card inside and offered the 12 special badge sets shown on this box back. (See pins-badges chapter) Values similar to 40% Bran Flakes boxes.

an Flakes box back had an ad for Hoppy's trading cards as ng inside each box. Such a deal! Other boxes advertised for stern badges (see above box).

In later years, cereal boxes had a box wrapper (similar to today) and is shown on the above box of Grape Nuts Flakes. Early in 1996 a Hoppy cereal wrapper sold at auction for over $1,100 (without a box inside). From the Jon & Charlie Cheek collection.

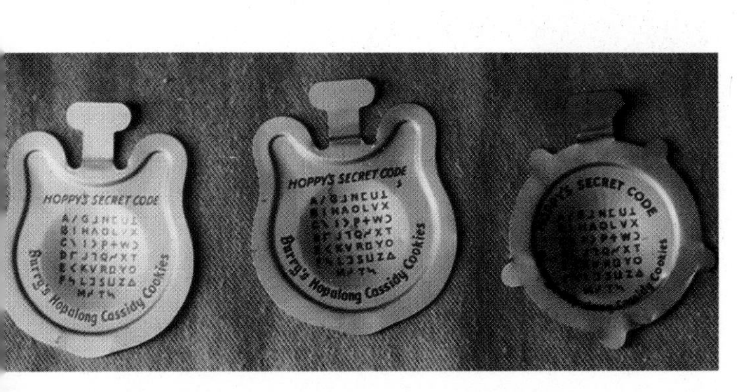

arry's Cookies Hoppy badges (backs) show secret code. (See adges chapter). From the "AJ" Siarkowski collection.

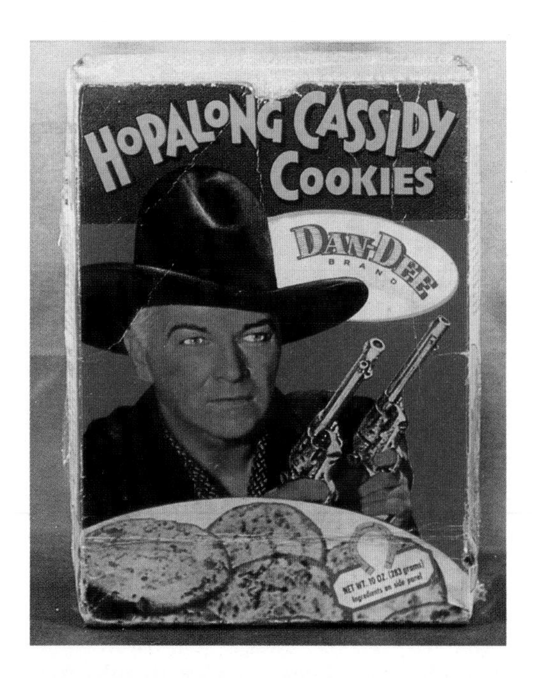

Hoppy Cookies were made by two different bakeries (above) and are both very rare and difficult to find. It is interesting to note that they both had the same box design, and wonder if the "Dan-Dee" brand became "Burry's" in 1954. In either event, they are a great (but expensive) find: #1. $550. #2. $425. #3. $350. (if the box is unopened, and has cookies inside, add $150). From the Jon & Charlie Cheek collection.

Crystal Pure Candy tried to get in the Hoppy craze in 1950 by making "Western Kid Pops" in containers shaped like holsters. Note that the young model is dressed in full Hoppy garb with stickers placed over the Hoppy identification points. Guess they were too cheap to get an endorsement.

Special packages of Hoppy's Burnett's Pudding had a send-away for premium which was the color, Hoppy cardboard mask. A great likeness of Bill Boyd, the mask had eye holes and a nose flap. Back of mask can be found in "Food Promotions" chapter. #1.$225 #2. $185 #3. $160. From the Jon & Charlie Cheek collection.

Hudson's Ice Cream quart cardboard container is similar to O'Fallon's except much more rare: #1. $140 #2. $110 #3. $85. From the Jon & Charlie Cheek collection.

Seldom found in one collection are all three sizes of Hoppy cereal boxes. Free sample size of Wheat Meal (L) Standard size of Raisin Brand and Grape -Nuts Flakes and large, economy size of Post Toasties. While all Hoppy cereal boxes are hard to find, the "family size" economy box is the rarest. Outside of the Wheat Meal box, the other three have colorful plastic sleeves or wrappers that covered the entire box. The small trial size Wheat Meal box is: #1. $375 #2. $325 #3. $275 (add $75 if sealed with contents). The two "standard" size boxes: #1. $1,000 #2. $850 #3. $775. The large box wrapper: #1. $1,200 #2. $1,050 #3. $975. (add $400 if sealed with contents). From the Jon & Charlie Cheek collection.

A great find for any collection would be the Post cereals shipping box which contained 12, 12oz. boxes of "Toasties." While not as valuable a find as the cereal boxes, a shipping box is still very collectible and a $350 price would not be uncommon. From the Jon & Charlie Cheek collection.

This pristine box of Delicia Hoppy ice cream cones had to be seen to be believed. There are also a few boxes of sugar cones known to exist. (the above cones are near perfect). #1. $1,350 #2. $1,200 #3. $1,050.

This wonderful Lehigh Valley metal store sign was a late arrival for the book but had to be shown. One of the prettiest signs I've seen. The size is about 3'x4' and is probably 1955 vintage: #1. $525 #2. $450 #3. $375. From the Jon & Charlie Cheek collection.

Paper store "trading cards" promotion poster is a late arrival and a great collector piece. Note the graphics and color. #1. $325 #2. $275 #3. $225. It is very hard to find one at all, much less in such good condition. From the Jon & Charlie Cheek collection.

Large cardboard container of "Royal Crest" cottage cheese is similar in design to O'Fallon's ice cream with similar colors. #1. $80 #2. $70 #3. $60. The small container is "Polk's" cottage cheese and is a difficult find: #1. $85 #2. $70 #3. $60. From the Jon & Charlie Cheek collection.

This Hoppy recepie brochure from White Star Tuna is a nice display piece. It carries the brand name on the reverse side as well as Hoppy's image. #1. $65 #2. $50 #3. $40. from the Ted Hake collection.

One quart box of Hoppy's "Victory" chocolate ice cream is similar to the "Puritan" brand shown earlier. #1. $85 #2. $70 #3. $60.

FURNISHINGS & ACCESSORIES

#1. condition: mint, showing no use #2. condition: excellent to near mint #3. condition: good to very good

The Furnishings & Accessories will begin at the most logical place; Hoppy furniture. Crafted from solid Maple, the Hoppy bedroom set was very sedate in design, and bore little, if any, identification marks, making it a big problem for collectors trying to find some. The bedroom set shown, all eleven pieces, is the largest set known to exist. It was part of an estate sale, and original delivery papers authenticate all pieces and identify the delivery date as May 15th, 1954. The complete set of course, qualifies as "investment value" grade which may be worth $10,000 to some lucky collector or museum.

Hoppy desk and chair from bedroom set.

Detail photo of leather identifying Hoppy patch attached to desk front. There were only two such patches used on the entire set.

There were two different Hoppy desks produced, al carried the leather ID patch. The desk not shown was a drop-leaf design with no leg space underneath The board or 'slat' design was used to make the pieces appear more rustic. Desk: #1. $2,500 #2 $2,000 #3. $1,800. Chair: #1. $650 #2. $450 #3. $375 (chair has no Hoppy markings, but has matching design features).

The Hoppy bureau (L) is the only other furniture piece that carried the Hoppy leather ID patch on the inset bureau panel (behind center white tin). The 'slat' door on the right, opened to reveal several sliding drawers. Note the iron-like, black drawer pulls, a distinctive feature. #1. $2,800 #2. $2,300 #3. $2,100.

Hoppy toy chest that came with the set (above) had a rounded ' top and an iron-like front plate, designed with a dummy hole. There were no Hoppy markings. For the critics out there: ı piece of furniture came with a stencil ID ber hidden on the bottom, and the distribu- name. All the numbers match. #1. $2,300 $1,900 #3. $1,600. Notice iron-like handles oy chest sides, they match the design and e of those used on other pieces.

Detail photo showing toy chest (L) open

: toy chest shown on the right is believed be the newer version, and has a color ppy decal on the front and the name ›palong Cassidy" on the lid. Notice that lid is flat. There are no iron-like handles each side. This trunk version seems to be re common and due to the Hoppy graph- more valuable: #1. $3,500 #2. $2,800 #3. 400. From the Jon & Charlie Cheek ection.

The ranch sign (L) is similar in all versions of Hoppy furniture sets. The sign support is grooved so that it will mount on the head-board of the Hoppy bunk beds. #1. $650 #2. $500 #3. $400.

Detail photo of desk chair design

Unique Hoppy stool (above) was included in the set and had a long neck with an attached metal ring fastened to the center. No one can come up with the actual use of this stool or the reason for the fastened metal ring and long neck. #1. $650 #2. $450 #3. $375.

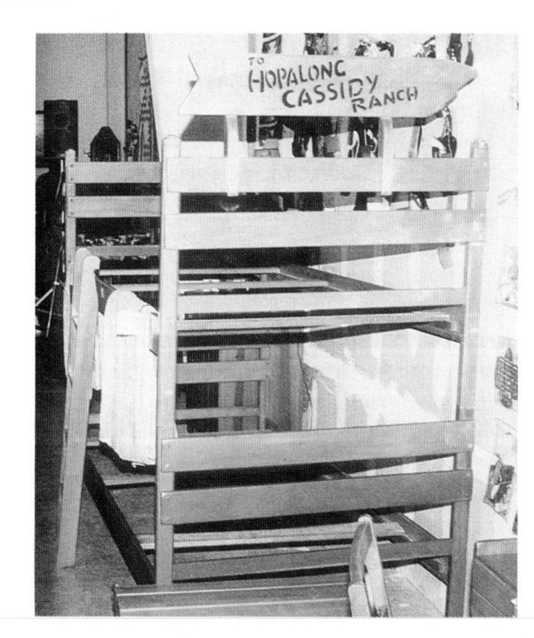

Hoppy bunk beds (above) are shown with "Hopalong Cassid Ranch" sign and wooden ladder. There are very few desig characteristics that would identify the beds without the remov able sign. #1. $1,500 #2. $1,200 #3. $1,000

'Standard' bureau and partially shown wall mirror of th Hoppy set. Note the similarity of key plate and drawer-pulls t other pieces. Mirror is similar. Bureau: #1. $2,600 #2. $2,200 #3 $1,900 Mirror: $650 #2. $550 #3. $475

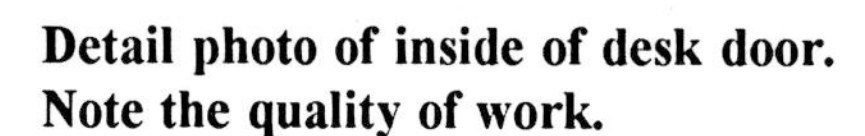

**Detail photo of inside of desk door.
Note the quality of work.**

ere are three sizes and several ferent designs of the popular ppy TV folding chair, all of m being very collectible. It is ficult to find these chairs in #1 even #2 condition because of deterioration of the vinyl ks and seat. Shown on the ht, are two excellent versions of chair with the most popular phics. #1. $525 #2. $450 #3. '5. From the Jon & Charlie eek collection.

unique Hoppy TV chair on the right has a brown leatherette seat with , and a brown studded back rest. #1. $900 #2. $800 #3. $650.

Hoppy metal rocking chair (L) came with a removable wooden 'Topper' and reins. Topper's head could be unbolted when child grew. Seat ms came in different colors (black, red, brown) #1. $675 #2. $550 #3. (deduct $250 without head) From the Jon & Charlie Cheek collection.

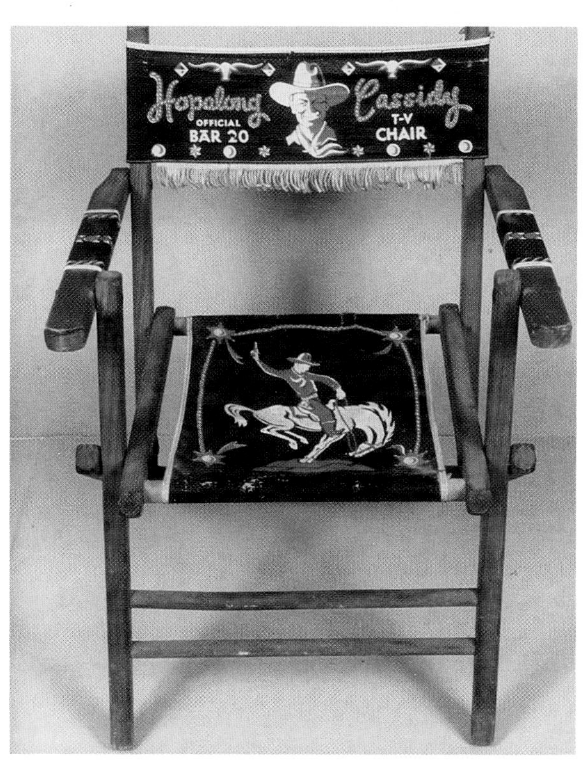

Detail photo of the Hoppy "director's chair" from the Ted Hake collection.

There were several versions of the Hoppy Clothes Corral and along with values, will be shown on the next page.

Photo (L) shows an assortment of wooden "clothes corral's" that were generally dairy premium items. Some collectors place a higher value on the clothes corral version that shows Hoppy with his hat on (not shown). #1. $325 #2. $285 #3. $250. From the Jon & Charlie Cheek collection.

The Hoppy "Shootin' Rack" (R) is a very rare wooden item that is similar to the "clothes corral." It was designed to hang gun & holster sets on, and note that the piece shown is an unmarked premium item as well. The bottom words also state "Hoppy's Favorite" but there is no dairy name imprint. #1. $525 #2. $475 #3. $425. From the Jon & Charlie Cheek collection.

Hoppy tie rack (above) came in brown and black colors with the black version the most rare. Made from a composit material with Hoppy superimposed on the face flanked by steer heads and crossed guns. #1. $340 #2. $285 #3. $245. (add $75 for the black version).

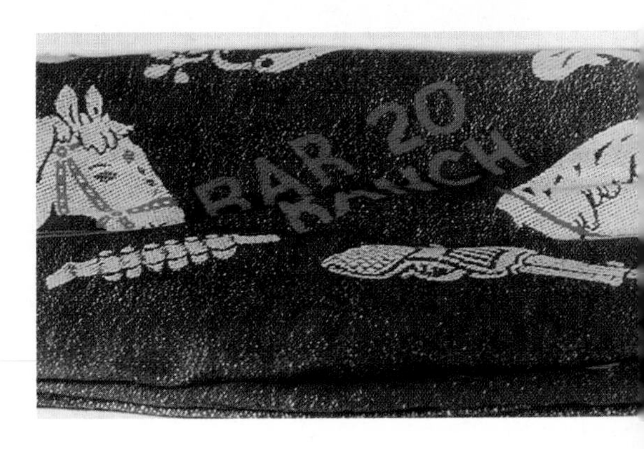

Light wool twin size HC blankets by Belcraft, Co. came in several colors. They are all very graphic and very rare. #1. $525 #2. $450 #3. $385. The blue blanket is from the Frank Smith collection.

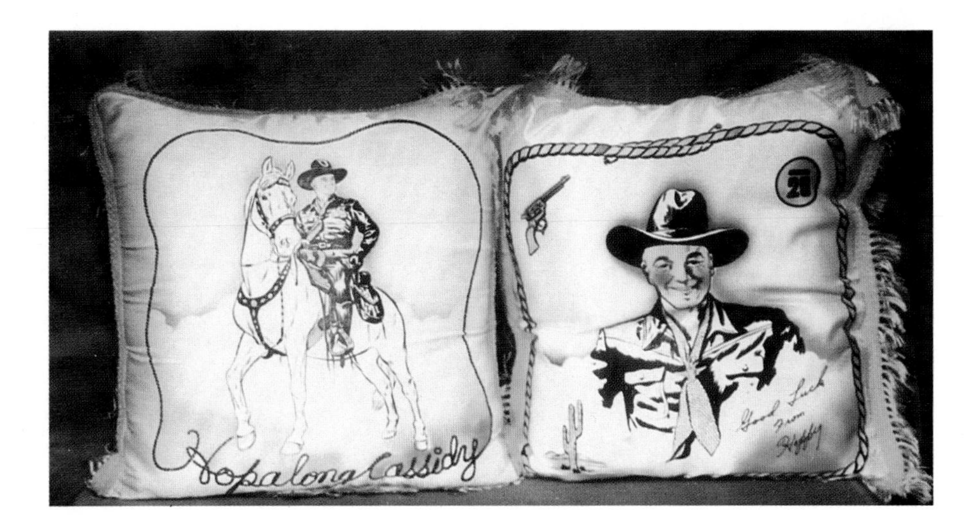

Two versions of the 16" Hoppy gold fringed, satin decorative pillow case (above right) show the most common version (Hoppy on Topper) and perhaps an earlier version showing just a Hoppy bust. Originally sold as empty pillowcases, they were later sold with a pillow. Hoppy TV pillow (above left) was made from a soft cotton fabric with brown fringe and repeat images of Hoppy on Topper on both sides. This item is quite rare with only two known to exist. #1. $275 #2. $250 #3. $225. Hoppy & Topper satin pillow case: #1. $275 #2. $250 #3. $225 Hoppy bust pillowcase: #1. $340 #2. $300 #3. $275. The satin pillowcases are from the Jon & Charlie Cheek collection.

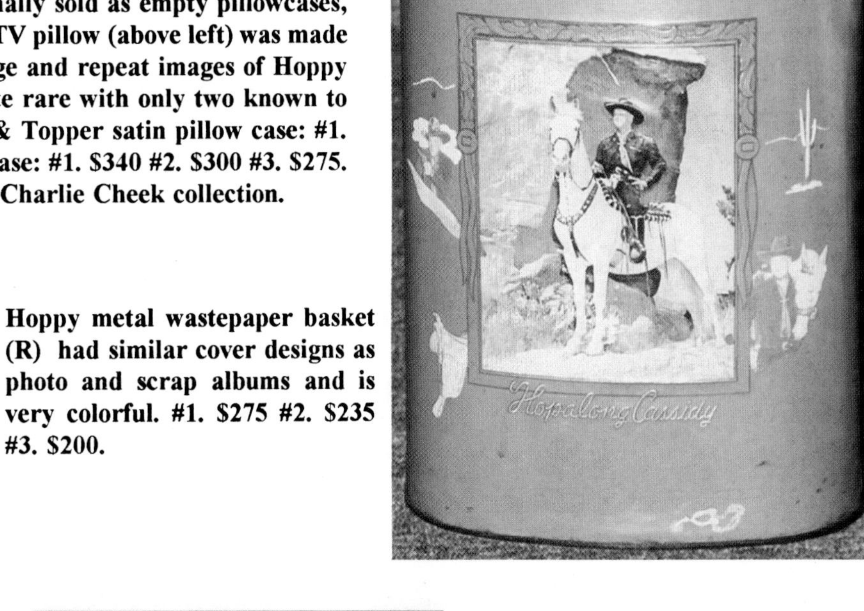

Hoppy metal wastepaper basket (R) had similar cover designs as photo and scrap albums and is very colorful. #1. $275 #2. $235 #3. $200.

Metal Hoppy clothes hamper (with lid) came in red, yellow and blue. Collectors value the blue hamper higher than the following: #1. $475 #2. $375 #3. $330. The yellow hamper is from the Jon & Charlie Cheek collection.

Two very unusual items are the Hoppy matress cover (above) and the Hoppy bed pillowcase (L). Both are the same shade yellow and have the same graphic designs. There probably were sheets to match. Hoppy pillowcase: #1. $195 #2. $175 #3. $150. Hoppy matress cover: #1. $325 #2. $250 #3. $200.

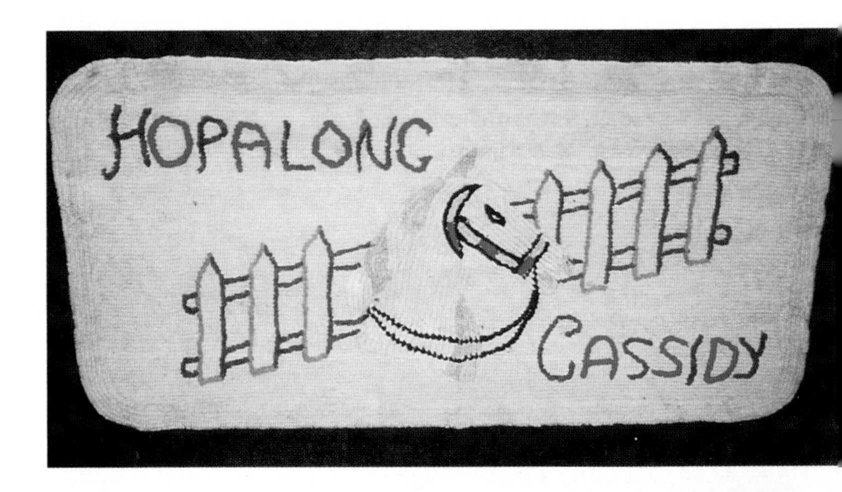

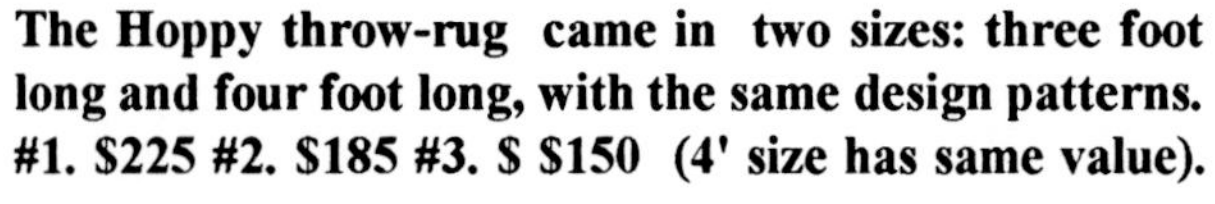

The Hoppy throw-rug came in two sizes: three foot long and four foot long, with the same design patterns. #1. $225 #2. $185 #3. $ $150 (4' size has same value).

Hoppy wallpaper is occasionally found in complete rolls with makers name decal. Sections and partial rolls are most common. The value of the full roll is: #1. $535 #2. $485. Partial rolls of Hoppy wallpaper have been selling for $17 a running foot.

Charles Lombard (L) and Ron Johnson display a Hoppy bedroom chenille rug that matched both the throw-rug above, and the bedspread. Rug is 4'x6' #1. $300 #2. $250 #3. $200. Photo was taken at the 1997 Hoppy Festival.

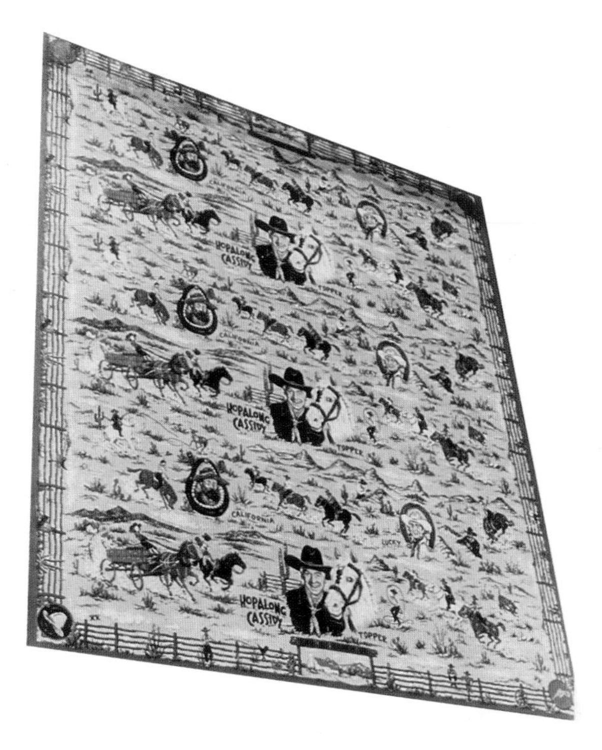

Photo of Hoppy linoleum floor-size roll. General size is 9'x12'.' All seem to have same design and colorations. From Ted Hake's Americana Auctions.

Detail photo of Hoppy linoleum design. This is a very rare collectors item and very much in demand. #1. (mint unopened roll 9'x12") $1,300 #2. $1,200 #3. $875. Needless to say, care must be taken when unrolling such a fragile item. From the Porter Albin collection.

There is a imitation Hoppy waste paper can that is popular with Hoppy collectors. The image on the can side is decidedly Hoppy riding Topper over the plains, but there is no name stated. Reverse side of can has a cowgirl riding a horse. While not "official" Hoppy, it is a very attractive item and worthy of consideration: #1. $150 #2. $100 #3. $50

Accessory items included an assortment of Hoppy vinyl shoe caddies that were generally stored in the closet. In addition to different colors (white, red, yellow, blue, black and black & white) the graphics on caddy sets also changed. The next page has several examples. #1. $400 #2. $350 #3. $300.

Hoppy shoe caddy's came in an assortment of colors and designs. Shown above, are a white and yellow vinyl set with similar patterns. #1. $400 #2. $350 #3. $300. From the Jon & Charlie Cheek collection.

The red vinyl garment bag (R) is an extremely rare Hoppy item find. Bearing the same design as the red shoe caddy (next page) it was indeed part of the full set of clothing protectors. (garment bag) #1. $600 #2. $520 #3. $480.

Detail photo of Hoppy closet shoe caddy sets. the only one missing from this collection is the red shoe caddy, which is found on the next page. From the Jon & Charlie Cheek collection.

Two different designs of the white vinyl shoe caddy sets. Fom the Phil Ellis collection.

Detail photo of the red vinyl shoe caddy

Detail photo of zipper front garment bag

nille Hoppy bedspread with graphics of Hoppy & per jumping fence. A nice piece but hard to display. #1. #2. $320 #3. $265. Chenille bedspread came in assorted rs as did similarly designed window curtains: tan, brown, n, gray and blue.

Detail photo of Hoppy wool blanket shown on previous page.

Hoppy chenille drapes completed the Hoppy room decor. The sets came in several colors including: tan, brown, green, blue and off-gray. #1. $450 #2. $400 #3. $325. (per set).

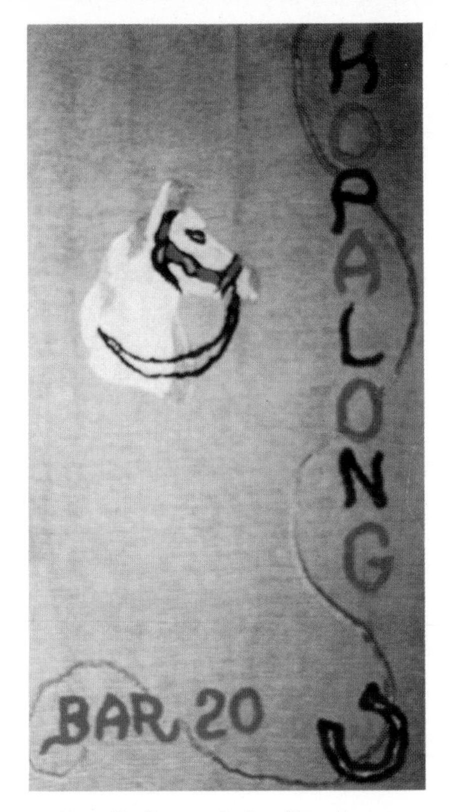

Detail photo of chenille drape

Photo of tan drape set. From the Bob Reed collection.

Display photo of another similar Hoppy dresser and Hoppy ranch sign from the Brian Beirne collection.

GUNS & HOLSTERS

#1. condition: mint, showing no use #2. condition: excellent to near mint #3. condition: good to very good

Hopalong Cassidy cap guns are the most controversial, the most sought after, carry the highest values and have the widest variety of models of any of the cowboy heroes of the 1950's era. The leather single gun and two-gun holster sets hold a similar reputation. To my knowledge, this chapter carries all versions of the North American made Hoppy cap guns except one . . . the Leslie Henry model made in Canada. The values indicated may appear quite high in many cases, but you must remember we are only appraising conditions #1 through #3. Listed values shown are a result of private sales, retail sales and auction results. I will talk about the famous "Buck N' Bronc" guns from Wyandotte, both in this chapter and in "Bikes & Trikes."

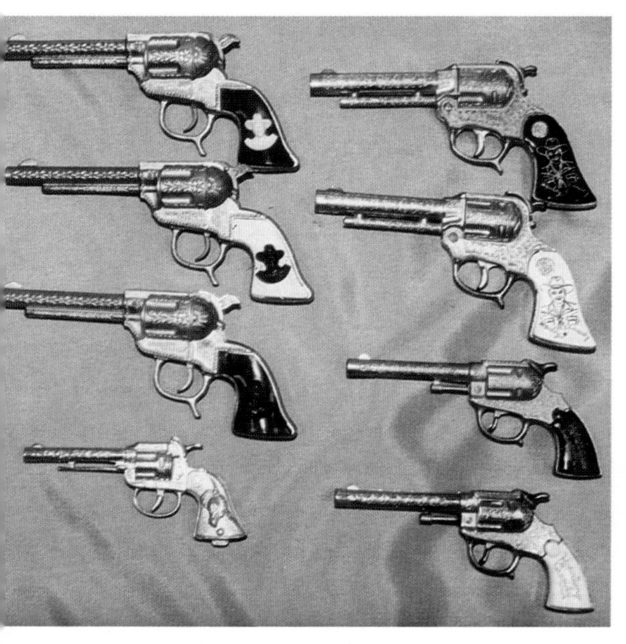

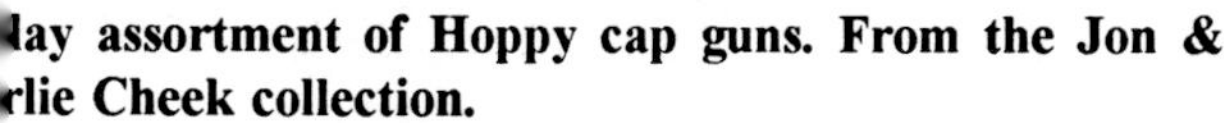

lay assortment of Hoppy cap guns. From the Jon & rlie Cheek collection.

One of the rarest Hoppy cap guns is this all metal, single-shot model that is about 5" long. Believed to be made by Hubley, Co. there is no known holster or box. "Hopalong" is stamped in the frame on the left side, "Cassidy" is frame stamped on the right. #1. $675 #2. $575 #3. $500. From the Jon & Charlie Cheek collection. There are only five of these guns known to exist.

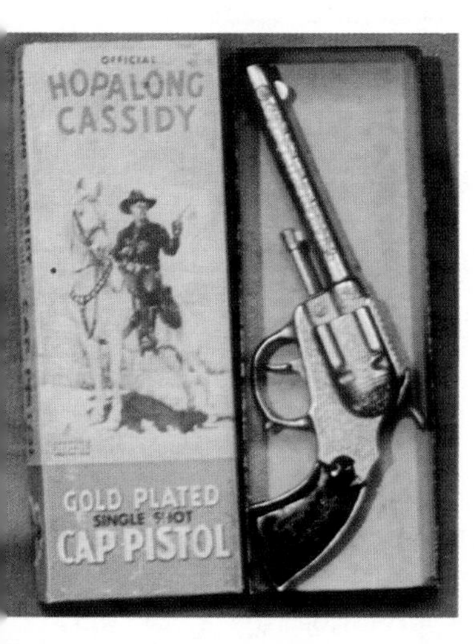

boxed Wyndotte gold & black gle-shot is: #1. $700 #2. $625 #3. 25. Deduct $200 if it is the silver rsion. From the Jon & Charlie eek collection.

Wyandotte produced two versions of a small single-shot Hoppy cap pistol that are shown on the right. The only difference between the two is the color scheme: silver with ivory grips and gold with black grips. The gold wash gun has a higher value: #1. $325 #2. $275 #3. $225. Deduct $50 if it is the silver version. The most often broken piece of this gun is the "ejector" rod, under the barrel.

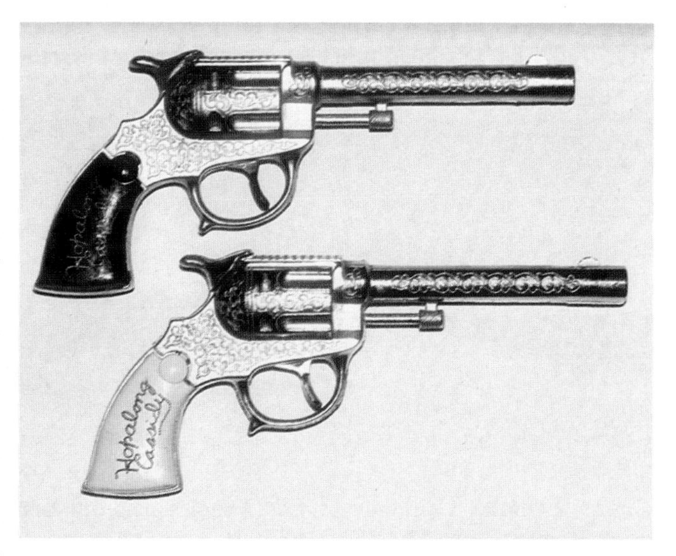

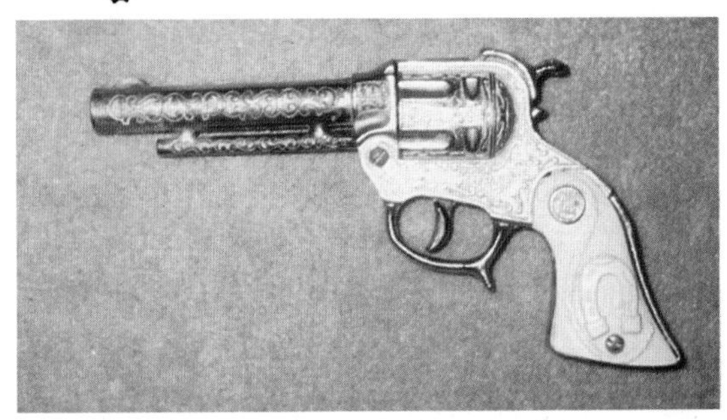

It is thought that the earliest Wyandotte Hoppy guns had generic grips as shown above and below. Note that the silver wash gun (below) has black grips and the gold wash gun had ivory, which was a reversal of what was to be the "standard" for all future Hoppy guns made. Many collectors prize these early versions: #1. $450 #2. $400 #3. $325. (single gun, no box). From the Robert Donovan collection.

Early version Wyandotte guns with generic grips were also used in boxed holster sets like the one shown above. Note the unique holster design. This set is valued further on in the chapter. From the Sharon Delaney collection.

The generic black "fluted" grips on the silver Wyandotte was not as striking as the engraved Hoppy grips designed later. T above photo shows both the earlier and later versions. Both guns are otherwise identical. The generic ivory grips on the ot hand, featured a horse's head relief on one side and a horseshoe on the reverse, which was a Wyandotte "standard".

The George Schmidt Company in Los Angeles was another main maker of Hoppy guns. The one shown is a very late model and carried the Schmidt "standard" Buck 'N Bronc grip. It is thought that at the end of the gun contract, Schmidt Company ran out of Hoppy grips and put a few "standard" grips on to finish the guns. The gun is a late model version as "Hopalong Cassidy" is cast in the frame. #1. $450 #2. $400 #3. $325. From the Bill Hamburg collection

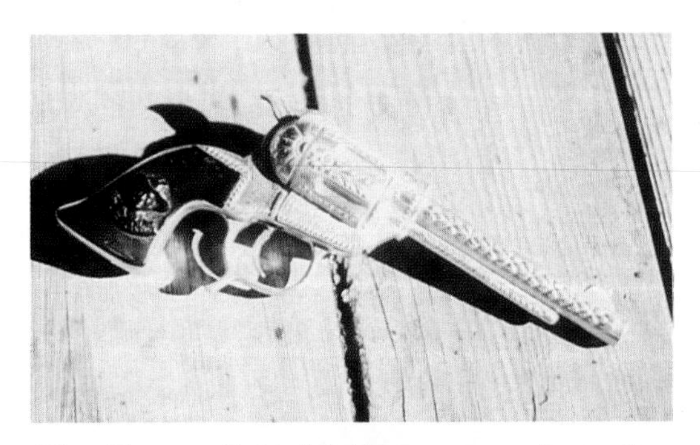

The George Schmidt Hoppy gun shown is a rare special edition. Note the black bust on black grip treatment and the bright gold wash that was produced by a 24 karat plating. From the Phil Ellis collection. A single un-boxed gun is $800 in #1 condition.

e George Schmidt Company, in addition to contracting to vide guns for the Hoppy bikes, made a few distinctive Hoppy s unknown in most collecting circles. The gun shown (above) is believed to be the earliest version known. Note the size and shape of the barrel, which is much longer and thicker (due to p ridge) than normal. Also note the small opening lever at base of hammer. Later Schmidt Hoppy guns had no such system. e name on this gun is "Buck 'N Bronc" but the name is small and directly under the cylinder. Also note the barrel on this gun lain - without the scalloped design typical of the newer design. Later versions had a much longer & wider name (shown above ht). The last Schmidt gun versions had the name "Hopalong Cassidy" stamped on both sides of the frame as shown on the vious page and following photos. This unusual long barrel gun was made in 1948-9 prior to the contract to make them for lfast bicycles. The big gun just wouldn't fit in the bike tank holsters! #1. $550 #2. $500 #3. $450 (gun alone).

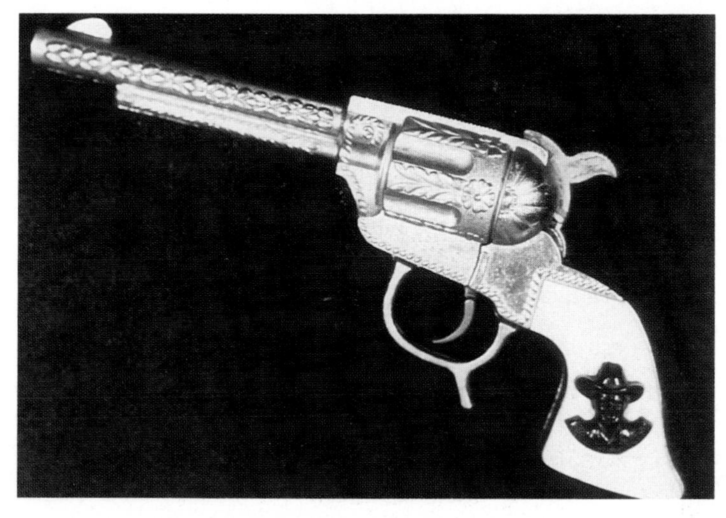

"Standard" model of the Schmidt gun with white grips and black Hoppy bust. Other guns had black grips and a white Hoppy bust. There is no value difference between the two. The above gun is a later version with "Hopalong Cassidy" stamped on each frame side: #1. $375 #2. $325 #3. $275. (gun only) From the Jim Mc Loughlin collection.

While the George Schmidt Company held the contract to produce guns for the Hoppy Rollfast bikes, many collectors' believe that the "Buck 'N Bronc" guns were made exclusively for bike use. Latest information contradicts this premise on the basis that several gun & holster sets contained "Bronc" guns, and several original Hoppy bikes had "Hopalong Cassidy" Schmidt guns. It is now reasoned that both bikes and holster sets contained whatever Schmidt guns were available at that time.

Rare 24K gold plated Schmidt Hoppy gun had "Hopalong Cassidy" stamped in the gun frame and had a black Hoppy bust on black grips. Note graphic on box shows the Hoppy bust in gold - to my knowledge, it was never produced that way. This special gold gun was also issued with holster sets. #1. $1,500 #2. $1,350 #3. $1,200 (deduct $700 without box). from the Jon & Charlie Cheek collection.

The above gun display shows the obvious beauty of the Schmidt gun compared to Wyandotte versions. The Schmidt gun had its drawbacks however, when the gun opening lever was removed. The Wyandotte gun was much sturdier of the two. From the Phil Ellis collection.

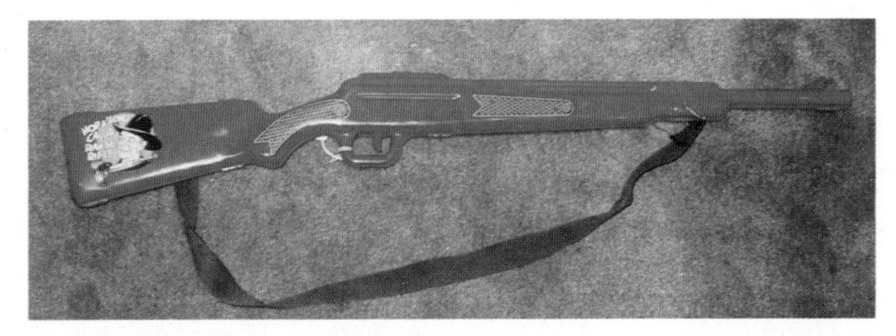

The Hoppy Range Rifle while not a cap gun, is shown here and in the "Toys" chapter. There is no known box for this great piece. This all metal rifle is a "clicker" gun with a military style sling. A great find. #1. $1,000 #2. $850 #3. $700. from the Brian Beirne collection.

Display photo showing the relative size between the Wyandotte repeater (above) and the Wyandotte single shot cap pistol.

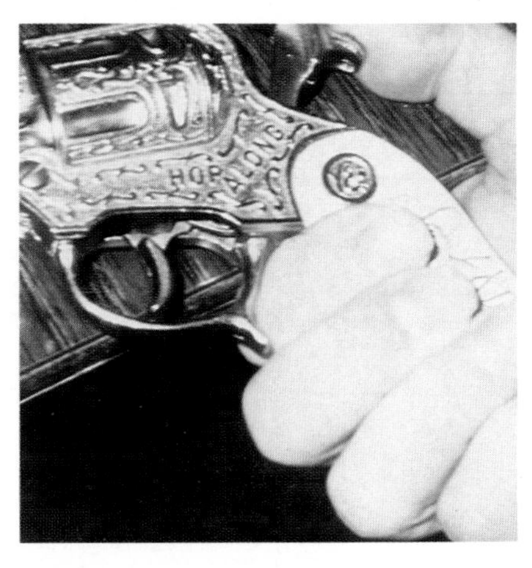

The hammer of the Wyandotte Hoppy "dummy" gun is shown above. Many states outlawed cap-firing guns and "dummies" were made instead. A narrow metal bar extends the length of the hammer preventing caps from firing. Schmidt also made "dummy" guns. These guns are quite rare and maintain a value increase of $75 over normal gun prices.

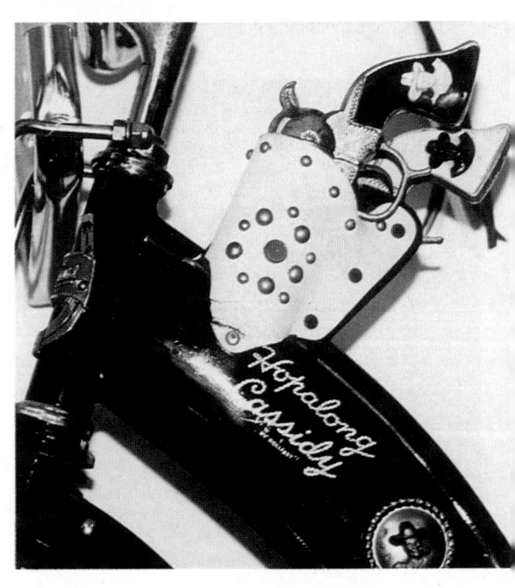

Display photo showing two Schmidt guns in girls' Hoppy bike. Ads for the bike showed o black grip and one white grip gun as show Nobody knows for certain if the bikes car this way. It is therefore reasoned that ea bike contained a set of similar guns and th the ad was designed to show that you could g either. Most of the early bikes contain "Buck 'N Bronc" guns, but in later years th were changed to the "Hopalong Cassid name.

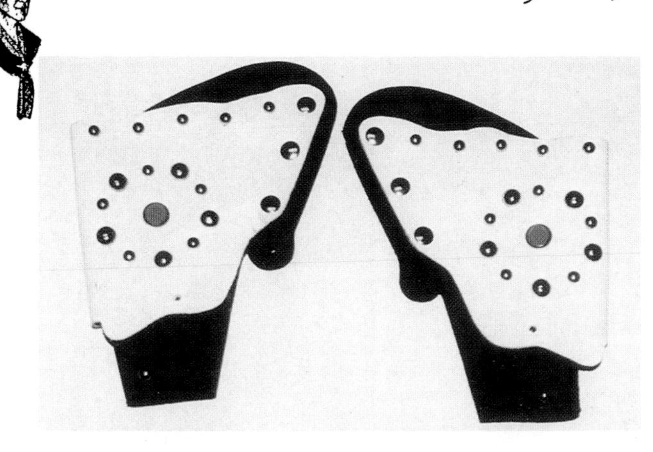

The above black & white studded holsters are designed for the 20" and 24" boys' & girls' Hoppy Rollfast bicycles. I doubt if many originals exist, but quite a few reproductions are available for $80 per set. (See "Bikes & Trikes" chapter.)

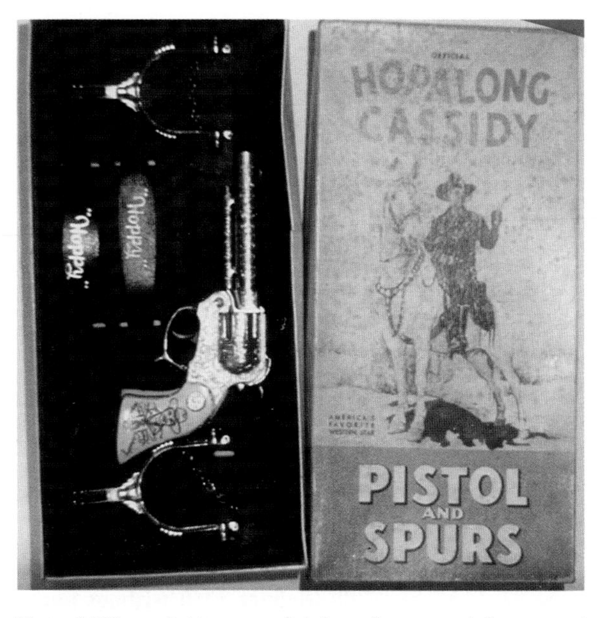

Boxed Wyandotte cap pistol and spur set is a great collectors' find: #1. $1,200 #2. $1,000 #3. $850

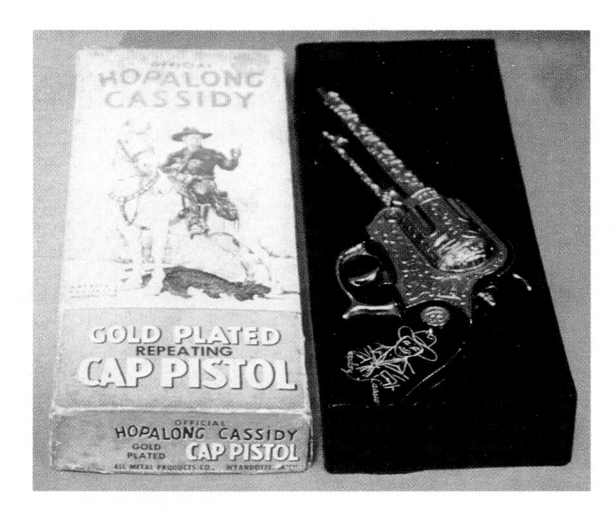

Gold plate w/ black grips Wyandotte repeating cap pistol in box (no holster): #1. $950 #2. $875 #3. $800. (deduct $300 without box). from the Jon & Charlie Cheek collection.

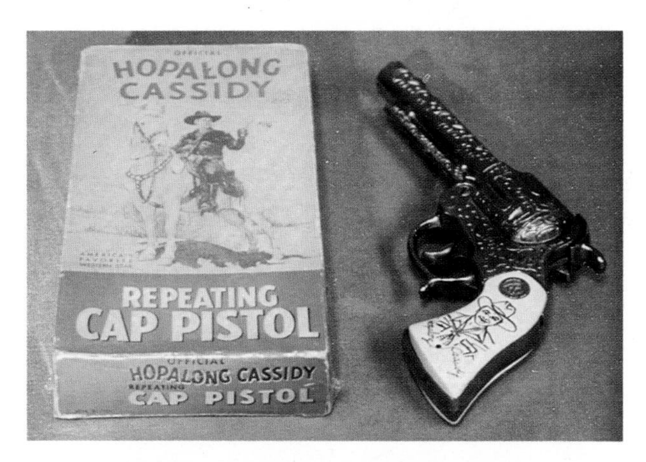

Boxed repeating Wyandotte cap pistol (silver) no holster: #1. $750 #2. $675 #3. $600. (deduct $250 without box). From the Jon & Charlie Cheek collection.

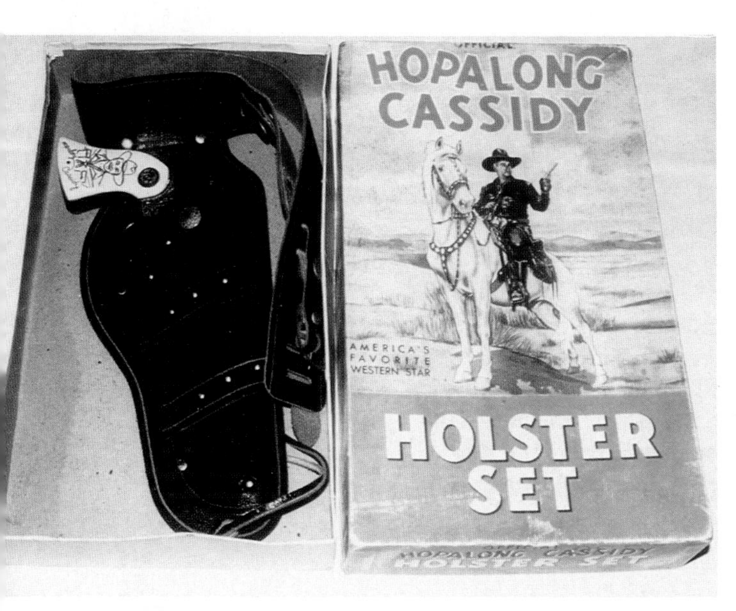

Unique Wyandotte single gun holster has hammer-strap to hold gun in. May be a prototype: Boxed set: #1. $1,200 #2. $1,100 #3. $1,000. The Ron Johnson collection.

Unique box on the right is an English gun & holster box. They are very rare and collectible. Some collectors will pay $1,000 for this box alone! From the Jon & Charlie Cheek collection.

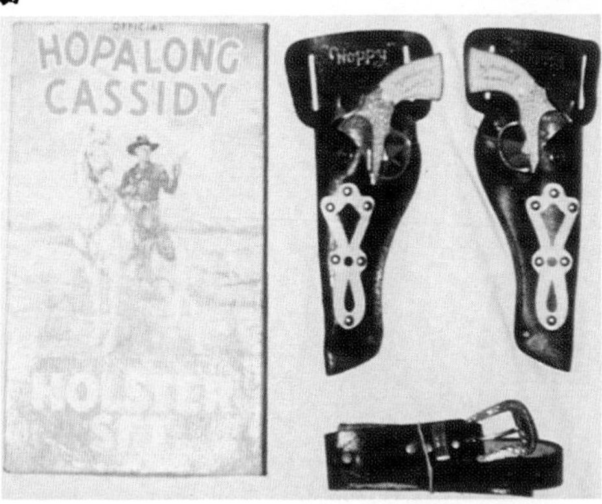

Single-shot Wyandotte holster set with slip-through belt. Holsters were made smaller to fit the size of the guns: #1. $1,000 #2. $850 #3. $700 (deduct $250 without box). From the Jon & Charlie Cheek collection.

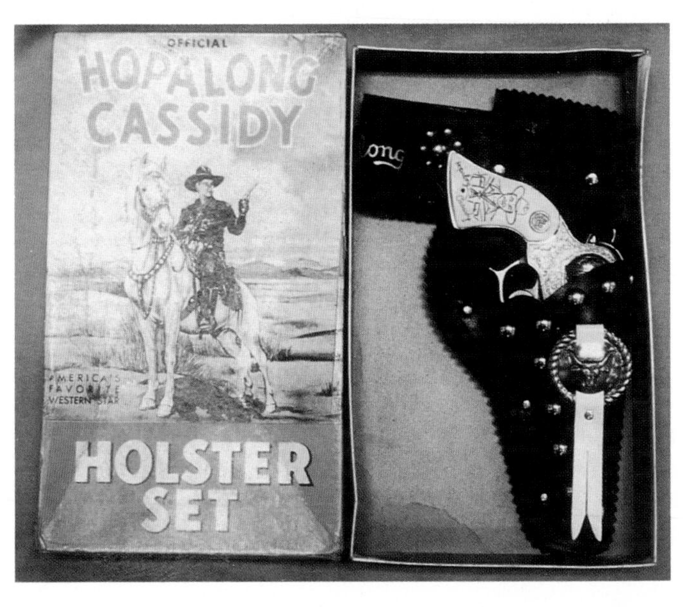

Single gun holster set by Wyandotte. Holster is deluxe version with black felt backing. Note gold steerhead conch. #1. $1,000 #2. $850 #3. $750. (deduct $300 without box). From teh Jon & Charlie Cheek collection.

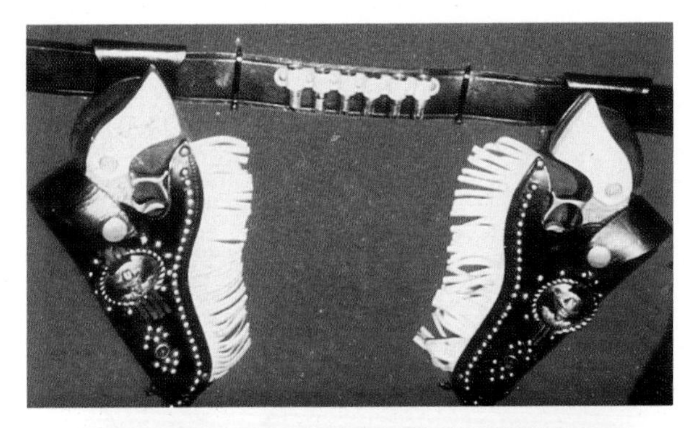

Perhaps the rarest holster set is the white leather fringed, hammer-strapped, swivel set shown in the photo above. Notice the strap completely covers the gun hammer of two "standard" Wyandotte cap pistols. Also note the holster belt has six chrome bullets. Each holster is made to "fast draw" swivel. Value of holster set only: #1. $750 #2. $675 #3. $600. (without box). from the Larry Seymour collection.

Wyandotte deluxe single gun holster set. Note: red wooden bullets on belt. #1. $1,050 #2. $950 #3. $875. (deduct $400 without box). from the Jon & Charlie Cheek collection.

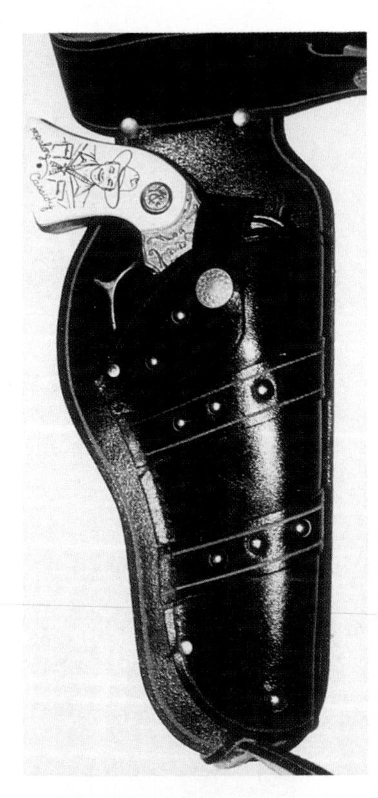

Detail view of the strap holster shown on previous page.

Shown earlier, is this unusual single gun holster set with the Wyandotte generic grips. In addition to the unusual grips, the holster is also unique: #1. $1,100 #2. $1,000 #3. $850. From the Sharon Delaney collection.

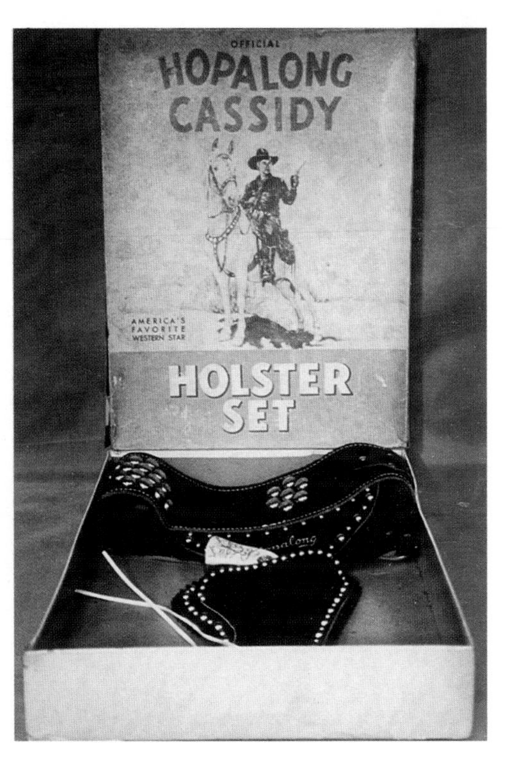

Deluxe Wyandotte single gun holster set: #1. $1,200 #2. $ $1,000 #3. $875. From the Jon & Charlie Cheek collection.

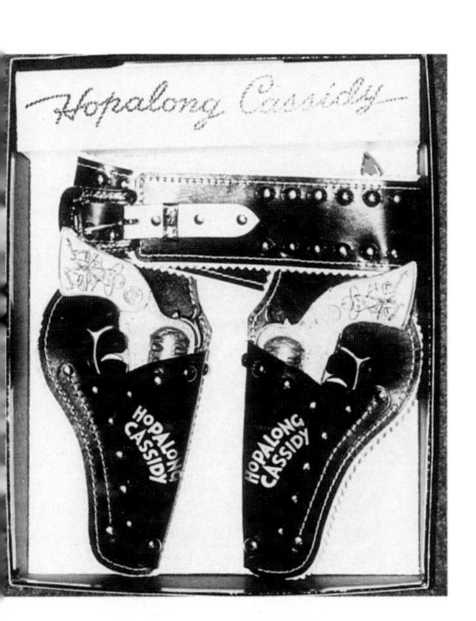

hown above is a limited edition two gun olster set that should not be confused ith an original. This set (guns extra) vas originally priced at $100.

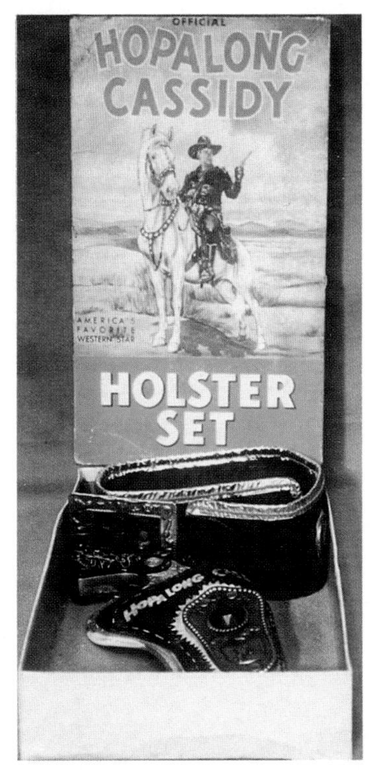

This extremely rare single gun Wyandotte gun & holster carried the gold & black repeating pistol and a very ornate holster which boasted a large red glass jewel mounted on a gold plate on the holster side. The holster belt was quite wide and trimmed in silver and boasted a gold buckle: #1. $1,000 #2. $875 #3. $750. From the Jon & Charlie Cheek collection.

Two gun holster set with traditional heart shaped stud design: #1. $1,400 #2. $1,250 #3. $1,000. Deduct $350 without box. From Jon & Charlie Cheek.

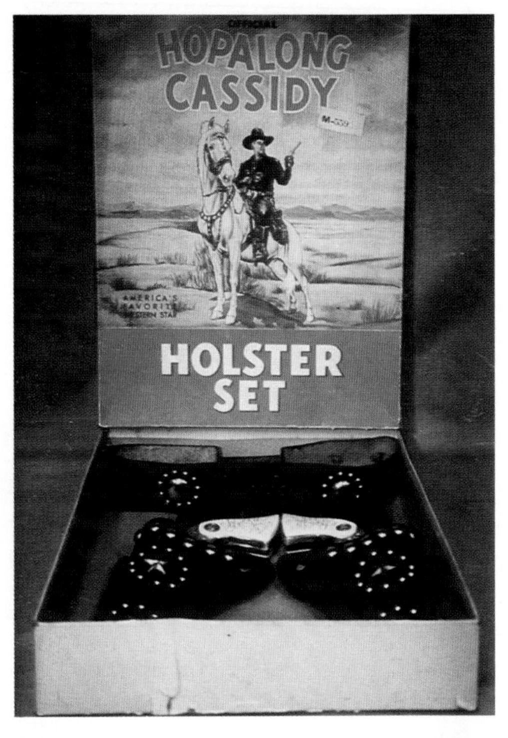

Note different holster patterns on "standard" Hoppy holster boxed sets: #1. $1,600 #2. $1,450 #3. $1,300. from the Jon & Charlie Cheek collection.

The above magnificently studded holster was designed by Tumbleweed Togs and carries two Schmidt guns: #1. $2,200 #2. $2,050 #3. $1,750. From Jon & Charlie Cheek.

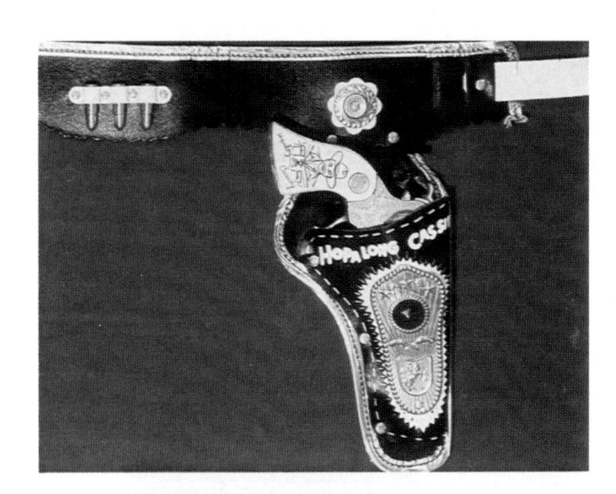

Display photo of the unusual Wayndotte single gun holster set shown on previous page: #1. $750 #2. $650 #3. $575 (no box)

Display of an attractive single gun holster. Holster and belt value alone is: #1. $275 #2. $220 #3. $175 (no box). From the Jon & Charlie Cheek collection.

Several deluxe sets came with matching wrist cuffs and gold-wash guns. Extremely beautiful-extremely expensive: #1. $2,000 #2. $1,750 #3. $1,600. From the Jon & Charlie Cheek collection.

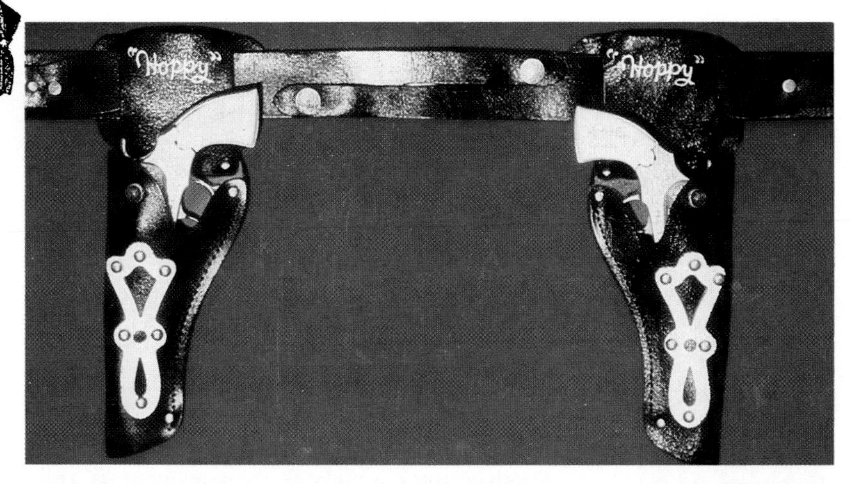

Detail photo of single shot holster set shown and valued earlier. Note that this holster set has "Hoppy" stamped in silver over belt slide holes. Similar designed holsters have "Cassidy" stamped in the same area. Holsters only are #1. $300 #2. $225 #3. $175. From Jon & Charlie Cheek.

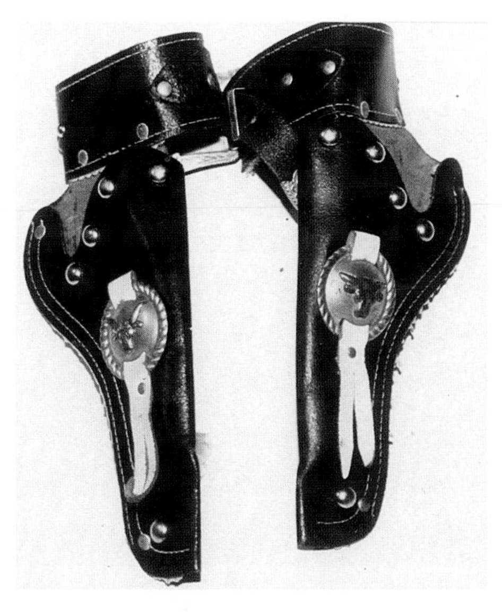

The above holster set is somewhat plain with steerhead conch on each holster. #1. $175 #2. $140 #3. $100.

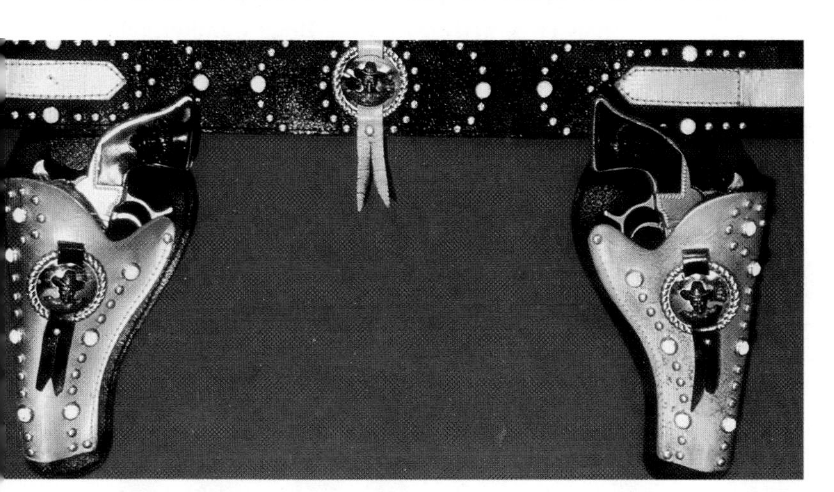

he most exotic holster set has to be this Tumbleweed Togs gold & black t with 24K gold plated Schmidt guns. It would be a collector's dream to nd such a rare and in-demand star of any collection: #1. $3,000 #2. 2,700 #3. $2,500 (deduct $500 without box). From the Jon & Charlie heek collection.

To keep the values listed in this chapter in some semblance of perspective, the above two gun holster set with Wyandotte repeating silver wash guns is in #3. condition (both guns & holsters) and is valued at $800. without a box. It is a "good" set, in "good" condition, no more, no less. If this book listed #4. or "fair" condition, such a holster set would be worth $650 to $700. Depending on which side of "fair" it was.

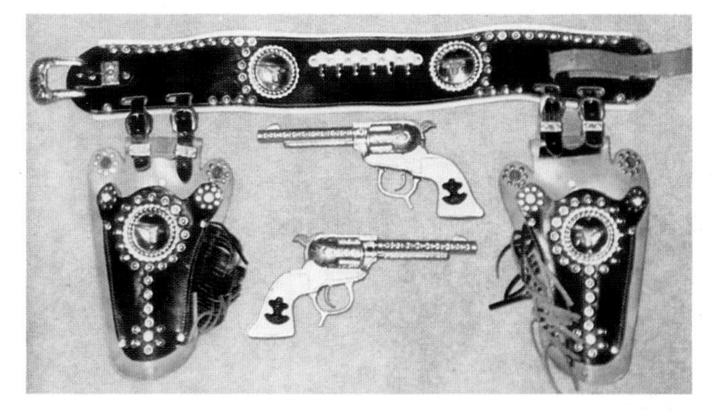

Most collectors' would question the authenticity of this holster set shown with "standard" Schmidt guns. The "Hoppy" name does not appear anywhere - but notice the gold steerhead conches are the same used on the less ornate holster shown above. This one would bear close examination. From the Robert Donovan collection.

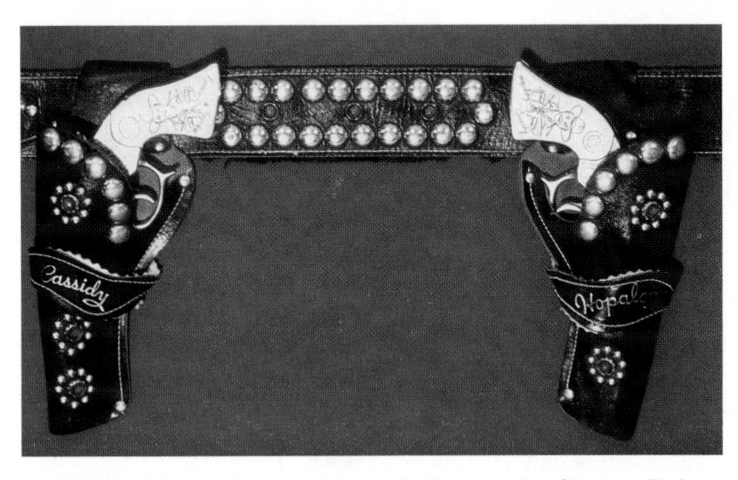

Wyandotte "tuck-in" holster set similar to the Sharon Delaney boxed single shown earlier. Holster tucked into its own strap and was not directly attached to the belt: #1. $500 #2. $400 #3. $300. (holster set and belt only). from Jon & Charlie Cheek.

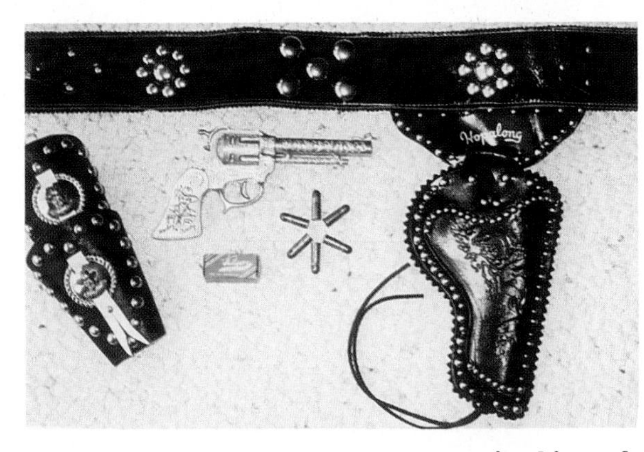

Another unique holster arrangement is this tooled leather version. The name "Hopalong" is clearly stamped at the belt attach point with a similar stud pattern. An unusual design from All Metal Products Company (Wyandotte). #1. $375 #2. $275 #3. $175 (holster & belt). From the Doug Candler collection.

I'm not a sexist or anything, but this just has to be a holster design for girls. Yes, I know Hoppy had a heart design on his real holsters too! #1. $450 #2. $350 #3. $250. (holsters & belt only). From the Jon & Charlie Cheek collection.

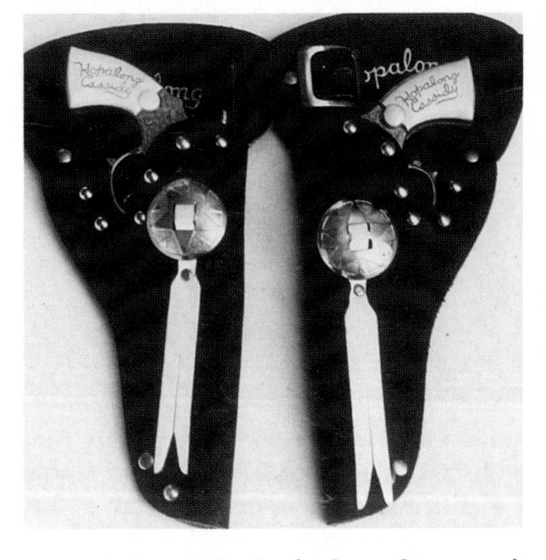

Deluxe holsters (both single and two-gun) had white or black felt padding on the back of each holster as well as the belt. The above set (and many others) lack this padding. While the single-shot pistols are too small for the holster set, note that the conches have a star design and not the steerhead or Hoppy bust: #1. $200 #2. $150 #3. $100. (for holsters only). From the Jon & Charlie Cheek collection.

Another gloriously ornate holster set is this Tumbleweed Togs version. The name "Hoppy" is in studs and gold colored leather: #1. $600 #2. $475 #3. $375. (holsters & belt). From the Jon & Charlie Cheek collection.

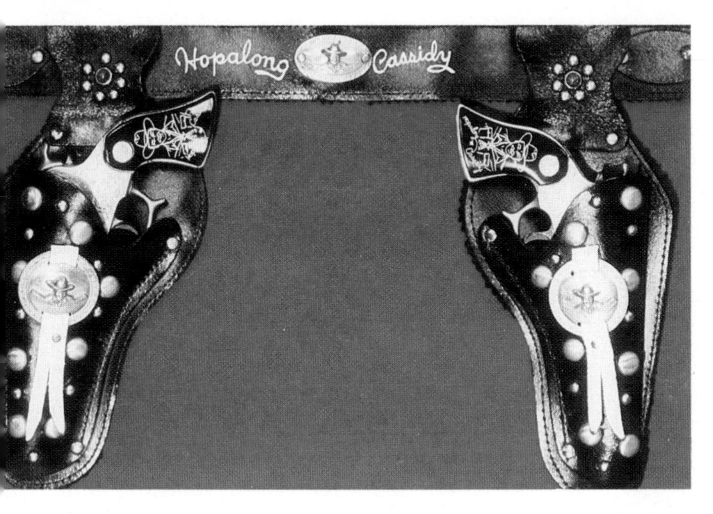

:corative holster set has an unusual Hoppy chrome emblem on ck of gunbelt between "Hopalong Cassidy." Slotted holster nches also have a gold bust of Hoppy in center: #1. $375 #2. 25 #3. $275 (holster & belt only). From the Jon & Charlie ieek collection.

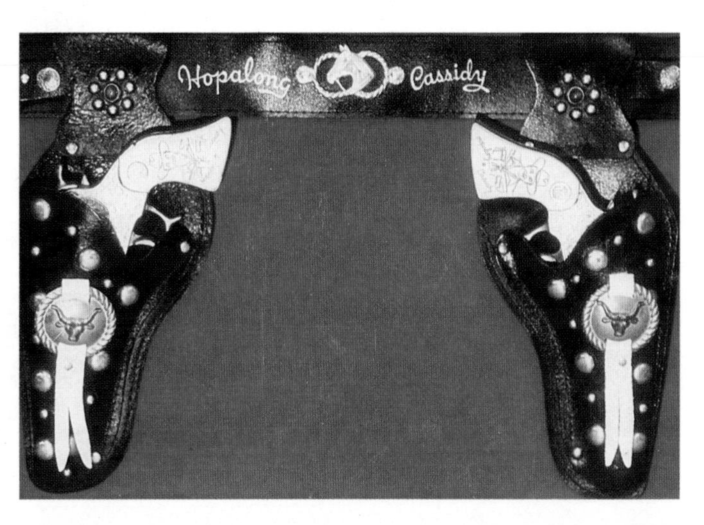

Similar holster and gunbelt to one on left, this version however, has a steerhead conch on holsters and a decorative horse emblem between the words "Hopalong Cassidy" on back of the gunbelt: #1. $375 #2. $325 #3. $275. (holsters & belt only). from the Jon & Charlie Cheek collection

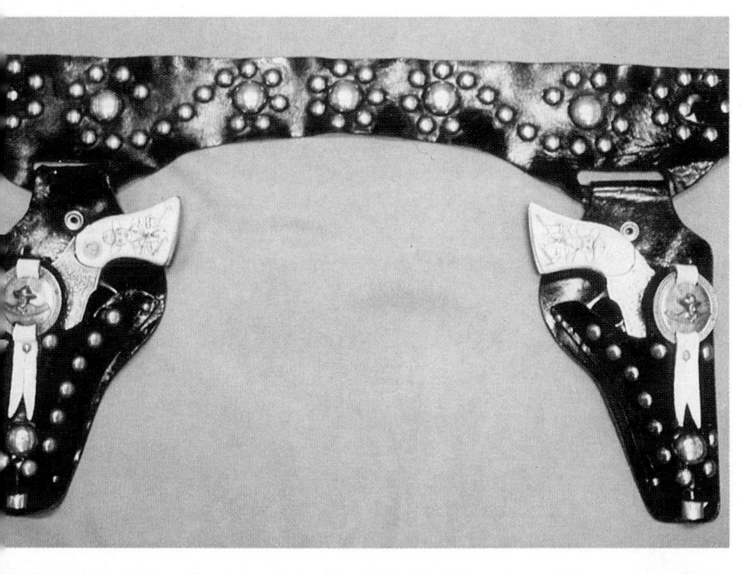

idded gunbelt is unusual for Wyandotte to make, especially thout Hoppy's name. Matching holsters are strap-rivited to belt ts. Note the unusual placement of the two Hoppy bust conches. e Hoppy name does not appear anywhere on this set: #1. $450 #2. 60 #3. $285. (holsters & gunbelt only). From the Jon & Charlie ieek collection.

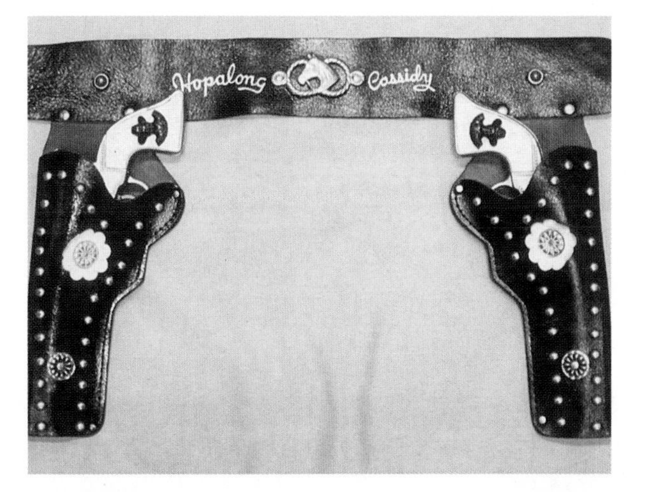

An All Metal Products, Inc. holster set with the same horse emblem as shown above. The holster design is more attractive and made to custom fit Wyandotte guns (and work well with the Schmidt guns shown) : #1. $400 #2. $350 #3. $300. (holsters & belt only). From the Jon & Charlie Cheek collection.

Similar to the holster set shown on an earlier page in "good" condition, note the name "Hoppy" printed on belt back: #1. $350 #2. $300 #3. $250. (holsters & belt only). From the Jon & Charlie Cheek collection.

Attractive holsters and matching gunbelt have similar chrome stud rosettes on both. "Hopalong" is stamped in silver on back of gunbelt: #1. $375 #2. $325 #3. $275. (holsters and gunbelt only). from the Jon & Charlie Cheek collection.

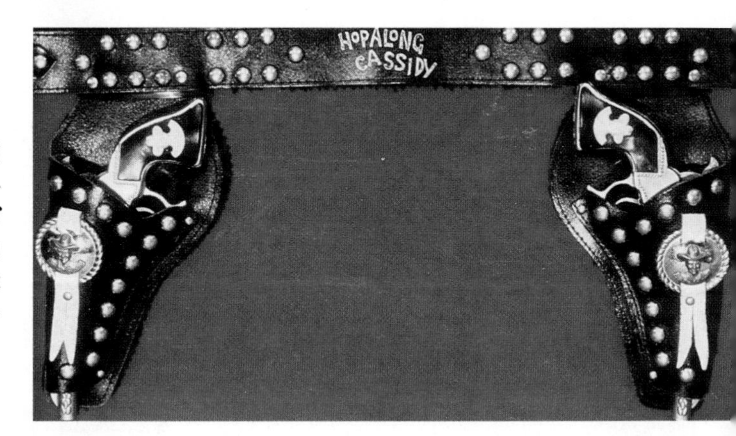

A very fine looking holster set has a good balance of design studs with the name "Hopalong Cassidy" in silver stamped on back of gunbelt. Holsters have the Hoppy bust conch: #1. $375 #2. $325 #3. $275. (holsters & belt only). from the Jon & Charlie Cheek collection.

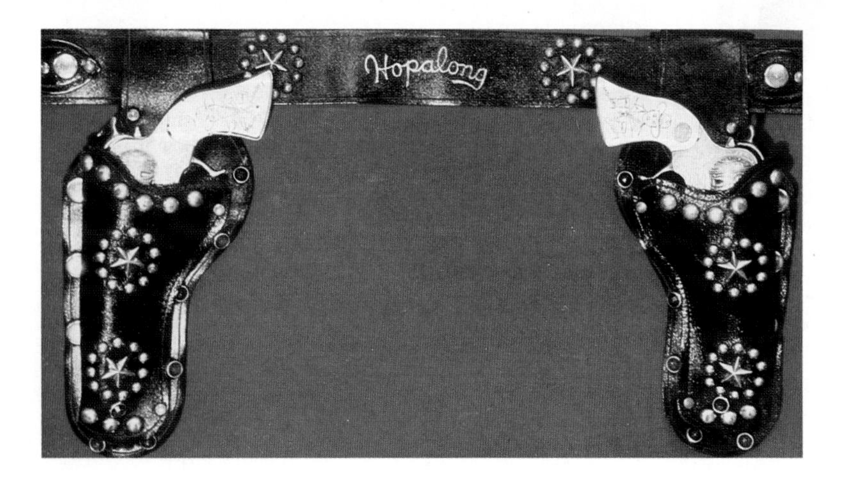

The "double star" holsters and matching belt are a nice variation design treatment. There may be as many as eighty different Hoppy holster designs in the US and European markets: #1. $375 #2. $325 #3. $275. (holster & belt only). From the Jon & Charlie Cheek collection

JEWELRY WATCHES & BANKS

#1. condition: mint, showing no use #2. condition: excellent to near mint #3. condition: good to very good

Colorful store paper sign pointed the way to the Hoppy watches and is a perfect lead-in for this chapter on jewelry, watches and banks. In addition to "real" Hoppy watches, you will also find the Japanese phonies and other reproductions. The store sign is from the Jon & Charlie Cheek collection and is valued at $600.

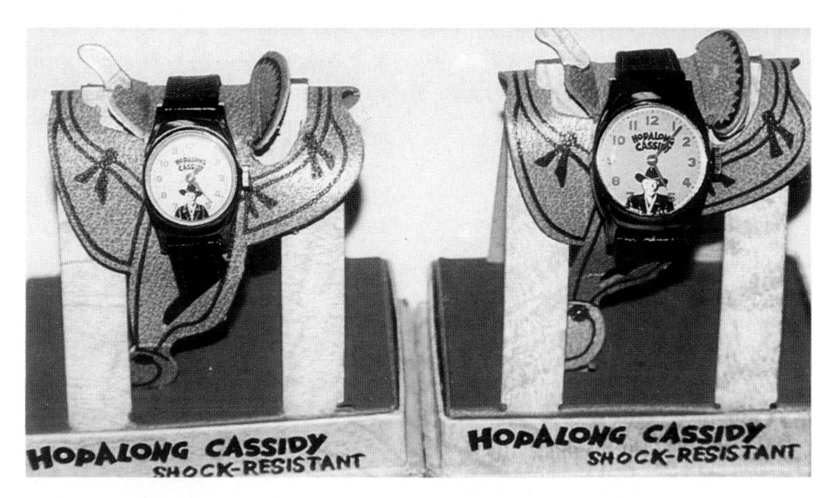

The two Hoppy watches (US Time, Inc.) shown above are the small size (L) which is called the girl's watch and the boy's watch (R) which is somewhat larger. The Boy's watch came both on the cardboard saddle (shown) and in a flat box. While wrist-bands varied, they were leather with western scenes in either silver or silver & red impressions. #1. $625 #2. $550 #3 $475. without box and saddle watches are worth: #1. $150 #2. $120 #3. $75

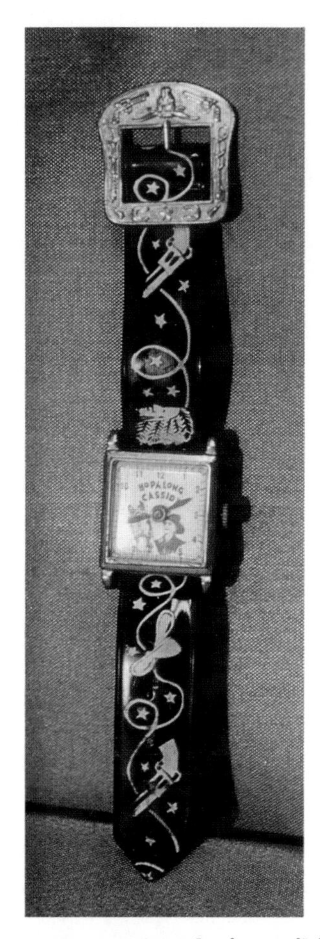

The above ornate watch is strikingly different than any others in the Hoppy line. It is a toy watch, without working gears, and the prized possession of Jon & Charlie Cheek. Popular opinion indicates that it may be a "one of a kind" and therefore an investment value item with a value of over $500.

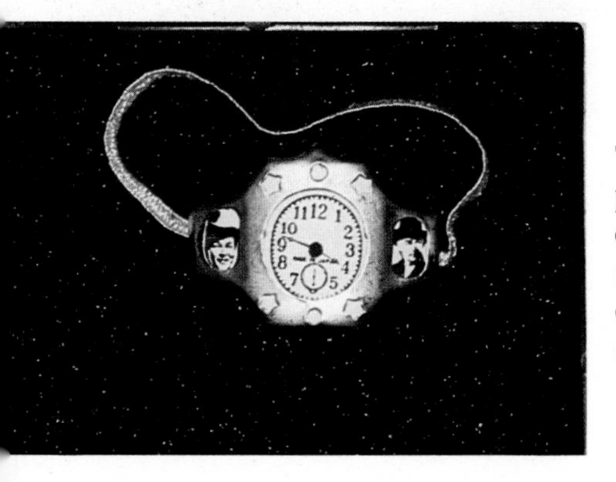

The toy metal watch shown (L) has a small photo of Hoppy on one side and Roy Rogers on the other. The band is elastic. It is a 50's rip-off item from Japan that has a high collector value. It does not come in a case, as shown. #1. $175 #2. $125.

Shown above, is the large wristwatch in the flat box along with instructions. Boxes of this type are very colorful and quite in-demand to a number of collectors. #1. $550 #2. $425 #3. $375. (without instruction book deduct $50)

Watch display from 1952 Wards catalog showing Hoppy and Disney watches. During this period, Hoppy watches outsold Mickey Mouse by three-to-one.

The majority of Hoppy watches sold had a metal case on both the top and bottom (top of photo). During later years (and in England) Hoppy watches came with black plastic top cases (see lower watch photo). Both versions were sold in similar watch saddle boxes. Watches made in England are so stamped on reverse side. In most cases, values of the two watches are similar. From the Phil Ellis collection.

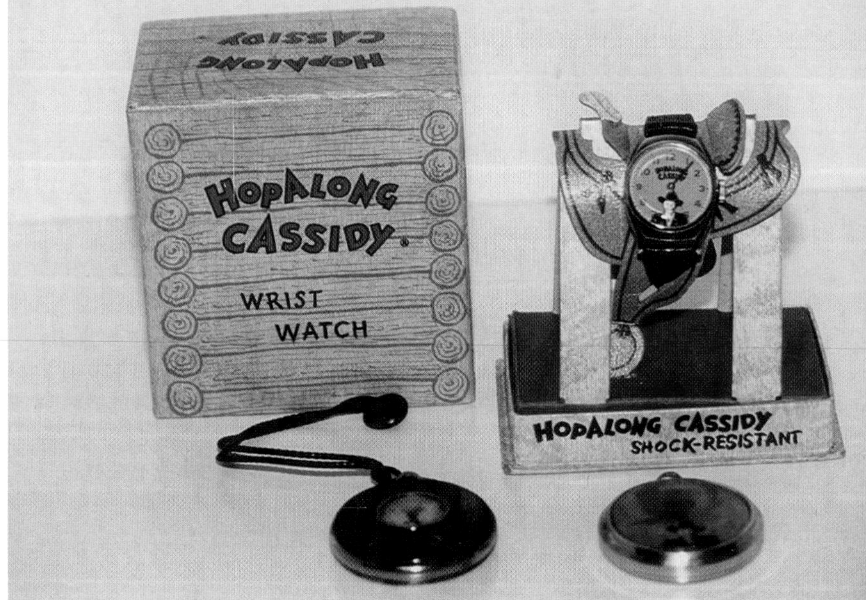

Display photo of large wristwatch in box and two pocket watches.

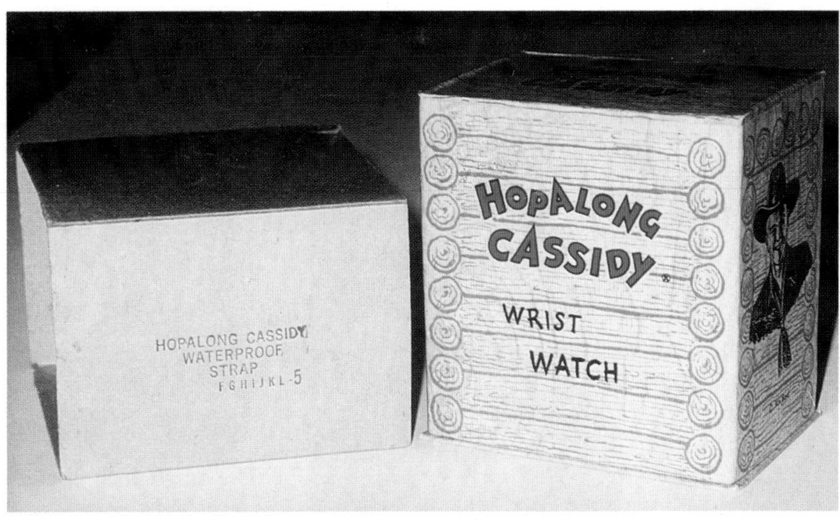

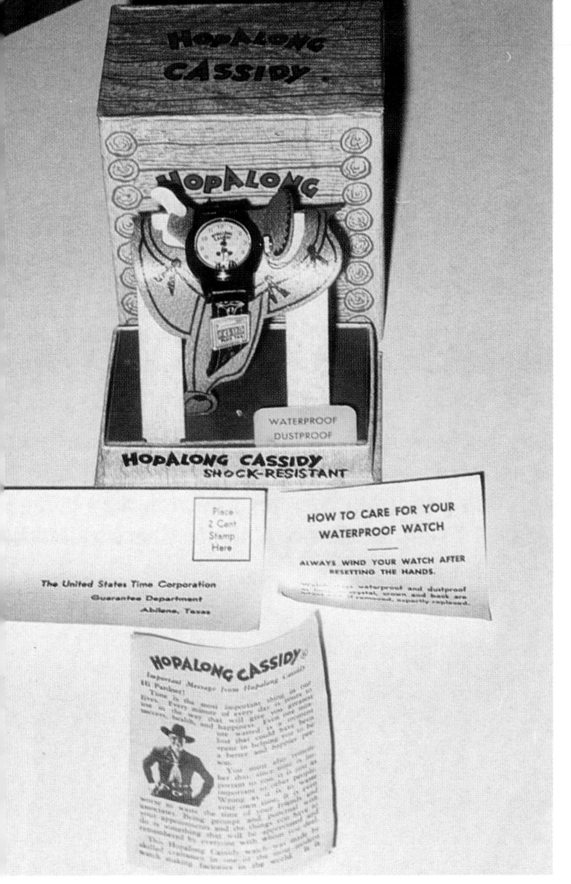

Recent findings show that a third, later version, Hoppy watch exists that has collectors scurrying to find. The watch is a Hoppy waterproof and dust proof version that has a black plastic front and back case and was made in America around 1960. The photo (L) shows an investment value watch from this era. Bearing a price tag of $6.95 (on watch band) this watch is complete in every aspect including: instructions, waterproof watch care note, warranty card, "waterproof - dust proof" sticker, original price tag, and never seen before box protector sleeve shown in above photo. A jewel item in the Charles Ringhel collection, this watch may be worth $1,000 as investment value grade.

Reproduction Hoppy pocketwatch made in the late 1980's is of very poor quality and seldom works. It is shown next to a plastic, recently made, pencil sharpener for size. The reproduction pocketwatch is hardly worth the $25 that some dealers ask for it.

lay photo of both the large face and small face Hoppy pocketwatches show a tantial difference in design. The small face is shown with its original leather p and leather fob: #1. $825 #2. $750 #3. $675 (deduct $50 without strap & The large face: #1. $750 #2. $675 #3. $525. (values are without box)

Unusual watch strap & fob. From the Jon & Charlie Cheek collection.

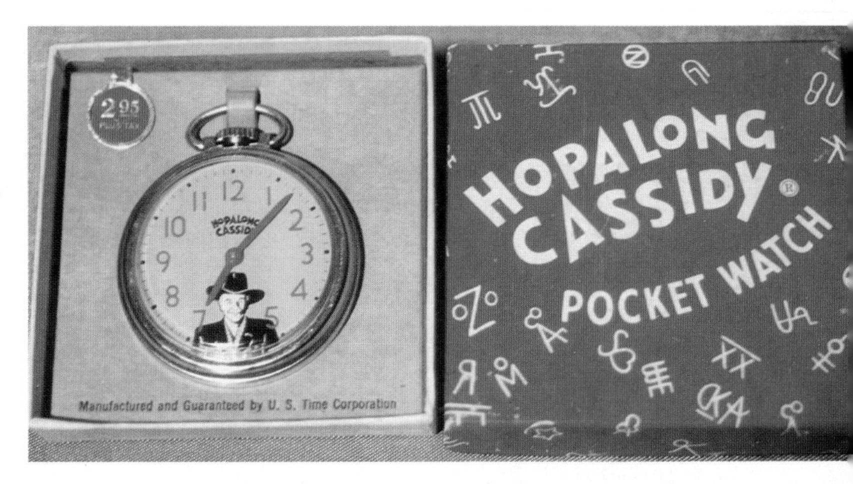

The small face pocketwatch (L) is shown with a wider leather strap and metal fob stamped "Hopalong Cassidy." There are no value chang between the two shown.

The above large face Hoppy pocketwatch is probably an investment val item as it has the original box and price tag of $2.95. Boxes f pocketwatches are extremely hard to find. This boxed watch may bring investment value of over $1,000. From the Jon & Charlie Cheek collectio

The two stamped metal watch figures (above) were made in Japan to resemble the Hoppy wrist compass design. The upper photo had a plastic strap very similar to the wrist compass and the lower version is a lapel pin watch. The quality of both was very poor. Some collectors prize these illegal imitations which has kept their values high: $175 (upper version) $145 for the lower lapel pin watch.

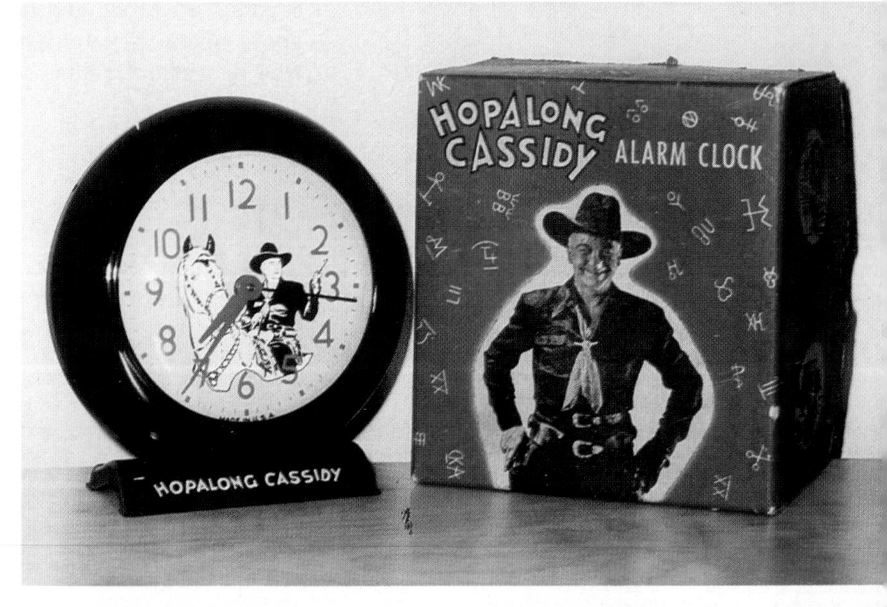

The Hoppy alarm clock (above) is a very popular collector item. Made by U Time (which became Timex) there are only two versions of this clock that ar genuine: the one shown above, and an earlier version of the same design bu with a slightly different graphic, the name insert on the clock face, and wider, open center pointer. Other versions are cobbled together and sold Hoppy clocks which are not. #1. $1,400 #2. $1,100 #3. $850. Deduct $30 without box, $75 without price tag and $50 without instructions & warrant From the Charles Ringhel collection.

The "Western Set" (R) is an obvious attempt to duplicate Hoppy by Japan. The stamped metal watch and badge were poor imitations. Notice that this particular band is plain without Hoppy name. Some collectors feel this card set is worth $250. as an unusual imitation.

hree items shown above are Japan made phonies from the 1950's. Even the t compass shown at the bottom is a fake. Notice it is a stamped metal on. The real Hoppy, (R) was actually cast plastic. If you examine the ey plastic bands you will also find some differences. From the Jon & lie Cheek collection. Phoney wrist compasses sell for $100-$175.

Close-up compass face photo is from the Ted Hake Americana auction.

The two Hoppy wrist compass items shown on the left are genuine originals. Notice that they came with a black or clear plastic band. The black being more rare. #1. $195 #2. $165 #3. $130. (black band + $20) From the Jon & Charlie Cheek collection.

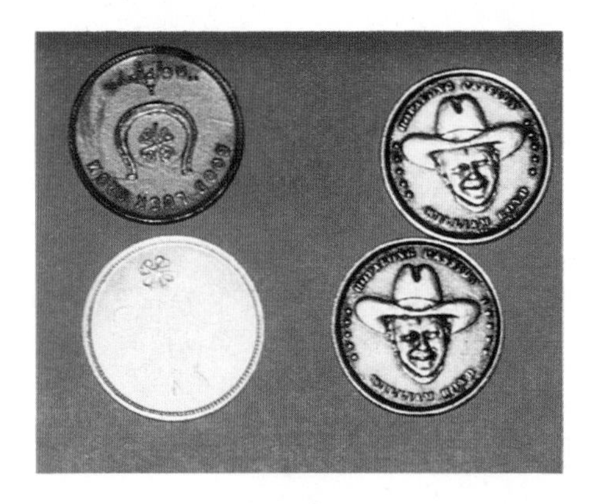

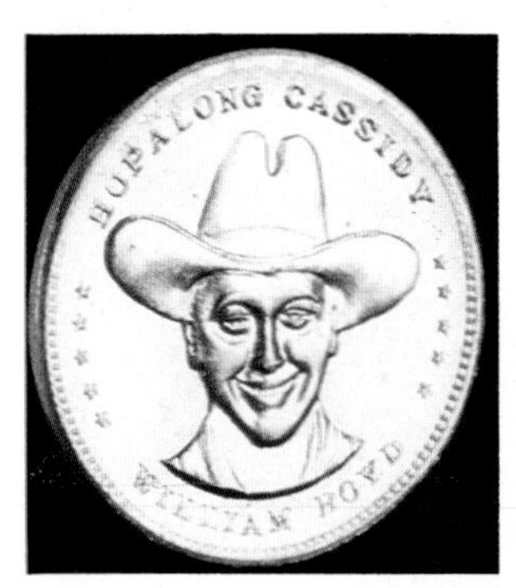

The Hoppy "good luck" coins were originally produced in 1948 for a Hoppy rodeo that was held in Hawaii. Cowboy actor Jack Elam worked for Bill Boyd during this time and helped finance both the rodeo and the coins that were to be tossed-out during the parade. They were made from lightweight aluminum and had "heads" on both sides. Variations of these coins were used for many years. The coins that were included in Pioneer wallets (see clothing chapter) were also made from lightweight aluminum with some having a horseshoe and four leaf clover on the "tails" side, with others also stating "Good Luck." There is a heavier, pewter-like coin currently made, with good image detail, that is not an authentic Hoppy coin. Original Hoppy coins sell for $20 each (two headed) and the good luck wallet coins are selling for $25 to $30. There is a gold coin which came with the Pioneer gold-capped wallet that some collectors buy for $60. There is a lot of Hoppy paper money around in various denominations that sells for up to $10 per bill. Each bill had a different Hoppy photo in the center.

The red Hoppy plastic bank shown above is one of the rarer versions, as is the box it is shown with. Hoppy banks were part of the Hoppy savings club promotion, but were also sold in stores in a different box and with no bank imprint on the back of the Hoppy bank. The rarest bank produced was this chrome and black version (R) of which only a few are known to exist. The most common bank was a bronze color, with a bank name imprint on back. Bronze bank: #1. $280 #2. $220 #3. $180 (deduct $100 if no box, $40 if it has bank imprint on back) Red Bank: #1. $375 #2. $320 #3. $285 (deduct $115 if no box, $40 if it has bank imprint on back.)

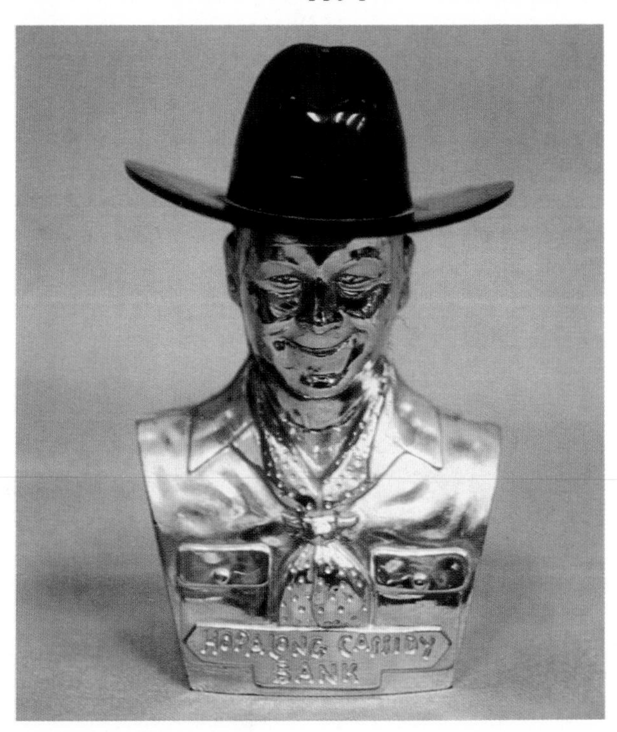

Chrome & black bank: #1. $575 #2. $525 #3. $450. (deduct $115 without box).

From the Jon & Charlie Cheek collection.

py bronze colored plastic banks wn above) were the most popular used bank savings clubs. Note the box s it is a "statuette bank" and not a ings club bank," indicating that it sold in a store. Un-boxed bronze ks are: #1. $140 #2. $100 #3. $75.
n the Phil Ellis collection

The above photo shows the almost complete selection of Hoppy banks produced, the most rare of which is the chrome bank shown in the middle. The one bank missing is a plastic marbled version. Values range widely between the bronze and chrome banks depending on collector interest. From the Jon & Charlie Cheek collection.

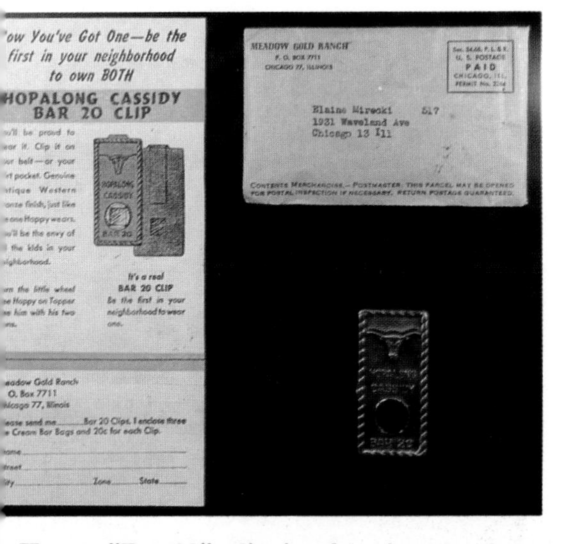

Hoppy "Bar-20" clip is often incorrectly re-red to as a money clip. It really was made as a belt hirt pocket clip with a polorized plastic lens and a ure of Hoppy. The above photo is of a Meadow d premium promotion of the clip, with envelope, motion material and clip. #1. $340 #2. $290 #3. 5. From the Jon & Charlie Cheek collection.

Above is a close-up "Bar-20" clip photo. Loose clips like this are: #1. $85 #2. $60 #3. $45.

Hoppy metal adjustable ring on card. While the Hoppy ring is a common item it is seldom found on the card. #1. $175 #2. $150 #3. $120 (deduct $70 without card)

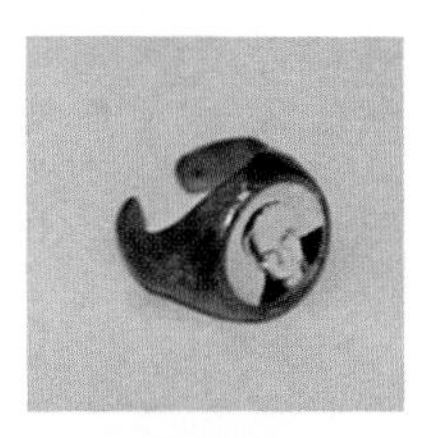

Detail photo of plastic premium ring. ($60)

The above selection of Hoppy rings show the diversity used. The three rings on the left are plastic, premium rings which are valued at $40, $60 and $75 respectively. The ring in the middle is a compass-hat ring ($375) and the three metal rings to the right are "standard" Hoppy rings ($60 to $100) with the exception of the silver ring (with tag) which is valued at $200.

From the Jon & Charlie Cheek collection.

Above card contains Hoppy pin with guns extending below pin bottom. HC charms and tie-tac's shown are reproduction from the same people that made the phoney coin. Pin: #1. $95 #2. $75. Deduct $40 without card.

Pin Hoppy gun opens in middle to reveal HC name. Gun has pearl grips. #1. $175 #2. $145 #3. $120

Detail photo of the compass-hat ring (hat is metal).

Girl's Barrett on card. Most barrettes came with no coloring (above). They are being reproduced. #1. $95 #2. $75 Deduct $40 without card.

Detail photo of plain and colored girl's barrettes. They both maintain a similar value.

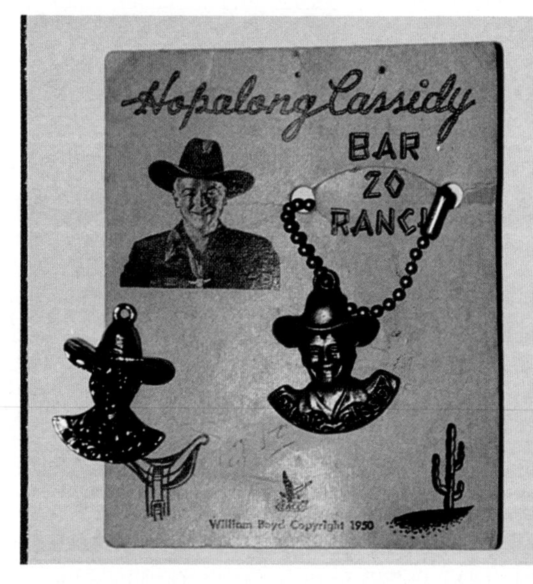

A difficult item to find is the Hoppy charm & chain on original card (above). Charms are being reproduced (L) and hard to tell apart #1.$130 #2. $100 (deduct $60 without card.

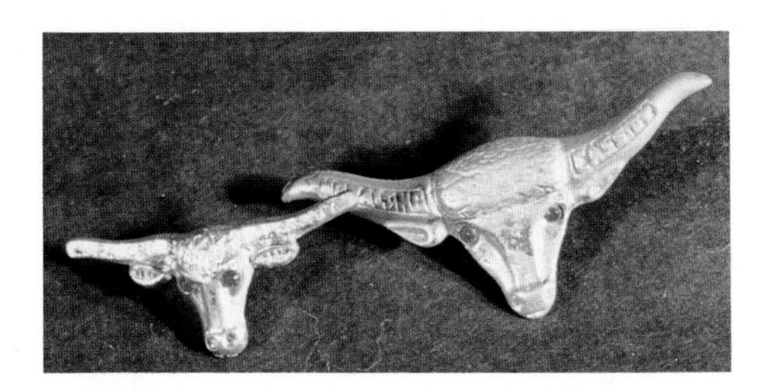

There are a wide variety of tie-slides for Hoppy neckerchiefs (see clothing chapter). The tie-slide on the left is a reproduction. Original slides in general are: $60 to $75. Reproductions are $15.

Most stores featuring Hoppy jewelry had an Anson jewelry display (above). A few of these displays made it into collector hands: #1. $1,200 #2. $1,000 #3. $900. (without shown jewelry). From the Jon Cheek collection.

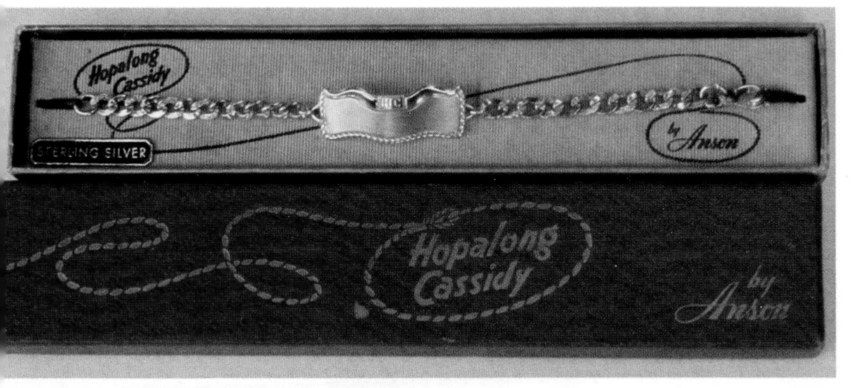

·ling silver ID bracelet made most 10 year old's happy. Bracelet had a steer
ɪ and "HC" in center. Room for engraving. #1. $345 #2. $290 #3. $230.
uct $100 without box.

HC gun & holster pin is quite novel with a tiny chain connecting the two. Gun can be inserted into holster. #1. $175 #2. $150 #3. $125.

ID bracelet has image of Hoppy in center, "HC" on left and "Bar 20" on right.
om bracelet has Topper in center with no change elsewhere. #1. $285 #2. $245 #3.
·. Deduct $100 without box. From the Jon & Charlie Cheek collection.

Another equally rare Hoppy card mounted pin is the crossed guns over Hoppy bust. There is no Hoppy identification on pin alone. #1. $195 #2. $175. (Deduct $75 without card). From the Jon & Charlie Cheek collection.

Another unusual card-mounted pin is this image of Hoppy on Topper in front of the Bar 20 ranch gate. #1. $275 #2. $225. (deduct $75 without card) From the Jon & Charlie Cheek collection.

Rare painted image of Hoppy (in black) with two guns drawn. Guns, holsters, boots and face are gold colored. No other Hoppy ID noticible. #1. $350 #2. $300. (Deduct $75 without card). From the Jon & Charlie Cheek collection.

Hoppy & Topper pin with scrolled rope. Has name "Hopalong" and "Topper" on pin. #1. $185 #2. $165. (Deduct $75 without card.

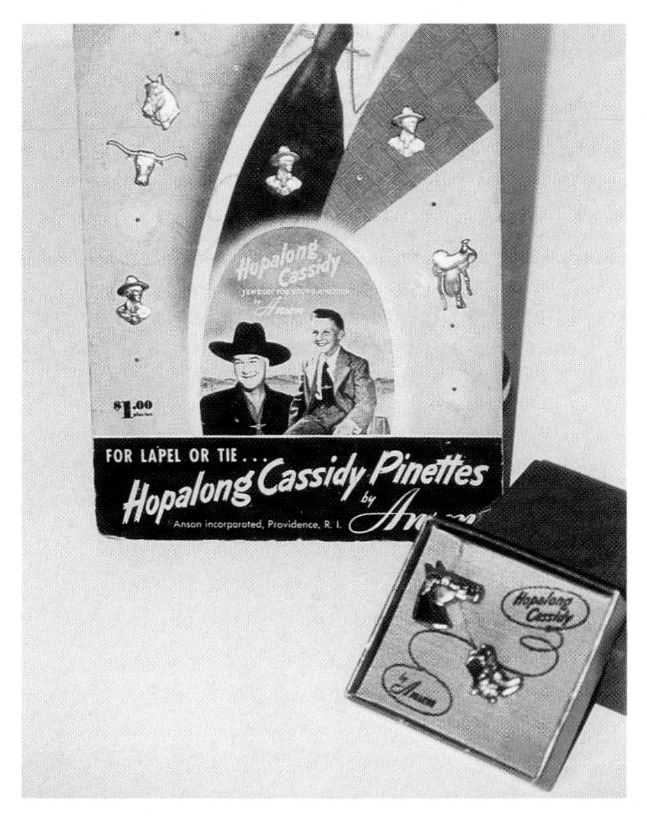

Store Hoppy "pinettes" display card for small Hoppy and western related silver colored pins. Produced by Anson. Boxed version of "pinettes" are gold colored. Display card: #1. $425 #2. $350 #3. $300. Pinettes are: $35 each. Box with two gold pinettes: $130.

Anson store card with ID bracelet. Sterling silver bracelet is stapled to card. #1. $450 #2. $375 #3. $325.

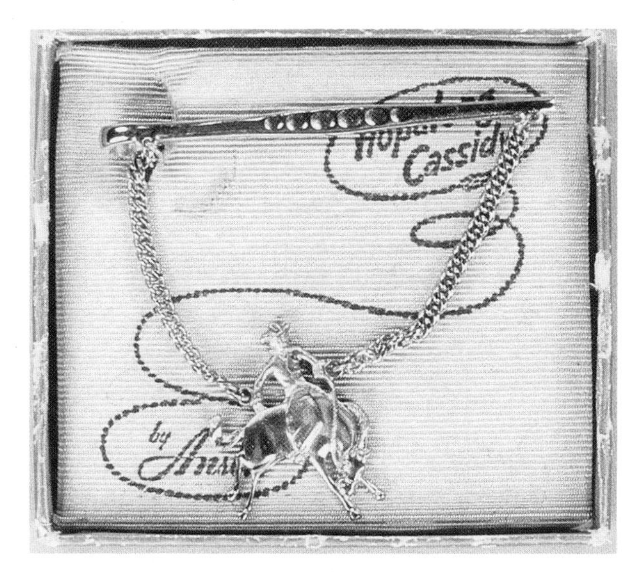

Detail photo of bucking bronc tie bar. No Hoppy ID evident. #1. $175 #2. $150 #3. $120. (including box) From Ted Hake's Americana auctions.

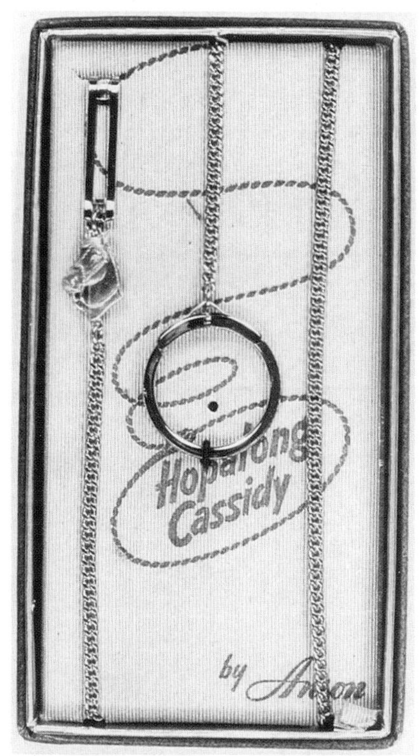

Detail photo of pocketwatch chain (or key chain) with horses head. #1. $225 #2. $185 #3. $165. From Ted Hake's Americana Auctions.

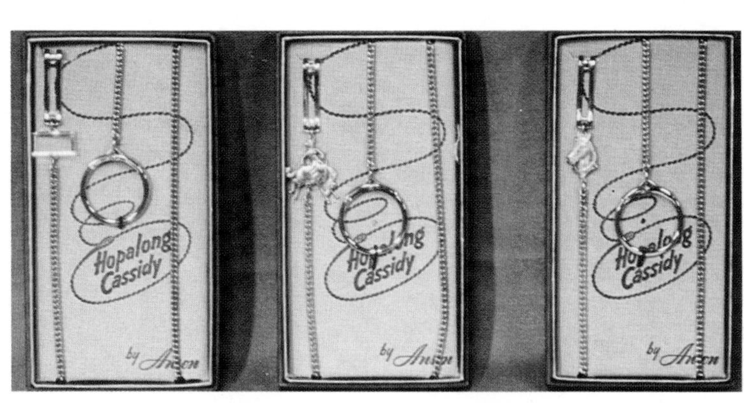

Three different chain sets with images. There is no Hoppy ID on any. Values are similar to those mentioned. From the Jon & Charlie Cheek collection.

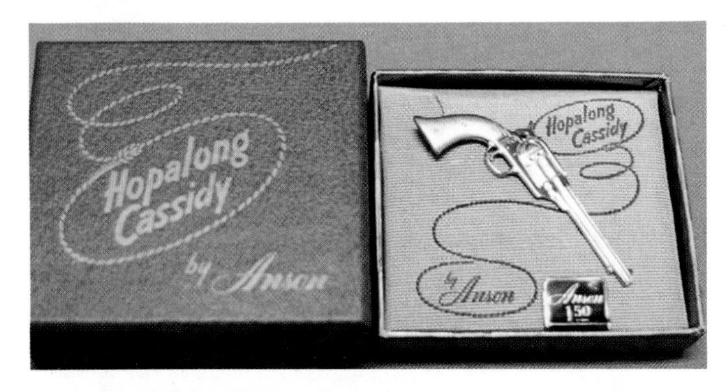

Hoppy Gun Tie Bar (Anson) is a great find. #1. $250 #2. $200 #3. $150. Deduct $125 without box. From the Jon Cheek collection.

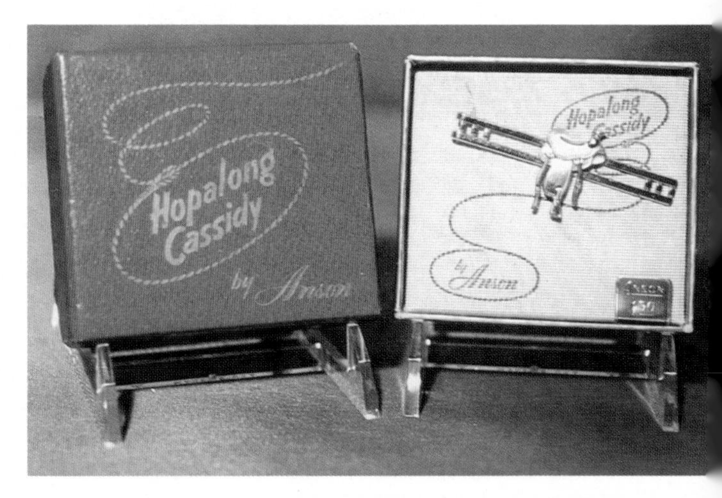

Saddle tie-bar with no other Hoppy ID. #1. $135 #2. $115 #3. $85 (includes box). From the Jon & Charlie Cheek collection.

Tie-bar has oblong center section which may bear an initial engraving. No Hoppy ID on piece. #1. $135 #2. $115 #3. $85. (with box) From the Jon & Charlie Cheek collection.

Two late arrivals from Jon & Charlie Cheek are the crossed pistols pin with chain segments and the Hoppy & Topper scrolled rope with hanging pistol. Both are valued at: #1. $225 #2. $195. Deduct $75 without card.

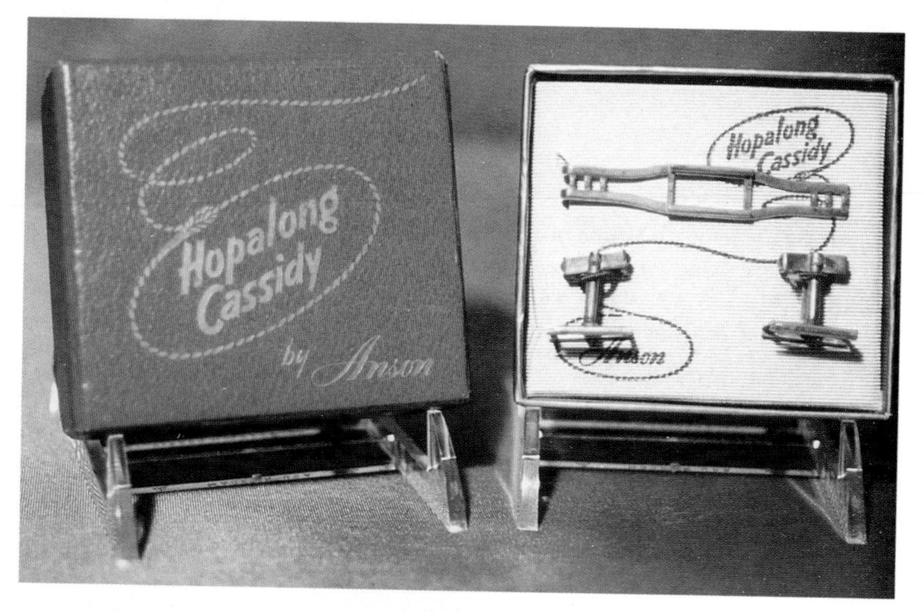

Tie-bar and cuff link set had rectangular open centers to allow something to be slid in. There is no Hoppy ID on the pieces. #1. $150 #2. $130 #3. $110. From the Jon & Charlie Cheek collection.

Steer head tie-bar. There is no Hoppy ID in evidence. #1. $135 #2. $115 #3. $85. From the Jon & Charlie Cheek collection.

Horseshoe tie-bar (in some cases horseshoe was gold color). Item has "Hopalong" on one side and "Cassidy" on the other side of the horseshoe. #1. $175 #2. $150 #3. $130. From the Jon & Charlie Cheek collection.

Hoppy head tie-bar was one of the few pieces where you could discern his identity. #1.$175 #2. 4150 #3. $130. From the Jon & Charlie Cheek collection.

Hoppy jewelry sets were quite rare, and the set to the right was rarer than most because of the chocolate box and brown box lining. Contained in the set are: Hoppy bust cuff links, a suspended gun tie-bar and a Hoppy bust key or pocketwatch chain. #1. $395 #2. $345 #3. $300.

A different variation of the Hoppy jewelry set is shown on the left. (Notice the box color has changed as well as the box insert). Contents are: Topper ID bracelet, Hoppy bust cuff links and a dog head tie-bar. #1 $440 #2. $395 #3. $360. From the Jon & Charlie Cheek collection.

LAMPS
LIGHTS & RADIOS

#1. condition: mint, showing no use #2. condition: excellent to near mint #3. condition: good to very good

The Arvin metal case, tube, table radio was the official Hoppy radio when it bore a special metal-foil front of Hoppy riding Topper over the speaker area. The radio came in two colors: red and black and two slightly different foil stampings: one with Topper rearing-up and one with only one raised leg. A few years ago, a collector bought the original dies to produce new Hoppy foil-fronts which were impossible to find, but now are available at the moderate price of $50 for either one.

Display photo of Hoppy radio and reproduced tin sign advertising it.

xed Hoppy radio is from the Sharon Delaney lection.

Photo of red and black Arvin radio's with two different foil fronts. There is no value difference between the two.

Arvin Hoppy radios': #1. $1,700 #2. $1,400 #3. $1,200 (deduct $400 without box, $150 without operating instructions. $75 without warranty, $75 without antenna suction cup) Photo (L) shows different colors and foil-fronts. From the Jon & Charlie Cheek collection

Wooden salesman's radio sample box for the Hoppy radio is a ni collector's find. #1. $450 #2. $375 #3. $325. From the Brian Beir collection.

Instruction booklet for the Hoppy radio had several nice Hoppy graphics and general radio instructions and guarantee form. While the instructions came with all Hoppy radios', few "boxed" radios' today have them. Deduct $150 if this is the case. #1. $150 #2. $120 #3. $95. From the Brian Beirne collection.

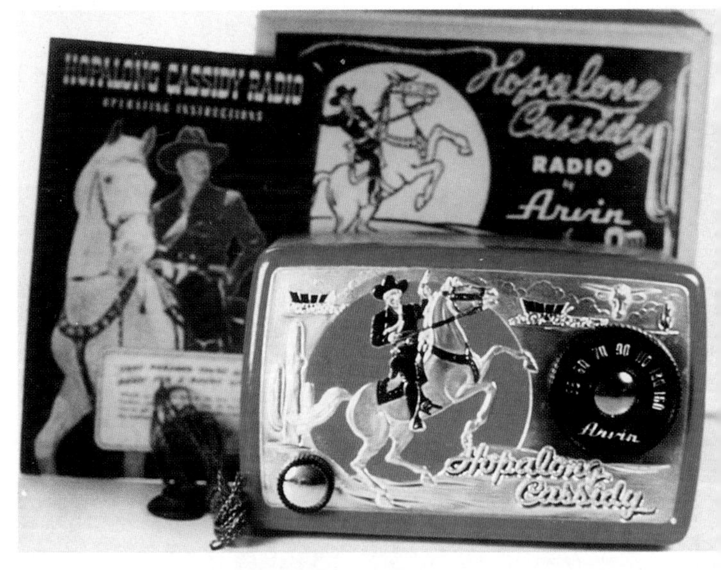

There are several "investment value" Hoppy radios' that hav reached record dollar heights at auction sales of $2,000 an $2,200. The radio shown above, is one of these rare exceptions. I is without doubt, a mint, unused and complete radio that a advanced collector would give almost anything for. There ar perhaps four such radios in existence and the "investmen value" will continue to increase. Note the suction cup on th antenna wire. From the Frank Smith collection.

Photo (L) shows the early Hoppy flashlight in its original box. Hoppy flashlight came with a Morse Code chart printed on the back. Notice box states the word "signal" on front and the statement: "with Morse Code" on side panel. #1. $520 #2. $450 #3. $400 (deduct $300 without box).

e only two versions of the Hoppy flashlight are shown ove) with the earlier 'signal' version on the right. The newer sion is the 'siren' flashlight. The 'siren' flashlight also came a special box (not shown). The flashlight on the right is a rare iation of the signal flashlight due to its decal, which is a aller version of the one used on full sized lamps. This flash-t carries a $50 premium value. From the Frank Smith llection.

Display photo (above) of the four Hoppy ceramic lamps and lights. Quite an impressive showing. From the Jon & Charlie Cheek collection.

: above photo is of the three most common Aladdin ceramic Hoppy lamps: gun olster night light (L) 'bullet' lamp - nite lite, (C) and standard table lamp. ile many table lamps exist, few have the original Hoppy 'Whip-a-lite' Aladdin de (R) which was easily damaged and destroyed. The gun & holster night light often suffered decal damage or a broken and reglued handle: #1. $395 #2. 0 #3. $285. (there was no known box). Bullet lamp (also a nite light) (C): #1. 0 #2. $410 #3. $380 (lamp is a great deal more difficult to find. Also, no known).

Most avid collectors would pay $800 for this #1. shade and tag. From the Phil Ellis collection.

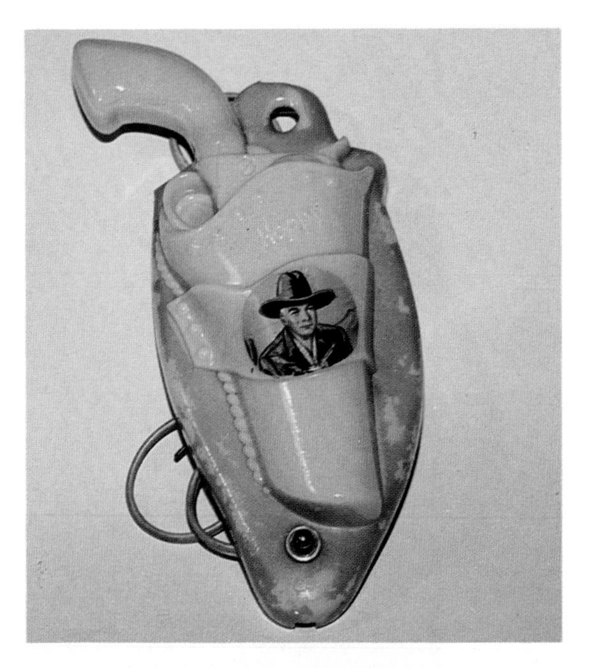

Detail photo of Aladdin gun & holster nite light. Always examine back of lamp for break lines as well as decal condition. Also examine electrical cord.

This Aladdin table lamp is clearly inve ment quality. Note original Aladdin ca on lamp and tag on shade. Other simil lamps are: #1. $1,250 #2. $900 #3. $8 (deduct $600 without shade). Add $150 f lamp tag and $150 for shade tag. From t Phil Ellis collection.

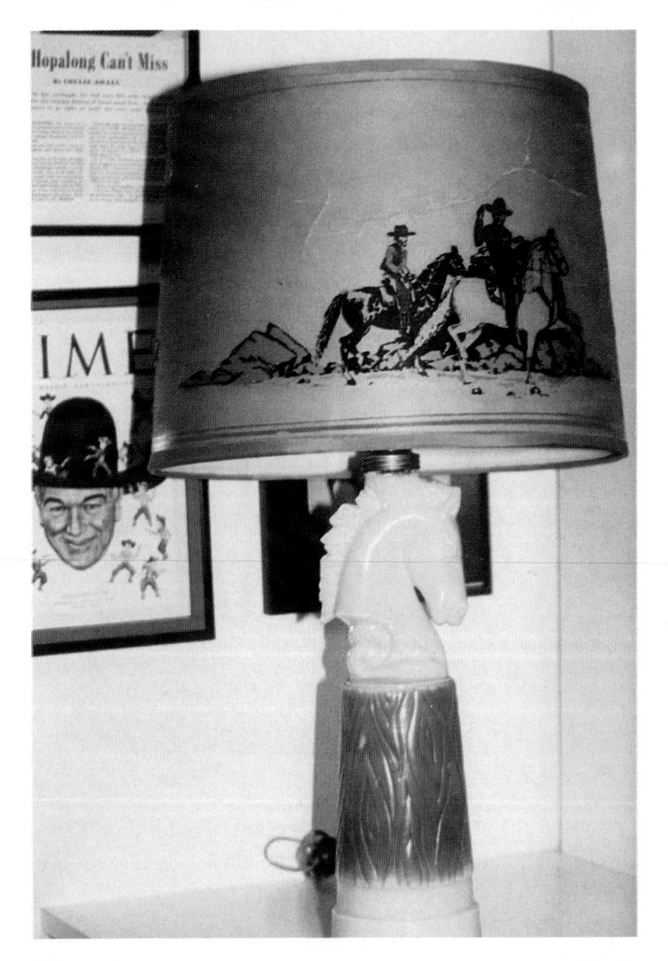

The 'Topper' Hoppy lamp is perhaps the rarest of the four. Some had 'Topper' name on the base in raised glass, others had 'Hopalong Cassidy.' #1. $1,600 #2. $1,300 #3. $1,100. (deduct $800 without shade).

Hoppy plastic 'action scene' lamps are very popular wi collectors. Red is the most common color, followed by bl yellow and gold. The above lamps were the later versions whe inside cylinder revolved to show 'action scene.'

Hoppy revolving plastic lights (used as a nite light) are very popular collectibles. When light was turned on, heat revolved an inner cylinder which made a scene appear to move. With the earlier version, (R) the waterfall and camp fire appeared to move and flicker. The later version (L) had a clear outer sleeve so you could watch the entire inner cylinder rotate which had the 'action scene' on it. Both scene types have similar values. Lamp colors however, have different values: Red #1. $650 #2. $575 #3. $500 Blue: #1. $700 #2. $625 #3. $550 Yellow: #1. $750 #2. $675 #3. $600 Gold: #1. $800 #2. $725 #3. $650. From the Jon & Charlie Cheek collection.

Note: red revolving light (L) is the earlier 'flickering' version but has a different scene in front of the waterfall and campfire. Blue light (R) has a similar 'action scene' as the others.

The two red lights shown on the left contain different scenes: the right one is the 'flickering' waterfall and campfire, the one on the left contains the 'action scene' as earlier described. There is no value difference between the two.

MAGAZINES ARTICLES

#1. condition: mint, showing no use #2. condition: excellent to near mint #3. condition: good to very good

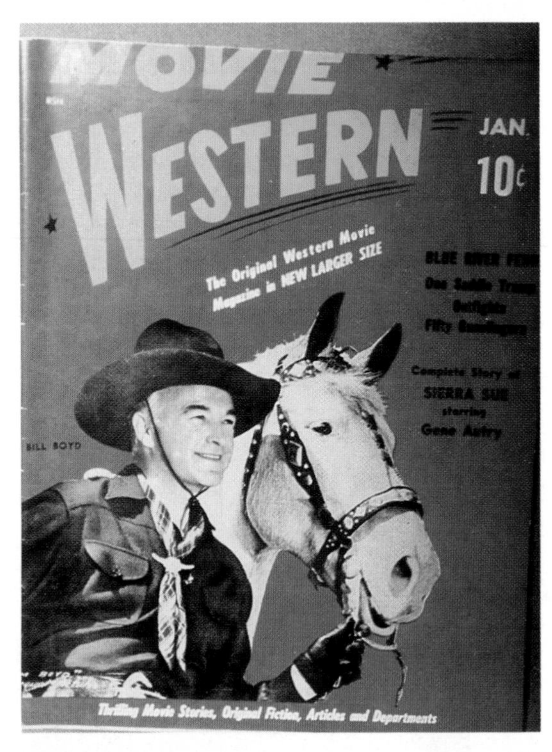

1950's issue of "Movie Western" magazine with Hoppy on cover is a great collector find. #1. $100 #2. $75 #3. $60. From the Jon & Charlie Cheek collection.

"Grit" Magazine from 1942 featured Hoppy on the cover (note sheriff's badge). Magazine is difficult to find. #1. $125 #2. $90 #3. $75. From the Jon & Charlie Cheek collection.

Western Stars magazine featur many cowboy idols including Roy Hoppy. In this issue, there were so great photos of Hoppy as well as multi-level contest taking sever pages. A Hoppy collector's "mu have." #1. $85 #2. $60 #3. $45. Fro the Mike Merryman collection.

BILL BOYD

"the case of hoppy and the little white lie"

by edgar buchanan

Edger Buchanan story about Hoppy in "Western Stars" (previous page). From the Mike Merryman collection.

"Men Only" magazine from England (1952) has caricature of Hoppy on cover and small article. Very rare: #1. $150 #2. $125 #3. $100. From the Ted Hake, Hake's Americana auctions.

The Role I Liked Best . . .

Article from Saturday Evening Post (1950) by Bill Boyd: "The Role That I liked Best" ($25-$45). from the Dick Stevens collection.

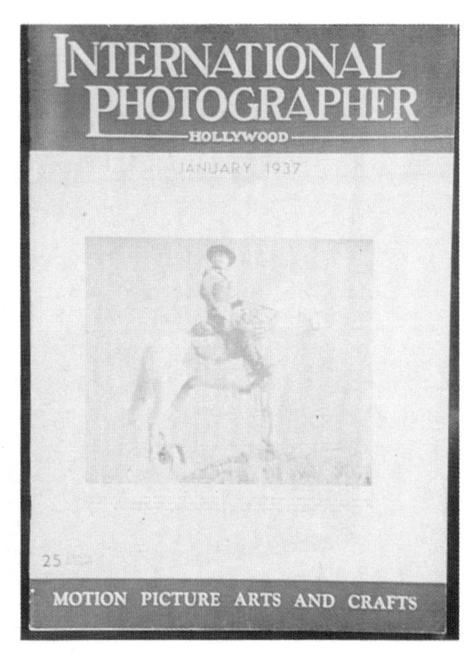

The January 1937 issue of International Photographer w/ Hoppy on cover is very rare: #1. $200 #2. $150 #3. $125. Jon & Charlie Cheek collection.

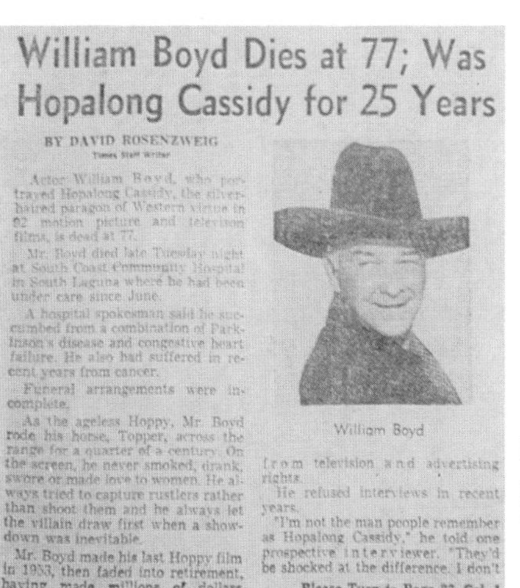

William Boyd Dies at 77; Was Hopalong Cassidy for 25 Years

BY DAVID ROSENZWEIG
Times Staff Writer

Actor William Boyd, who portrayed Hopalong Cassidy, the silver-haired paragon of Western virtue in 82 motion picture and television films, is dead at 77.

Mr. Boyd died late Tuesday night at South Coast Community Hospital in South Laguna where he had been under care since June.

A hospital spokesman said he succumbed from a combination of Parkinson's disease and congestive heart failure. He also had suffered in recent years from cancer.

Funeral arrangements were incomplete.

As the ageless Hoppy, Mr. Boyd rode his horse, Topper, across the range for a quarter of a century. On the screen, he never smoked, drank, swore or made love to women. He always tried to capture rustlers rather than shoot them and he always let the villain draw first when a showdown was inevitable.

Mr. Boyd made his last Hoppy film in 1953, then faded into retirement, having made millions of dollars from television and advertising rights.

He refused interviews in recent years.

"I'm not the man people remember as Hopalong Cassidy," he told one prospective interviewer. "They'd be shocked at the difference. I don't

William Boyd

Please Turn to Page 33, Col. 1

Newspaper death articles (1972) with photos are also a collectible item of sorts. They are valued at $15 to $30.

POST

Old Hopalong Can't Miss

By COLLIE SMALL

June 14, 1947 article from Post magazine. Photos were taken by Gene Lester, the "Hollywood Photographer." Hoppy is not on cover but the article is extensive. #1. $65 #2. $45 #3. $30

Hoppy on cover of "Time" magazine is a very in-demand collectors' item. Article is also very interesting. #1. $95 #2. $75 #3. $50

"People and Places" magazine featured Hoppy in July, 1950 and is a hard issue to find: #1. $95 #2. $75 #3. $50.

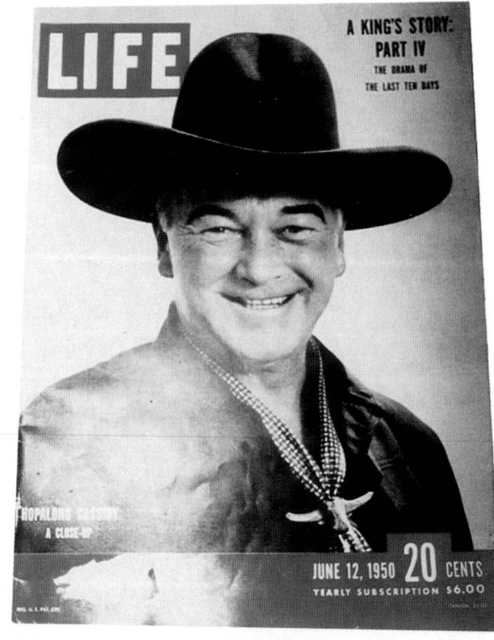

"Life" magazine featured Hoppy in its June, 1950 issue with an extensive article. This magazine is one of the more popular collector items: #1. $100 #2. $75 #3. $50

1951 "Coronet" magazine with Hoppy article is quite rare: #1. $65 #2. $50 #3. $30

Quick magazine featured Hoppy on May 1, 1950 cover with a feature story. #1. $65 #2. $50 #3. $30

"TV-Radio Life" magazine ran a great Hoppy caricature in one issue. Hard to find: #1. $75 #2. $60 #3. $40

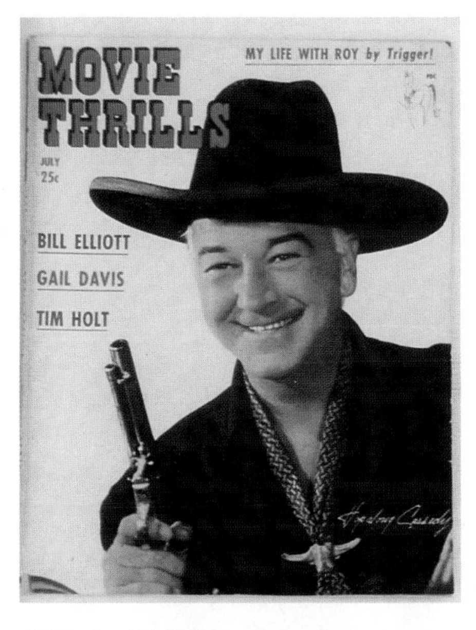

"Movie Thrills" magazine ran a great cover Hoppy photo with gold autograph. #1. $85 #2. $70 #3. $60.

Very rare edition of "Video" magazine (June, 1950) ran a cover photo of Hoppy plus a splendid article. #1. $120 #2. $90 #3. $65. From the Jon & Charlie Cheek collection.

The Pittsburg, PA issue of "TV Digest" (along with other areas) is a very hard find and a strong demand item: #1. $85 #2. $70 #3. $60.

a nice piece, is the "Hopalong Cassidy's stern" magazine (R). The yellow cover e (L) contained the "Tex" Burns story ail to Seven Pines" (Louis L'Amour's t western book). That issue is valued at 0 in #1. condition. Other issues are: #1. 5 #2. $100 #3. $75. From the Jon & rlie Cheek collection.

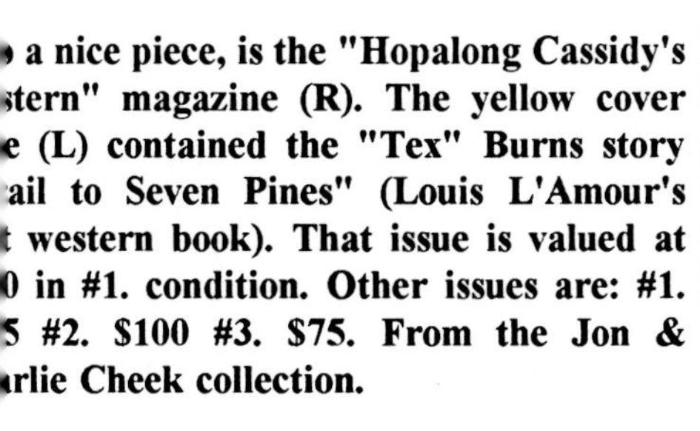

By far, the most sought after Hoppy cover magazine is "Look" where he is seen with "Hoppy's Kid" Roger Hall. Unautographed issue values are: #1. $120 #2. $90 #3. $70. from the Phil Ellis collection,.

"Friends" magazine was an automobile promo. publication which is quite rare. The August, 1950 issue featured Hoppy with an unknown "Hoppy's Kid." #1. $120 #2. $90 #3. $70.

"TV Forecast" January, 1953 featured Hoppy and several others. Very rare issue: #1. $125 #2. $100 #3. $80. From the Mike Forthun collection.

"Lazy Rolls the Rio Grande" is shown as an example of the many song sheets that featured Hoppy on the cover. We do not have the space to cover all of them.: #1. $50 #2. $35 #3. $20.

"Colorama" section of the Feb. 21, 1954 Philadelphia Inquirer newspaper featured a great photo of Hoppy with both guns drawn: #1. $65 #2. $50 #3. $30. From the Dick Stevens collection.

"Song & Saddle" (r) is a western folio with both songs and pictures. Has the photo of a very young Hoppy on the cover. Contains many "folk" era pieces: #1. $100 #2. $80 #3. $70.

While the famous photo of Hoppy and a confused "Hoppy's Kid" (note the Roy boots) is widely known, few collectors know the source. It is the September 12, 1949 issue of "Life" magazine with Marshal Tito on the cover. The story is "Life Goes on Tour with Hoppy" and has extensive photos. A great value: #1. $60 #2. $45 #3. $30.

'arade" is a newspaper magazine ction that in 1953 featured Mr. & rs. Bill Boyd with many photos. #1. 0 #2. $30 #3. $20.

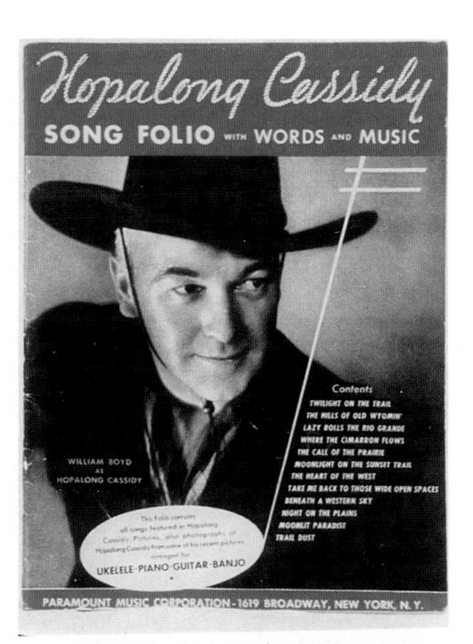

The Hoppy "song folio" (above) contained many western titles plus a wonderful cover photo of Hoppy: #1. $100 #2. $80 #3. $70. from the Gene Douglass, M. Saxen collection

"Box Office" was a trade magazine and extremely hard to find. Contained great Hoppy promos: #1. $125 #2. $100 #3. $80. From the Mike Pellow collection.

MISCELLANEOUS ITEMS

This chapter contains many great Hoppy items that were late arrivals, or could not be readily placed somewhere else. Some items are found in other chapters and are shown again here, in a display photo so that you will see what they look like from a different perspective. I have also included a few phoney production items and several licensed production items that are really neat!

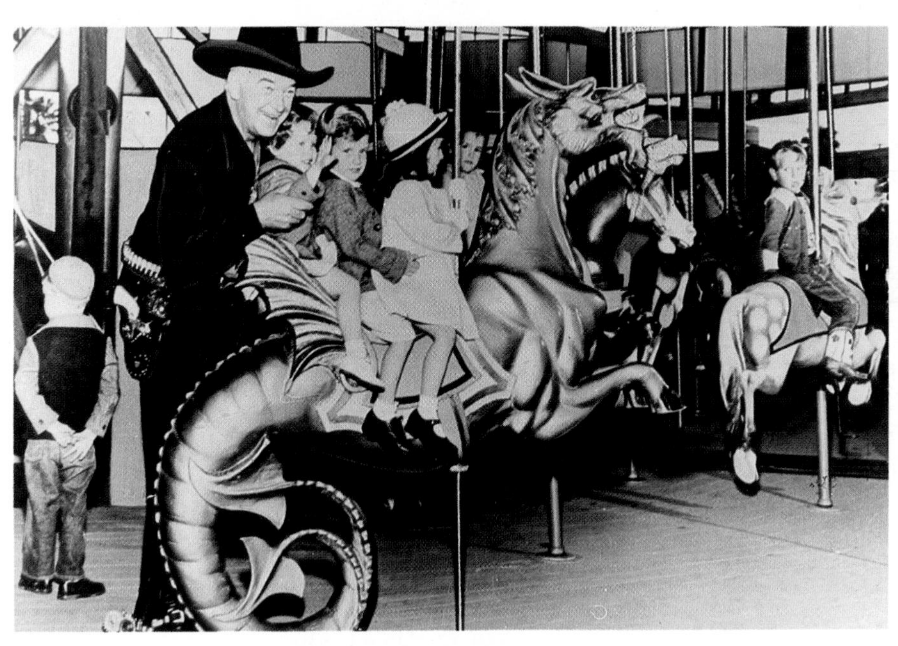

Photo of "Hoppyland" opening day, May 27, 1951

Cited by many as America's first "them park, "HOPPYLAND" opened its doors May 27, 1951 in the beach front community Venice, California, about 25 miles west Anaheim, where cartoonist Walt Disney wou open his theme park several years lat Nearly 100 acres of rides and attractions we designed for family enjoyment: a small mou tain populated by goats, a watery lagoon ki could splash in, or paddle around in a b and a two-mile pony ride around the park personally interviewed the lady who as young girl, ran the pony ride attraction. S clearly remembers the "special saddle Hoppy had made for the nearly 100 li ponies used. The saddles had the Hoppy ima on both "fenders" and came in black a brown. The pony saddles that collectors' pri today are thought to have come from t Hoppyland stock, and are truly "Hoppylan memorabilia. The park closed in 1954.

There is precious little memorabilia known that came from "Hoppyland" with the exception of the pony saddles mentioned earlier, a few "Press Passes" given to newsmen for opening day and an occasional ticket. I have not been able to find any Hoppyland postcards or other related amusement park items usually sold. I personally feel that the two versions of the Hoppy carnival chalk figures also originated at Hoppyland, but at this time, cannot substantiate this claim.

One recently discovered item showing Hoppyland on opening day does exist however, and I am proud to be part of its preservation. The item is a 10 minute, 16mm film (theatre short subject) covering the Hoppyland grand opening. The film shows the park and many of the rides and interviews with Hoppy and many Hollywood elite including Pat O' Brian and Richard Widmark, and hundreds of kids dressed in Hoppy outfits. The film has been transferred to VHS tape and can be ordered through Cowboy Collector Publications for $24. It is worth it just to see Hoppy on his roller coaster ride!

Electric train ride around "Hoppyland" park.

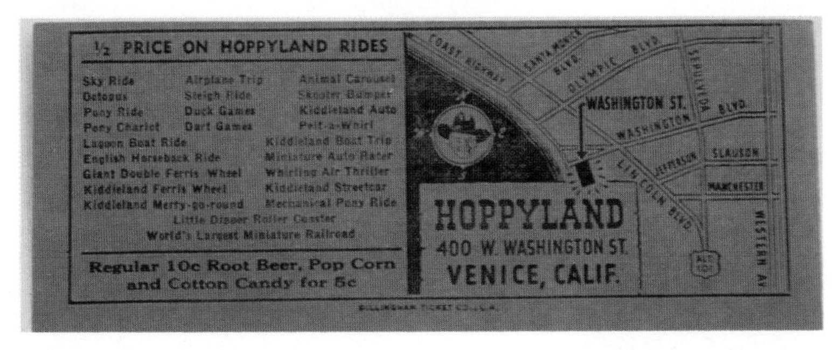

Thrifty Drugs had discount "Hoppyland" tickets and there may be others: #1. $225 #2. $180 #3. $150. From the Mike Merryman collection.

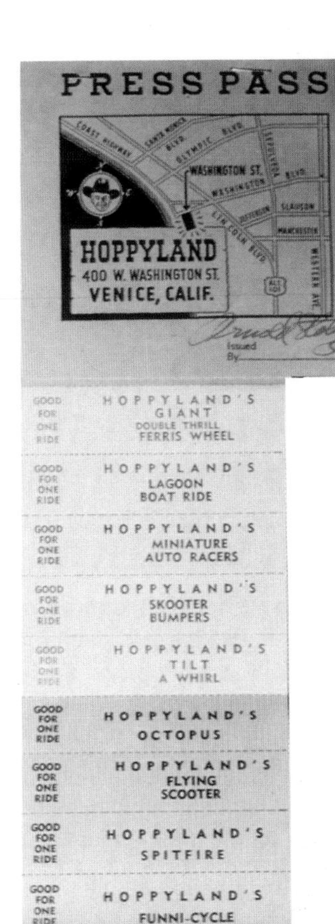

There are only two "Hoppyland" Press Passes known to exist that contain 25 ride coupons: #1. $450 #2. $400 #3. $350. From the Mike Forthun collection.

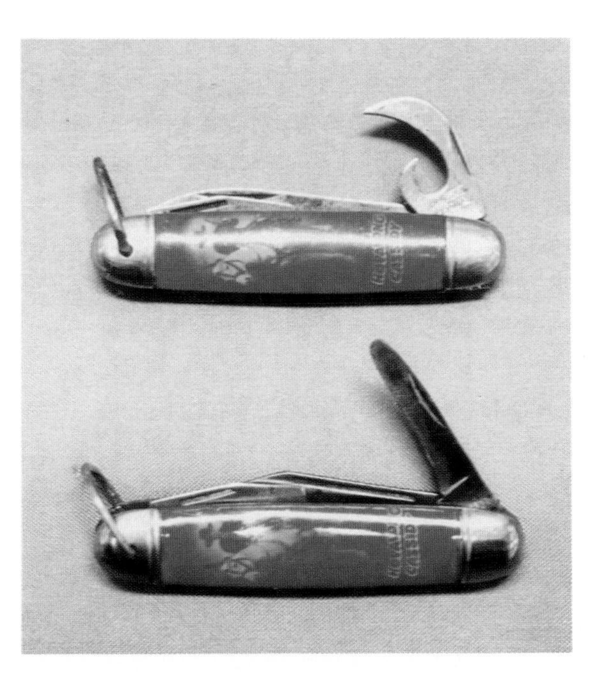

Shown in the "Bath-Personal" chapter, the red Hoppy Trail Knife is again shown for identification. It is the rarest of all three Trail Knives with a red side (shown) and a black reverse side: #1. $450 #2. $340 #3. $300. Deduct $30. if no fob. From the Jon & Charlie Cheek collection.

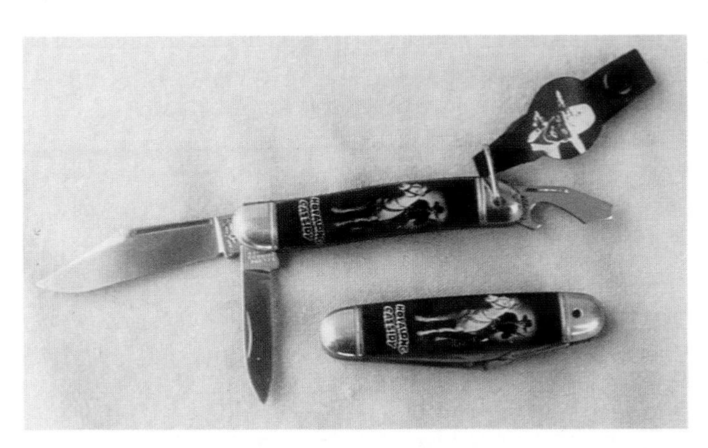

The open knife shown above is a "serpentine" version of the Hoppy Trail Knife and is slightly longer and narrower than the standard version. Look closely and note the slight difference in the end and body shape of this knife. Perhaps a one of a kind. Estimated value is: #1. $500 #2. $450 #3. $400. From the "AJ" Siarkowski collection.

Nice Hoppy Sheriff Badge on original card. Never saw one quite like it. Badge has color photo of Hoppy & Topper. It could be a "fantasy" piece. From Gary Bondy's collection

The Hoppy wagon shown here is a "fantasy" item and never was "original Hoppy." It was made a few years ago by an enthusiastic collector.

The unknown brown vinyl Hoppy box. I have seen three similar boxes, all with no contents. The box is very well constructed, but not, I think, to house a product. The Hoppy image, rope and saddle seem to be hand-painted in gold leaf on each one. As is, I would value it at $300 in #1. condition until more is known about it.

Intact sheet of Hoppy "Zoomerang" gun paper. Paper was cut into strips and attached to gun front. Value? My guess is around $100. From the Frank Smith collection.

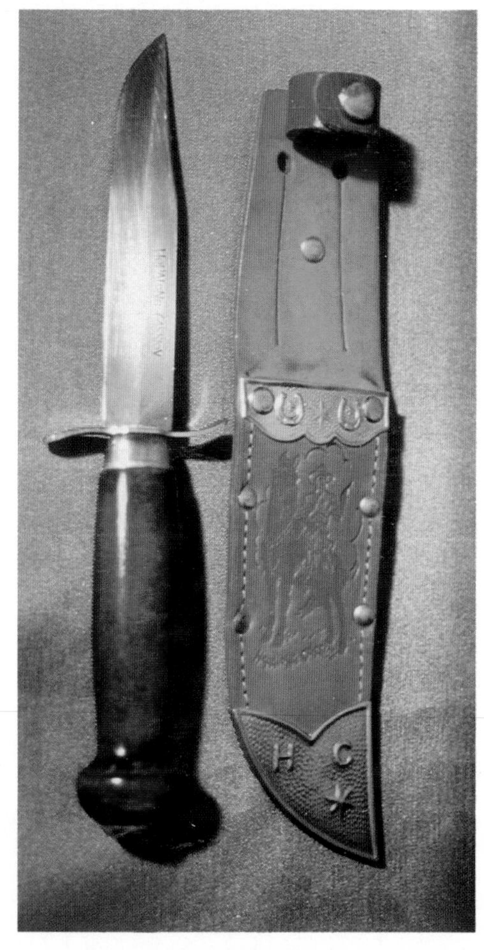

Rarer than rare is this Hoppy sheath knife and sheath. Knife is aprox. 8" long and has a solid wood handle. Very good workmanship on both the knife and sheath. Knife has "Hopalong Cassidy" stamped into the blade. #1. $1,450#2. $1,275 #3. $1,100. From the Jon & Charlie Cheek collection.

On first glance this may look like a special Hoppy book but look closer! It is a box of cigars! It was a Christmas present from the Hoppy film maker to his friends: #1. $825 #2. $750 #3. $625. from the Jon & Charlie Cheek collection.

Inside view of Hoppy cigar box looks normal.

is Hoppy cut-out figure was said to be a store splay with several reportedly found. I have examed one and it sure looks like a phoney item to me. e Hoppy cut-out is slipped into a slotted pine stand be displayed. I personally see no reason to have e.

Small but rare is this deck of Hoppy miniature playing cards with a photo of Hoppy on each card back. Jon Cheek says it was found in a box of "Cracker-Jack" candy. #1. $150 #2. $120 #3. $90

Shown in "Toys" this is Lee Mitchell's marionette with box. An investment value item for around $1,300.

While most collectors are familiar with Producer's Dairy paper milk containers few of their glass bottles are known to exist. Shown is a 1/2 gallon size: #1. $125 #2. $100 #3. $85.

Interesting Purity Maid paper milk container has an unusual top: #1. $185 #2. $140 #3. $100From the Jon & Charlie Cheek collection.

Early version of the "tent top" paper milk container from Lawrence Dairy is quite rare: #1. $200 #2. $150 #3. $100. From Steve Axelson.

Shown under "Promotions" ice cream cup lids often featured Hoppy and mention his current film. Lids shown all pre-date 1940 and are great collection pieces: $25 to $45 each.

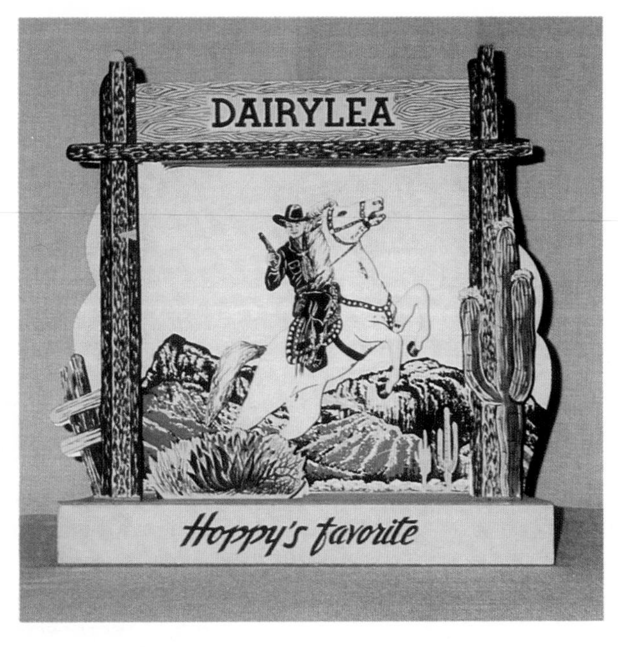

This Dairylea dairy products counter display is electric driven and rocks Hoppy & Topper back and forth. Very rare: #1. $1,875 #2. $1,600 #3. $1,450. From the Phil Ellis collection.

little known Golden Book "Here omes The Parade" has Hoppy as art of it. A nice addition to any llection.

A display of paper milk containers from 1/2 pint to 1/2 gallon including "Tent type" and "flat-top" designs from the Jon & Charlie Cheek collection.

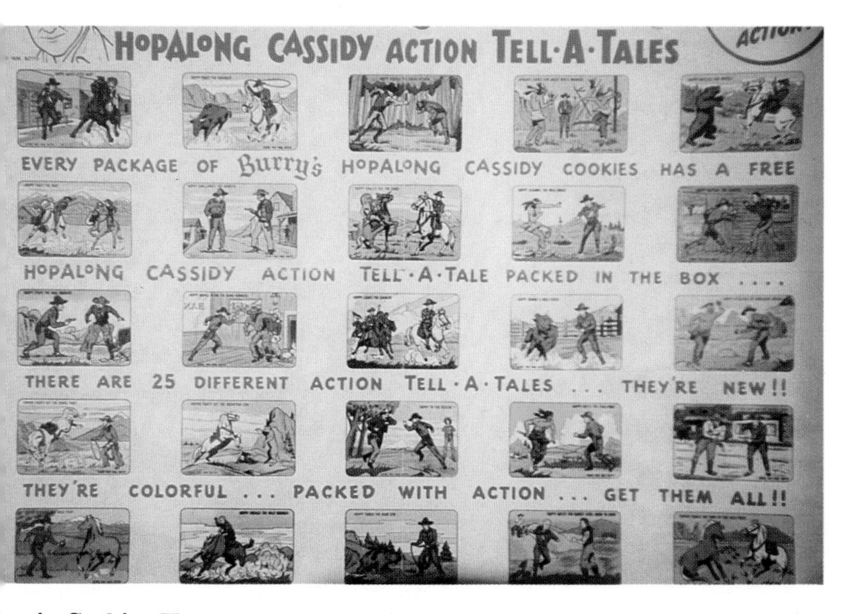

rry's Cookies Hoppy card store display. Card shows all 25 color Hoppy ds that come free, one in each box. Sorry that the top graphics of the play isn't shown: #1. $900 #2. $800 #3. $700. From Phil Ellis.

Hoppy's Singing Lariat is as rare as it looks. It is a special promotion item from W.T. Young Foods. String was held in hand and "lariat" was swung around head to make a strange noise. #1. $300 #2. $250 #3. $200. From the Jon & Charlie Cheek collection.

rry's Cookie Hoppy badges are a great find for $25 -$35. Detail photo of -backs is found in another chapter. From the "AJ" Siarkowski collection.

Nice version of the girl's vinyl brown book bag. Notice strap instead of handle: #1. $360 #2. $300 #3. $240. From the Frank Smith collection.

Hoppy book bags (School Items chapter) include this boy's black & white vinyl version with a plastic handle: #1. $360 #2. $300 #3. $240. From the Jon & Charlie Cheek collection.

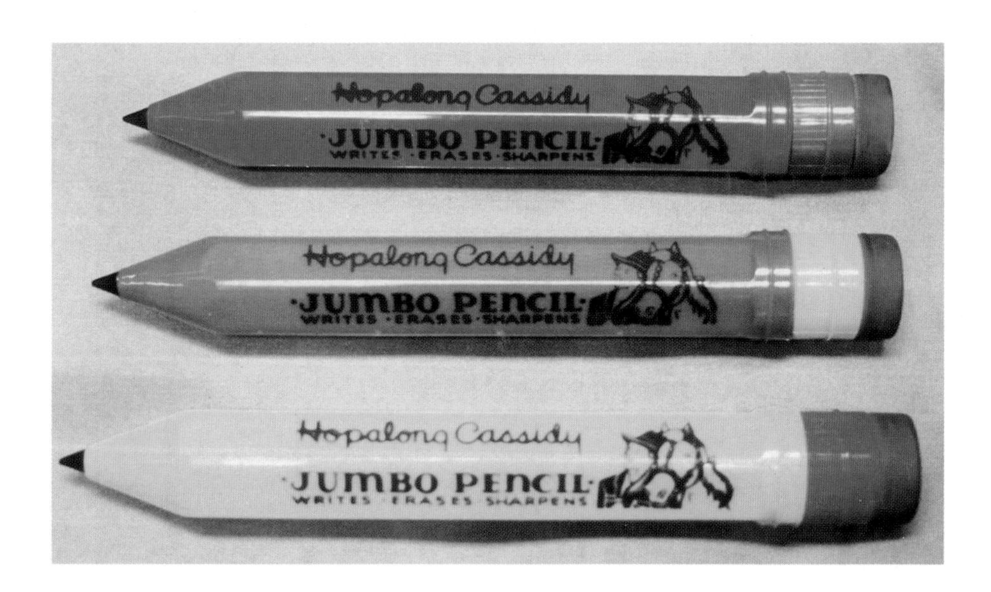

Another "School Items" chapter item are these three plastic "jumbo" pencil cases which came in three colors: Red, Green & yellow: #1. $400 #2. $325 #3. $280 (with contents). from the Jon & Charlie Cheek collection.

This is an unusual vinyl Hoppy patch about 3" in diameter. I have no idea where this item came from or was used with, and neither does its owner. An item like this is worth at least $50 and maybe more if an application is known. From the "AJ" Siarkowski collection.

The game of "Hopalong Snap" is a British card game that I'm not very familiar with, but would like to have. Box contains a blue & white Hoppy & Topper on each card back and color western scenes on card face: #1. $350 #2. $275 #3. $200 (with box). From the Frank Smith collection.

Shown in the "Endorsements" chapter, the above item is a large die-cut metal sign that was attached to Producer's Dairy home delivery trucks. A very nice piece: #1 $650 #2. $575 #3. $525. From the Charles Ringhel collection.

This wonderful Hoppy cookie jar was a limited edition produced by Happy Memories, Woodland Hills, CA. Originally selling for $360 they are now bringing $500+. Only 500 were made.

oppy slippers were shown in "Outfits" chapter and due to their rarity eserved a display photo: #1. $350 #2. $225 #3. $175 There is no known ox.

All metal toy (3" high) of Hoppy on Topper is made in England and originally came on a card: #1. $130 #2. $95 #3. $65. Deduct $40 without card.

There is no such thing as a genuine Hoppy shaving kit for kids. It is a "fantasy" piece designed just for the heck of it, for collector's as silly as me. The kit actually had a lot of work put into it and makes a good conversation piece if you find one for under $40.

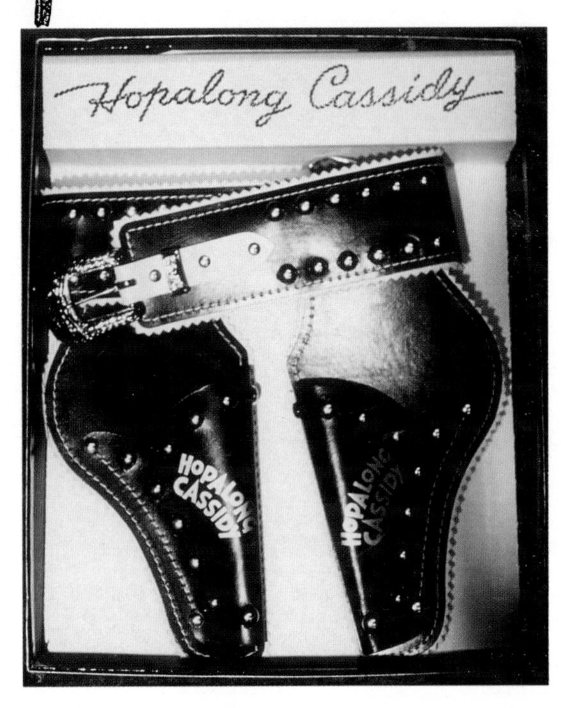

This Hoppy boxed holster set is a licensed limited edition item made two years ago. The quality and craftsmanship are excellent. It is so good it could easily become confused as an original. Only 200 were made, I'm told, selling for $150 per set. No guns were included. This set is also shown in "Guns & Holsters" chapter.

This bronze Hoppy statue is about 18" high and a thi[illegible] of beauty. It is expensive though ($4,000+) and [illegible] produced in limited quantity by Happy Memories, Inc[illegible]

A very recent discovery is this size 12, Hoppy leather winter jacket. In all probability, it is made by the same company that produced the jacket on the first page of the "Clothes" chapter. They both have fringe, similar cuff striping, color design and lining. The only identifying element are the two red Hoppy on Topper leather patches sewn on each sleeve. While the jacket shown is in #4 condition and probably worth $200, the higher values are: #1. $575 #2. $475 #3. $300. From the Doug Candler collection.

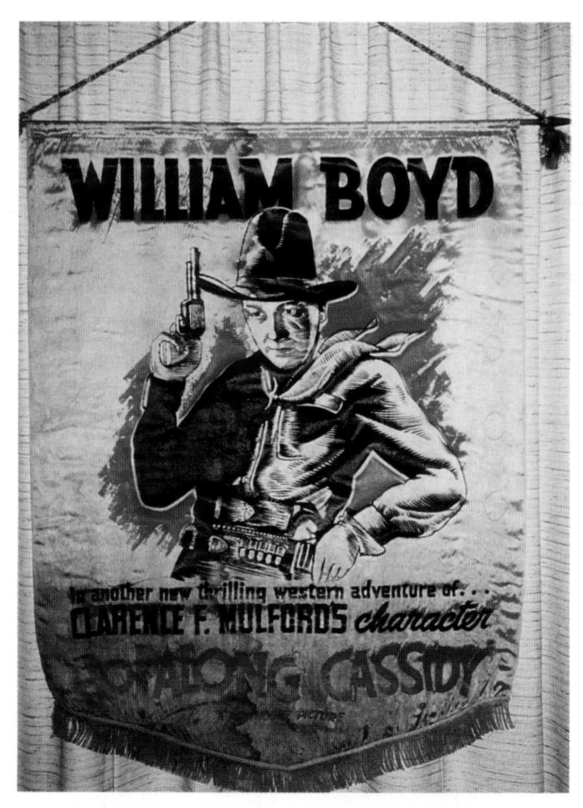

There are only a few of these theatre banners known to exist. Featuring a gold, satin-like fringed material with a William Boyd headline, these banners are thought to have stood, pole mounted, in front of theatre featuring a new Hoppy film. Definitely 1930's vintage and an investment item for sure. Value is probably in the $1,500-$2,500 range. This photo is from Phil Ellis although collector John Rizzo sent me a similar photo that was damaged.

Theatre promo card (4'x2.5') states Hoppy will be there in person: #1. $375 #2. $225 #3. $175. From the Brian Beirne collection.

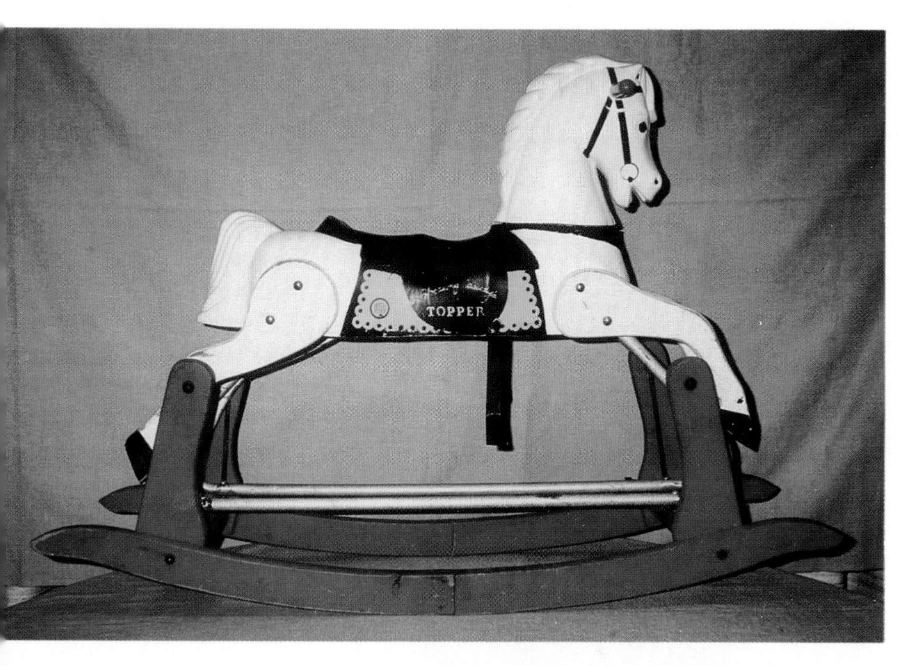

s Topper "glider-rocker" is similar to "rockers" shown in the "Toy's" chapter ept larger and more rare: #1. $875 #2. $750 #3. $600. From the Phil Ellis ection.

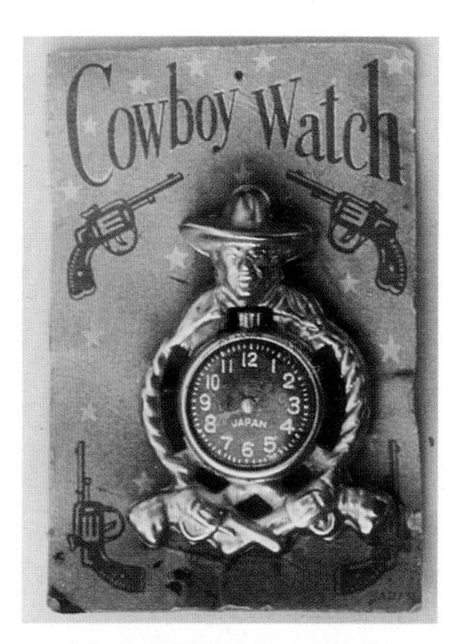

Japan rip-off Hoppy watch on card. Note that this pressed metal watch looks like the genuine Hoppy wrist compass: #1 $175 #2. $150 #3. $100 Deduct $50 w/o card. From the "AJ" Siarkowski collection.

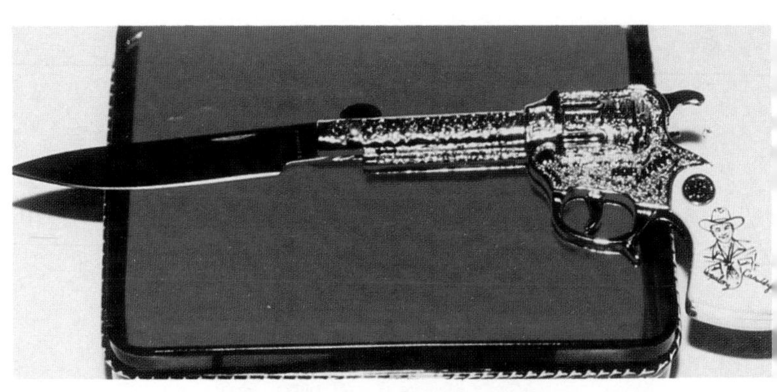

United Cutlery recently offered a Hoppy Wyandotte gun/knife that had to have. It came in a small metal lunch box container and i really quite a high quality item for around $35. It measures about 8 with the blade extended, and is a limited issue.

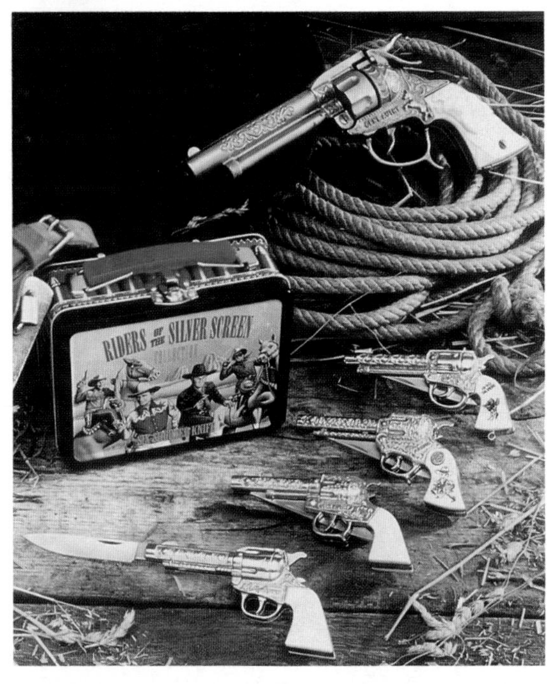

United Cutlery ad showing several versions of collector gun/knives including Hoppy's.

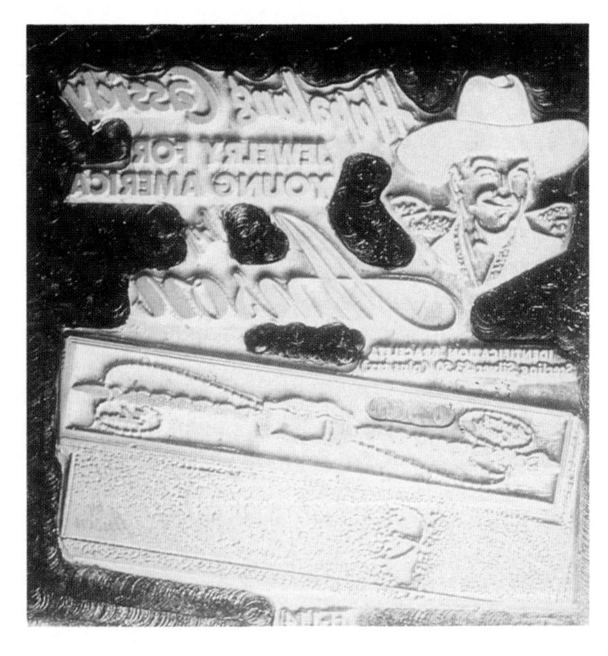

Anson Jewelry designed it Hoppy ads on metal plates Several specimens foun their way into the possessio of Collector John Rizzo. A investment item to be sure the plate shown would prob ably bring $200 at auction.

"Donut" Topper is an inflatable toy (see "Toy's") used in and out of swimming pools. Very rare and unique. A full-page ad for "Topper" is worth $20-$25.

Hoppy straw decanters came in white & blue glass. Neither one is "genuine" Hoppy. From the Steve Axelson collection.

'he Ivan Anderson Hoppy print is very popular and ıcreasing in value. Poster is $75 unsigned, $250 signed ınd $350 if also signed by Grace Boyd. Frame extra.

Many collectors' have a deep interest in "early" Bill Boyd before he became Hoppy. This ad for cigarettes is one example as well as the promo card also shown. A 1930's ad like this will easily sell for $50. From the Mike Forthun collection.

Front of Bill Boyd "Luckies" promo place card

This view of the Bill Boyd promo card for Lucky Strike cigarettes was not shown in "Ads" chapter and is quite noteworthy. From the Mike Forthun collection,

Daily News paper Hoppy clicker gun was used as a free give-away promo. Quite rare: #1. $200 #2. $165 #3. $120. From the Jon & Charlie Cheek collection.

This set of card-mounted Hoppy film viewers was sent by Phil Ellis. Look in "Film" chapter for values.

Many collectors have purchased the blue glass and pitcher as "original." They are new licensed products.

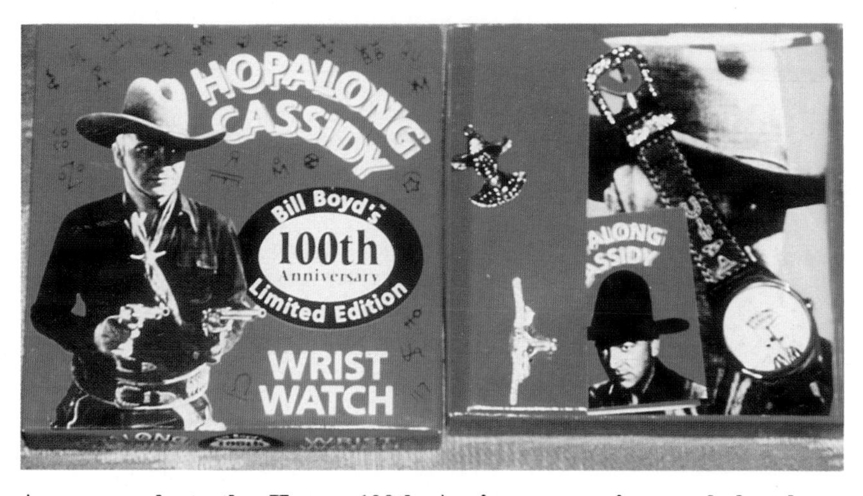

A new product; the Hoppy 100th Anniversary wrist watch has been mistaken as an original when found without the box. Always check the back for "USTime" or "Timex" markings.

Display photo of an early 35mm plastic Hoppy camera with box and instructions. See "Camera" chapter.

Hoppy had a lot of soap but none like this. It is a phoney that has been around for at least three years. A nice curiosity piece for $10, but don't pay more.

A pre-Hoppy Bill Boyd poses for this song sheet cover from his film "The Flying Fool" produced around 1930. The song sheet is valued at $60. in #2. condition. From Gene Douglass.

NOW TURN IT ON

Turn the knob in the lower left hand corner 'til it clicks. That feeds the power in. The farther you turn the knob, the more power you feed in — and the more volume you get. Don't get all up in a fuss if it doesn't start right out playing because it has to warm up. Takes about half a minute.

The other knob is for tuning in the stations you want. Tune it so the number you want is right under the steer head. When you get the station, turn the knob just a little bit, back and forth, carefully, until you get the deepest tone and the least background noise. Then you're right on the station. Always tune it right on the station. Most grown-ups don't tune a radio right. You show 'em how!

THIS RADIO IS FULLY GUARANTEED

This is something special, Pardner! Your Hopalong Cassidy radio is fully guaranteed (except tubes) for one year when the guaranty registration card in the carton is filled out and mailed to the factory. Repairs, if needed, within one year, will be made at the factory if you return the radio to Arvin Industries, Inc., Columbus, Indiana, postage prepaid, with a dollar bill. The radio will be put back in tip-top shape and returned to you postage prepaid. But, you aren't likely ever to need the guarantee. It's just nice to have.

ARVIN INDUSTRIES, INC. • COLUMBUS, INDIANA

Part No. A23870

Hoppy Arvin radio instruction booklet is a very rare find. Any collector owning a radio would pay $50 for one. From the Brian Beirne collection.

Sheet of official Hollywood "Stamps of the Stars" has Hoppy included. A very hard find: #1. $120 #2. $95 #3. $70. The Hoppy stamp alone is valued at $15. From the Gene Douglass collection.

his autographed print of a young ill Boyd is noteworthy because it signed "Thanks To You Hop-Long Cassidy" Bill Boyd. His utfit in this photo is from the Frontiersman" which he filmed everal years before taking the rst Hoppy part. The original 5x7 r 8x10" print would be worth at ast $1,000.

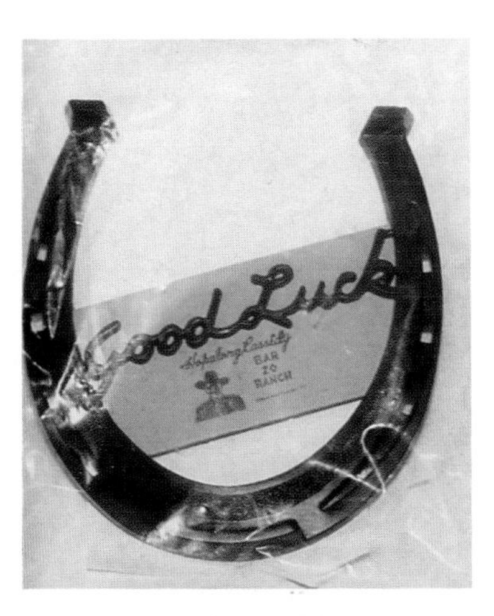

This "Good Luck" plastic horseshoe is reported to be one of the first "phoney" Hoppy products made in the last 10 years. It has no value except for the curious collector.

Rare ad for the Hoppy pistol flashlight to store owners. Also shows the retail Hoppy bank. Both were made by Topper Toys. Full page ad is valued at $50.From the Jon & Charlie Cheek collection.

OUTFITS & ACCESSORIES

#1. condition: mint, showing no use #2. condition: excellent to near mint #3. condition: good to very good

President Bill Clinton - 1955

I proudly wore a "full dress" Hoppy outfit when I was eight years old, so did millions of other children that I fondly call "Hoppy's Kids." My hat was from Bailey's of Hollywood and my two-gun holster set was the very best that Wayndotte ever made. I played in it, did chores in it and even slept in it, with both guns always loaded with full rolls of caps. In our house, next to the Bible, "Hoppy's Creed" was taught and adhered to, on an almost daily basis. No, that's not me pictured on the left, flanked by parent types in front of a rather tired looking 1952 Buick (we had a much tireder looking 1947 Chrysler). The "Hoppy's Kid" shown in this slightly out of focus photo, grew-up to be the most famous of all the "Hoppy's Kids" to date. His name is Bill Clinton and he became a two-term United States President! A quote from his mother, Virginia Kelly, during an interview with the Saint Paul Pioneer Express newspaper: "Before John F. Kennedy rode into the picture, Hopalong Cassidy was Bill's hero, and I treasure a photograph I took of him standing on the sidewalk in front of the house wearing a black cowboy hat, boots, and a black short-jacketed cowboy suit with Hoppy's picture on it. As a Cassidy myself, I heartedly approved of Bill's taste" she said. Ms. Virginia Kelly sadly passed-away in 1994 after writing her biography; "Leading With My Heart" Published by Simon & Schuster.

The above photo is noteworthy because of the Hoppy mannequin and the lad who apparently was the model for it. The Hoppy mannequin came in both boys' and girls' versions and in several sizes. There must be a few around, but nobody admits to seeing them. Value? Dressed accordingly, my guess would be over $5,000!

The upper right photo of "Hoppy's Kids" was borrowed from a magazine article because of the various outfits worn.

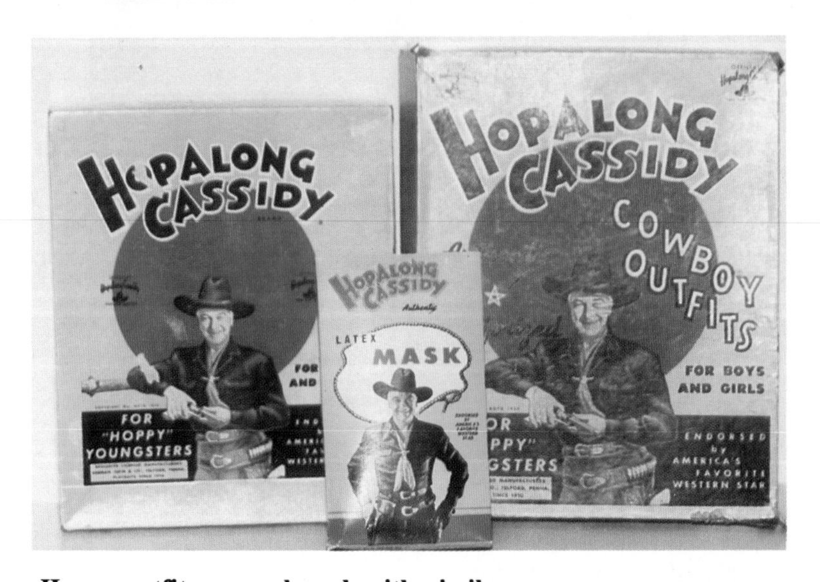

Hoppy outfits came boxed with similar graphics for boy's or girl's outfits. Shown also, is latex Hoppy mask box.

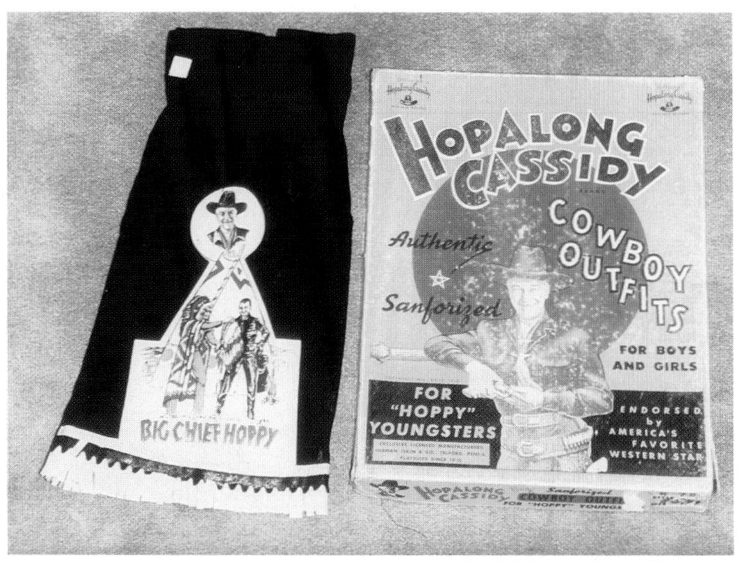

The rarest Hoppy outfit is without doubt, "Big Chief Hoppy" Indian wear, with the girl's set (above) perhaps somewhat easier to find. Set consisted of decorative shirt and matching fringed skirt: #1. $550 #2. $400 #3. $325. (without box deduct $250). From the Brian Beirne collection.

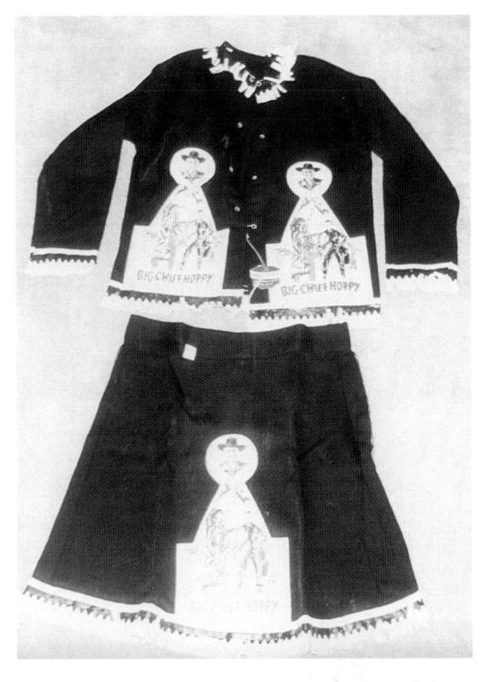

Display photo of both the blouse and fringed skirt of the girl's "Big Chief Hoppy" outfit. There were only two clothing pieces with this set. From the Brian Beirne collection.

*** Boy's set is found on last page.**

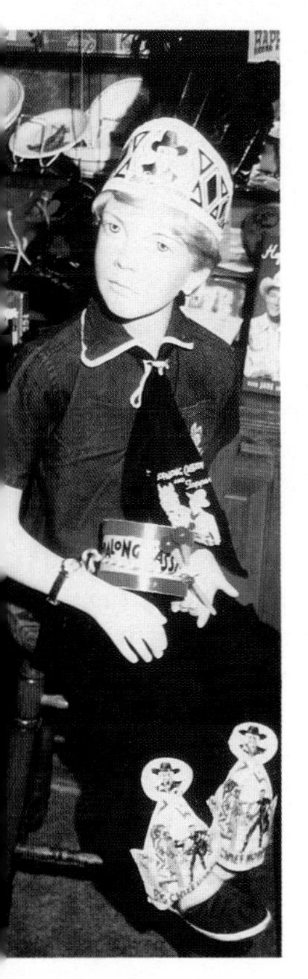

ve mannequin displays the rarer boy's "Big Chief Hoppy" Indian it. The shirt shown is not an original part of the set. Notice similar ts design pattern as the girl's outfit. #1. $650 #2. $500 #3. $425. hout box deduct $250) Loose "Big Chief" pants are valued at $175 2. condition, "Big Chief" shirt (not shown) is $125 in #2. condition.

Detail photo of "Big Chief" pants design and Hoppy slippers which were often used as Indian moccasins. Hoppy slippers: #1. $350 #2. $225 #3. $175 (no box)

Loose (no box) "Big Chief" feathered headdress (upper left) is valued at: #1. $275 #2. $200 #3. $150.

Hoppy "Big Chief" headdress (L) came in a similar box as other Hoppy outfits. Headset boasted "genuine" feathers and included a five feather "train." #1. $450 #2. $350 #3. $300. (deduct $150 without box). From the Jon & Charlie Cheek collection.

Child mannequin neatly dressed in girl's outfit. Note: she is wearing Hoppy rubber boots.

Deluxe girl's Hoppy "plaid" outfit was high quality and very colorful. Note that the dress design is different than the one pictured on the left. Accessories included steer-head Hoppy neckerchief slide, neckerchief, holster & belt with plastic gun.

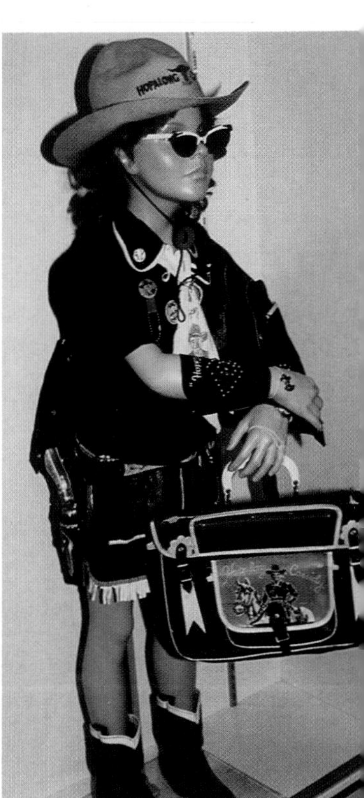

A used store mannequin ($1 makes a great Hoppy item disp piece. Note that girl is wearin Hoppy fringed skirt, Acme cowb boots and a gray, authentic Hop hat. And don't overlook the gi Hoppy sunglasses!

The plaid Hoppy girl's outfit is valued as follows: #1. $375 #2. $300 #3. $250 (deduct $150 without box).

Boy's Hoppy outfits came with either short or long sleeved shirts, with the short sleeved the more common. The shirt shown (above) had a large Hoppy graphic over the left pocket with the words "Hoppy" in red, underneath. #1. $350 #2. $275 #3. $225 (deduct $150 without box).

Boy mannequin (12-14yrs.) makes a great display piece for Hoppy items difficult to show. Note sunglasses and Hoppy chaps & vest.

Difficult to find, but worth it when you do, is this girl's black leather fringed vest & skirt outfit. Set has Hoppy bust on vest and color Hoppy & Topper on skirt sides. Outfit was fringed in white leather tassels. #1. $360 #2. $290 #3. $240.

Hoppy leather chaps & vest outfit for boy's wasn't nearly as colorful as the girl's set but still very popular. #1. $375 #2. $300 #3. $250.

Ms. Haley Ellis (granddaughter of Phil & Rose Ellis) models this delightful Hoppy ensemble consisting of a cotton short-sleeve shirt and vinyl-fringed cotton skirt. She is sporting the ever-popular Hoppy overnight kit (sleeping bag).

Modeled by Krista Abramson, this super rare Hopp outfit is quite notable; both the chest and cuff areas ar brightly silver-scaled and note the red fringe over th shirt slash pocket and red piping on shirt and pants #1. $425 #2. $350 #3. $300 (deduct $150 w/o box)

Hoppy pants-chaps are very unique and rare. Featuring an elastic waist-band this item is quite colorful and practical, for it seems it could be worn as "regular" pants. #1. $275 #2. $225 #3. $175 (no known box).

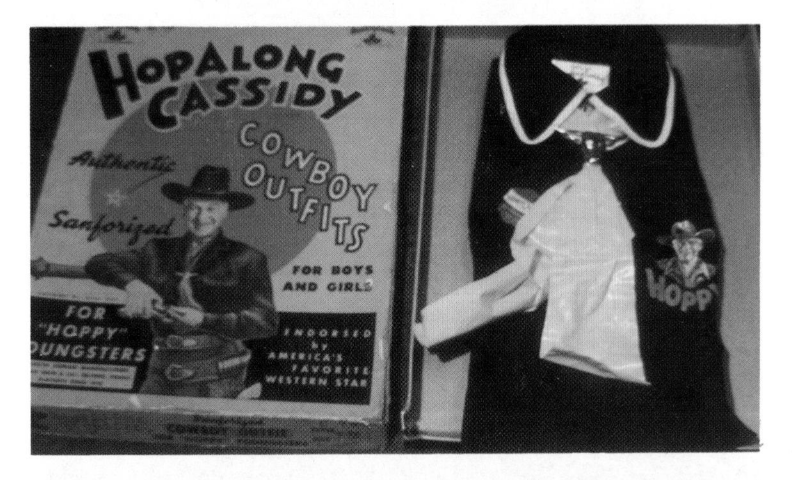

Not all outfit boxes came with complete outfits. The above boxed shirt, neckerchief and slide is believed to have come that way. #1. $280 #2. $240 #3. $200 (deduct $150 without box).

Hoppy trick lariat (above) is interesting for two reasons: the rope is black-stripped and it contains a "Hoppy" fob of sorts. No known box. #1. $285 #2. $240 #3. $200. From the Jon & Charlie Cheek collection.

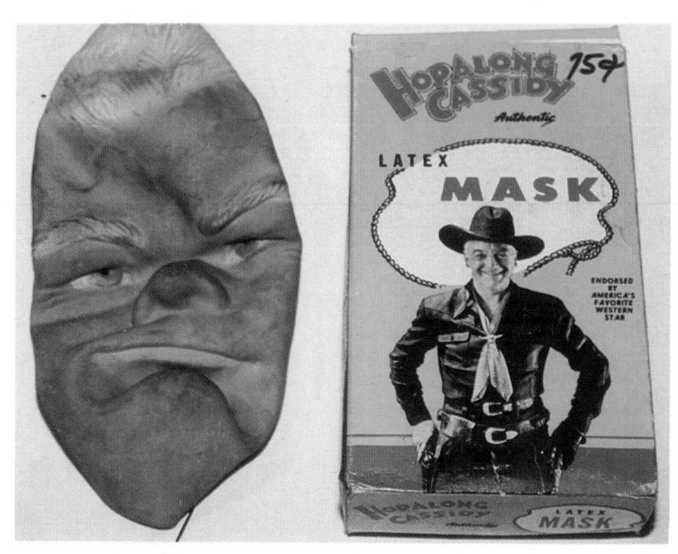

The latex Hoppy mask is as good an "accessory" item as any and compliments the "outfits" chapter. The mask box above, still bears a grease-pencil price of seventy-five cents: #1. $375 #2. $300 #3. $250. (mask value without box is $75 to $100). Mask must be pliable and soft.

The Hoppy hat above, is called a "deputy" hat and is so marked. While it bears the hat-cord and "Hoppy" leather fob on strap, it was not the quality of the Bailey's hats shown below. #1. $285 #2. $240 #3. $185.

The "Bailey of Hollywood" imprint is clearly seen on the sweat-band of all their hats.

Note: A red hat is shown in the "Clothing" chapter.

The traditional Bailey Hoppy hat was as well made as most adult western hats. Note that the imprinted Hoppy name does not use the word "deputy." The Bailey Hoppy hat comes with a satin hat band and without the hat cord/neck strap used on the "deputy" version hats. #1. $385 #2. $350 #3. $285. (add $150 if hat came in a Bailey of Hollywood box). From the Jon & Charlie Cheek collection.

Another variation of the Bailey Hat is known as the "Sheriff" (L) This hat lacks the Hoppy imprint but has a unique Hoppy band with Hoppy image. Similar values to other Bailey's Hats.

Perhaps the most sought Hoppy accessory item are Hoppy gloves. Excellent quality material with good stitching, "gauntlet" type gloves are a boon to any collection. The above photo shows several pair. Each is distinctive and handsome. From the Jon & Charlie Cheek collection.

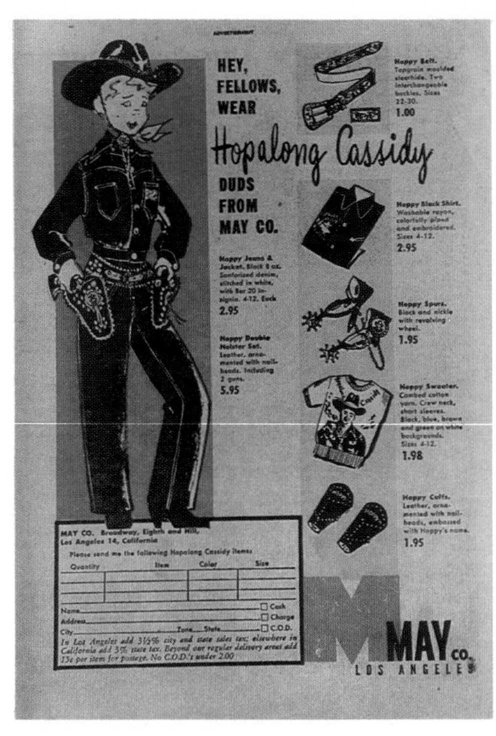

Hoppy outfit & accessory ad from May Company stores is a great display piece. Ad shows spurs, wrist cuffs, shirts & sweaters. Color ads (1/2 -3/4 pge.) are valued at $20 - $40.

Most Hoppy gloves were made from fine grade leather and were soft and pliable. The gloves shown above are quite unique as they feature white leather gauntlet fringe and the conch used bears the image of a horses head. #1. $425 #2. $350 #3. $275. From the Charles Ringhel collection. There is no known box.

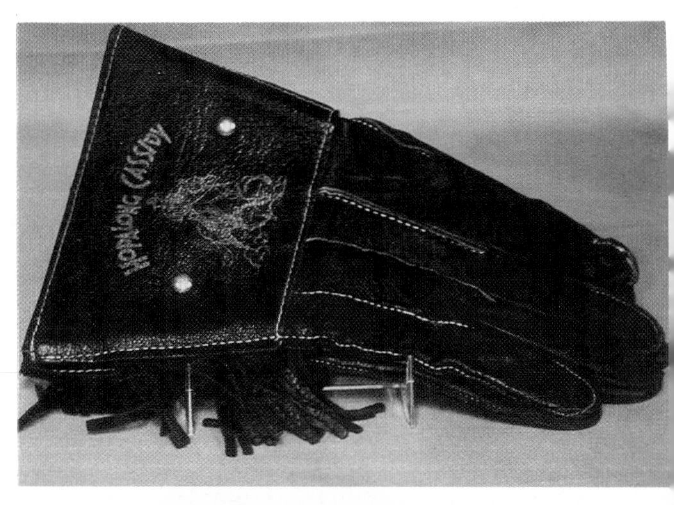

Perhaps an early glove version bearing a light imprint of Hoppy riding Topper, note the black gauntlet fringe. There are two metal studs showing, which may have been simply for decoration. #1. $350 #2. $300 #3. $275. From the Jon & Charlie Cheek collection.

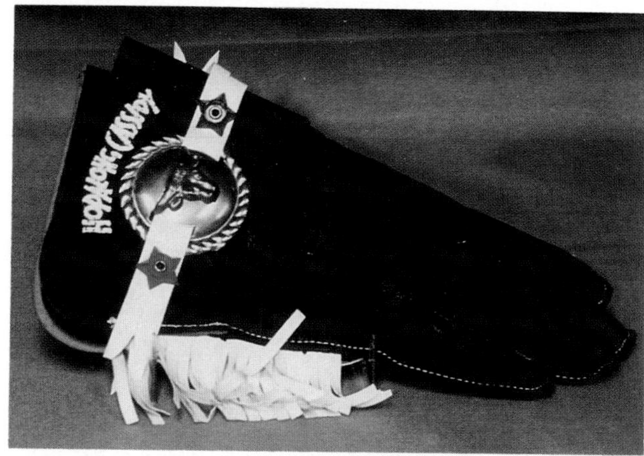

Hoppy gloves with white fringe, gold steer head and red & blue stars. Set is very colorful: #1. $375 #2. $325 #3. $300. From the Jon & Charlie Cheek collection.

Not quite ornate as the others this glove set bears two red glass jewels adjacent to "Hopalong Cassidy" imprint. Note gold steer head similarity: #1. $350 #2. $300 #3. $275. From the Jon & Charlie Cheek collection.

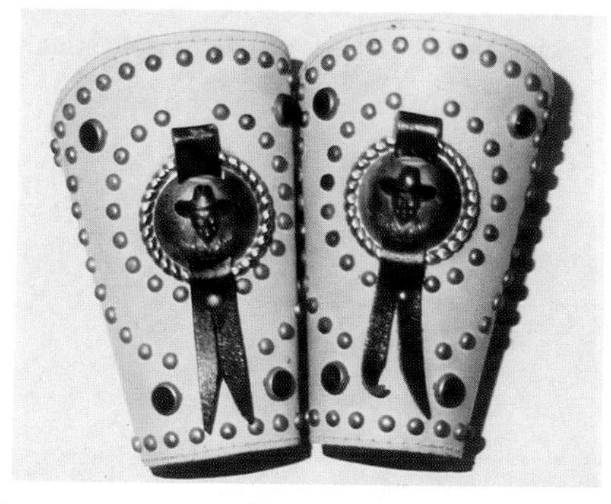

Perhaps the rarest Hoppy wrist cuffs (above) are beautifully studded white leather. Cuffs had snaps on the back that would fasten them to the wrist. Note gold bust of Hoppy on conch. #1. $475 #2. $400 #3. $350 (deduct $200 without box). From the Sharon Delaney collection.

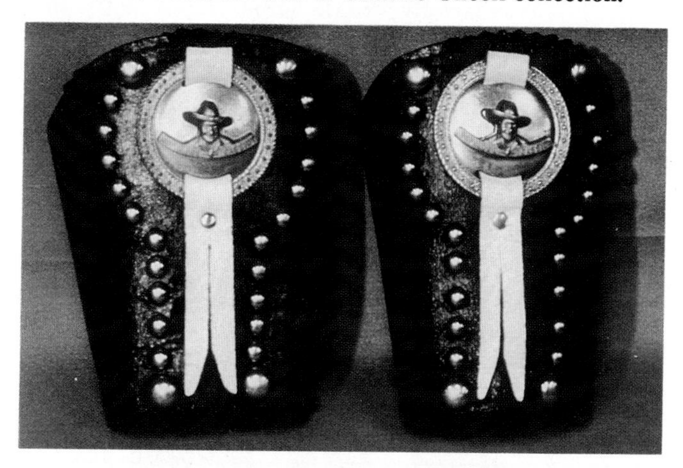

"Keyhole" design cuffs had a different gold Hoppy bust on conch. #1. $425 #2. $375 #3. $325. (Deduct $200 without box). From the Jon & Charlie Cheek collection.

Another "keyhole" design has a gold steer head conch under "Hopalong" imprint. These cuffs are shorter in length than others shown. Very attractive piece. #1. $375 #2. $325 #3. $275. (deduct $200 w/o box). From the Jon & Charlie Cheek collection.

Much more simple in design is this "heart" cuff with a gold Hoppy image on conch. Most cuffs were backed with a black felt material. #1. $375 #2. $325 #3. $275 (deduct $200 without box).

Wonderfully ornate large Hoppy cuffs show large imprint and has several white jewels. Cuff box is shown. #1. $425 #2. $375 #3. $325. (without box deduct $200). From the Phil Ellis collection.

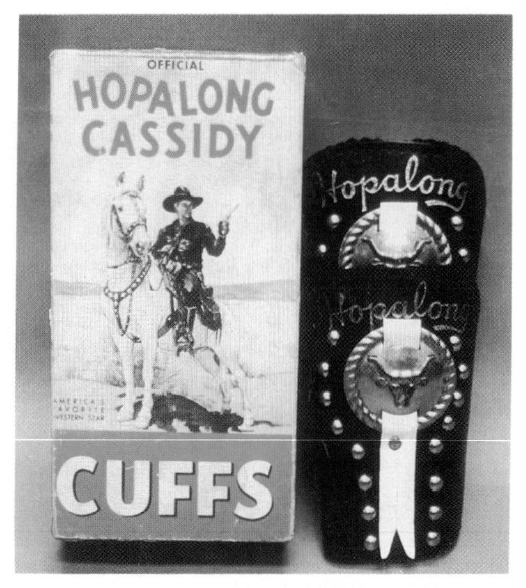

Another cuff version is the steer head long cuff. Note the keyhole design and the gold steer head. "Hopalong" is printed in silver across cuff top. #1. $400 #2. $350 #3. $300. (deduct $200 without box). From the Jon & Charlie Cheek collection.

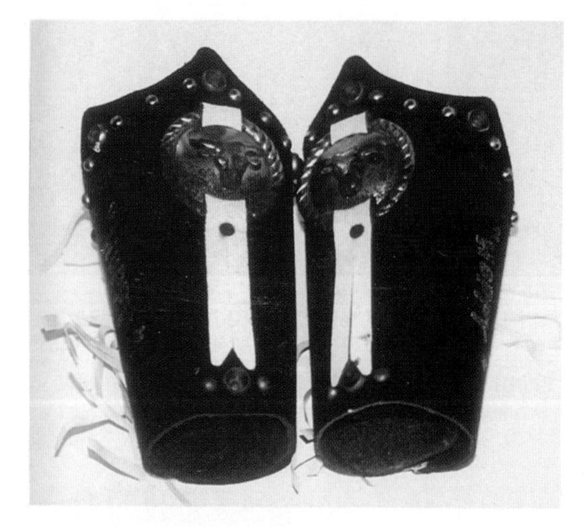

Perhaps the most unusual Hoppy cuffs were the large length cuff with leather fringe. "Hoppy" was imprinted on cuff side. Conch had a gold steer head. #1. $450 #2. $400 #3. $350 (deduct $200 without box).

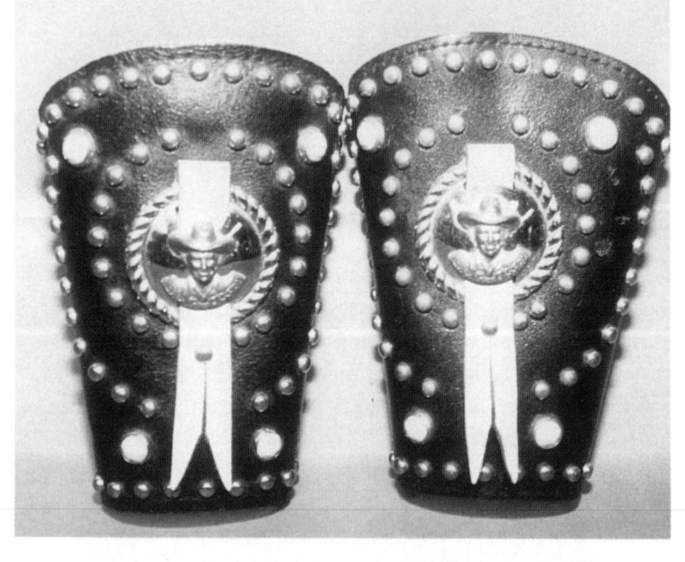

Another version of the non-imprinted Hoppy cuff is the impressive large size with many studs and jewels. A gold bust of Hoppy is attached to the conch. #1. $425 #2. $375 #3. $325 (deduct $200 without box). From the Jon & Charlie Cheek collection.

Several cuff versions were shorter in length like the "diamond" pattern cuffs on the left. Note the red glass jewel centers. #1. $375 #2. $ 325 #3. $275. (deduct $200 without box) From the Jon & Charlie Cheek collection.

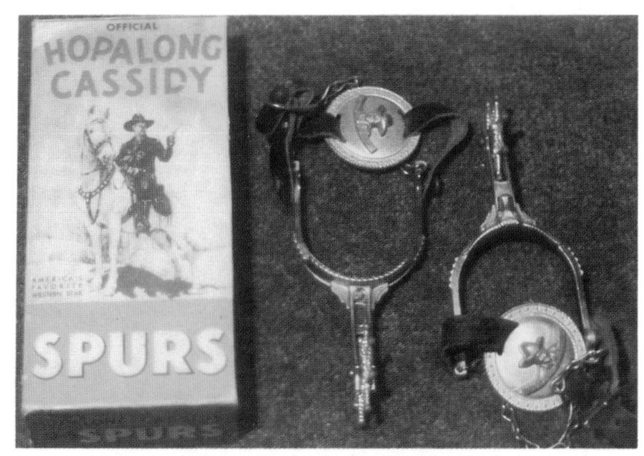

The most common Hoppy spur sets were either silver or gold colored and had a conch mounted Hoppy bust on the ankle strap: #1. $375 #2. $325 #3. $290. (deduct $175 without box).

Box design indicates this may be an early spur set. Note spurs are black and have felt cushion on ankle strap. #1. $525 #2. $450 #3. $400 (deduct $200 w/o box). From the Jon & Charlie Cheek collection.

Note that there is no Hoppy imprint on this set. Conch carries gold steer head. #1. $375 #2. $325 #3. $290. (deduct $175 w/o box). The Cheek collection.

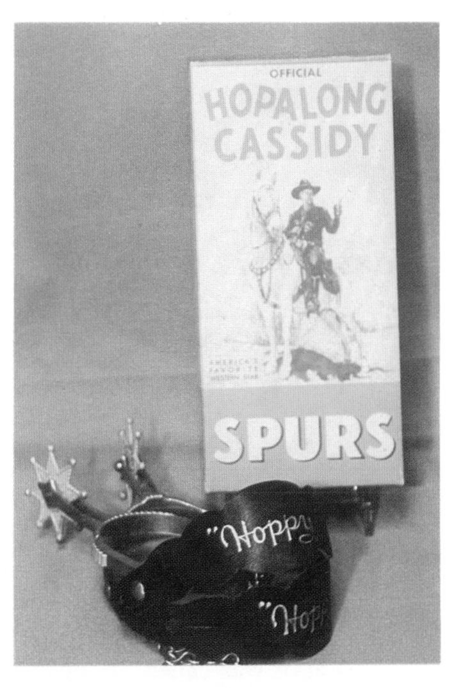

Silver & gold coloring and wide leather ankle strap with imprinted "Hoppy" makes an attractive set. #1. $450 #2. $380 #3. $325 (deduct $175 without box). From the Jon & Charlie Cheek collection.

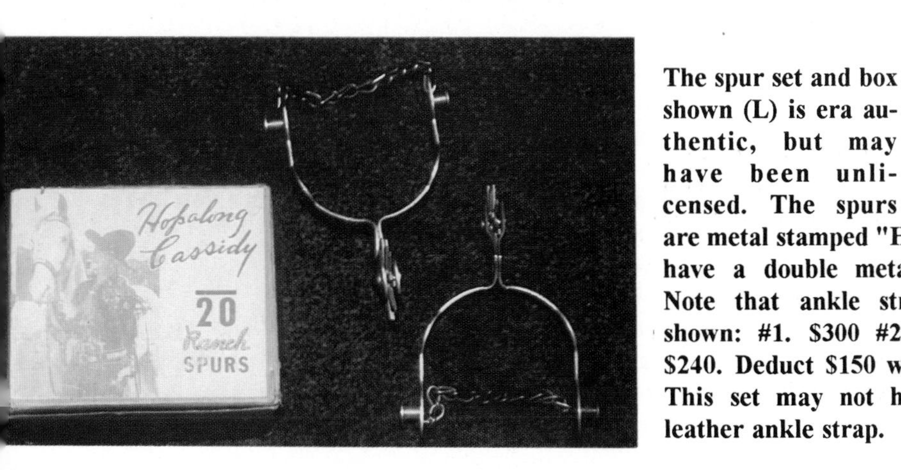

The spur set and box shown (L) is era authentic, but may have been unlicensed. The spurs are metal stamped "Hoppy" and have a double metal roundel. Note that ankle strap is not shown: #1. $300 #2. $260 #3. $240. Deduct $150 without box. This set may not have had a leather ankle strap.

The above ad is for a different Hoppy "trick rope" than shown on previous page: #1. $425 #2. $350 #3. $300 (deduct $200 without box).

Ad from retail store magazine shows boy mannequin they can buy for $39.00 to display Hoppy garb. A collector would pay over $5,000 for the mannequin today!

Small business ad for Hoppy "Frontier Suits" Outfit was called "Hoppy's Vigilante" of all things. In 1950 they cost $72. per dozen.

Two ads related to this chapter are the Hoppy Bailey hats. The ad states that they came in: black, silver, red and tan. Style H-1003 was a wool felt material and cost to the store was $15. per dozen! The jackets cost $3.50 each!

The ad on the left is for a product hardly known to exist! Called the Hoppy "Saddle Bag," it is actually the "box" for a 22x44" Hoppy & Topper bath towel and a 12x12" wash cloth. I have heard that one exists in #1. condition but was not able to contact its owner. No idea of its value.

Unique set of black spurs with gold roundel from the George Schmidt Company. Narrow ankle band has "Hoppy" imprint. #1. $350 #2. $300 #3. $275. From the Jon & Charlie Cheek collection.

No Hoppy outfit would be complete without genuine Acme Hoppy cowboy boots made from the finest leather. Designs varied on most boots and the boots shown are among the most attractive. #1. $750 #2. $650 #3. $550. (deduct $350 without Acme box. From the Phil Ellis collection.

Another different spur set has a wide ankle strap, studs and white jewels. Made by George Schmidt, Co. who also made several versions of the Hoppy cap guns. #1. $475 #2. $425 #3. $350. from the Jon & Charlie Cheek collection.

A late arrival is this later version Hoppy hat that is quite hard to find (1951-1956) Made by Bailey. It is called the "Topper" hat and boasted the round Hoppy seal. There were two other hat styles with this seal, all are valued accordingly. #1. $385 #2. $350 #3. $285. From the Jon & Charlie Cheek collection.

A recent "new find" are the above pair of Hoppy boots that were made in Canada by the Canada West Shoe. You can clearly see both pull tabs in the above photo. The name "Hopalong Cassidy" is embossed in silver, into the white leather trim near the boot top as well. #1. $475 #2. $425 #3. $350. There is no known box. From the Steve Axelson collection.

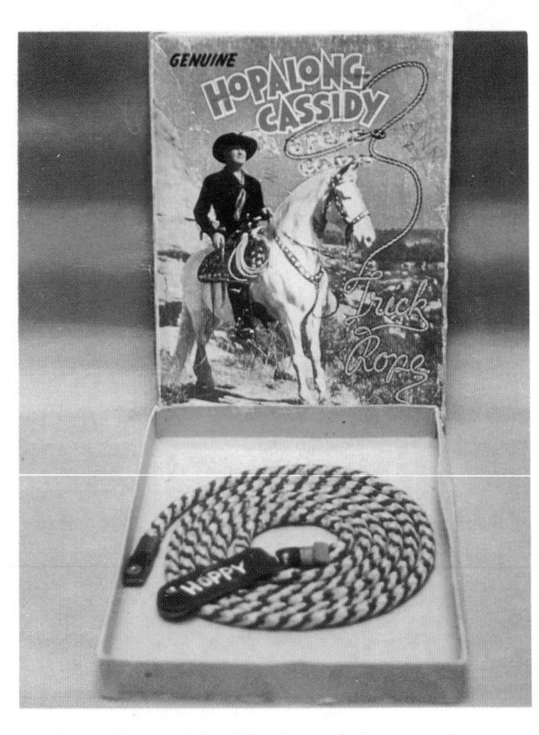

The above late arrival is the trick rope shown on previous page. It does come in a box! Unique ro has leather "Hoppy" fob, which I imagine, is t part you hold. #1. $535 #2. $455 #3. $400. Dedu $250 without box. from the Jon & Charlie Che collection.

Another important late arrival is this boys' "Big Chief Hoppy" shirt, which is part of the rare set shown on a previous page. This set came complete with: pants, shirt, headdress and something like "spats" which were worn around the ankle. This complete boxed set is an investment value item with a range of: #1. $1,100 #2. $975 #3. $800. Deduct $300 without box, $150 without "spats." Shirt as shown is valued at $250. From the Frank Smith collection

Baliey Hat ad shows different hat models styles

PLATES - PARTY & GLASS ITEMS

#1. condition: mint, showing no use #2. condition: excellent to near mint #3. condition: good to very good

There are several different 4 glass sets of Hoppy tumblers. One is solid black (most common) one is black & red (shown above) and there is a blue set known. Each glass has different graphics as: "breakfast, lunch, dinner and snack" The "snack" is the most hard to find.

From the Jon & Charlie Cheek collection

above detail photo shows the black & red tumbler set, the photo on right shows the color difference between the two most common Of the four glasses, the "snack" glass is the most rare, especially lack version "snack" glass for some reason. You will note that the boxed set shown above, black & red "snack" glass instead of the proper black version. While individual tumblers widely sell for $65 to $90 each (blk. & red or blk.) the plain black "snack" glass has been ging $350 to $400 by itself. The black & red set is: #1. $575 #2. $485 #3. $425 (deduct $240 out box). The black set is valued $200 higher because of the rarity and demand of the black ck" glass. Photo from the Phil Ellis collection.

Detail photo of glass sizes

As you can see in the photo on the left, there are three different size china white glasses with his image. The smallest (L) is a juice glass, the center glass is from the "Bar-20 Chow Set" compared to the (R) standard tumbler. All three glasses maintain similar values (other than the "snack" glass) of $65 to $90 each, depending on condition. The black & red "snack" glass would bring $125 to $150.

The blue image glas (above) is assumed t have come in a set, bu little else is known. I hav no value indicators.

The two Hoppy tumblers shown to the left are plastic versions of the glass item. Note that one is "solid" looking while the other is opaque. The "solid" plastic tumblers were also sold as a set and came in various colors (including blue) and bore "breakfast, lunch., dinner and snack, similar to the glass versions. I don't think a complete boxed set exists today, but loose plastic tumblers are available, and bring higher values than that of glass: (solid version) #1. $135 #2. $110 #3. $90. The opaque version will be covered below.

Detail photo of reverse sid small "Bar-20Chow Set" glas

On the left is a unique photo of the opaque plastic 10 oz. tumbler and a Cloverlake cottage cheese plastic lid. You may note that the tumbler is the "dinner" version. This shows that opaque Hoppy tumblers were used as premiums, and contained dairy products when sold in stores. This could account for the difference between the two plastic versions and the poorer quality of image printing on the opaque tumblers. While opaque tumblers maintain values of $65 to $90 each, the plastic tumbler lid has sold for $250 and more.

rom the Bill Hoffman collection

Hoppy glasses came in a wide variety of colors, sizes and applications too numerous to list and value them all. Many "endorsement" glasses are shown in that chapter of this book. One of the most unique Hoppy glass known, is the brown imprinted 'bust' glass on the left. Note the fluted bottom. This glass is from the Bill Hoffman collection and may carry a value of $170. as would the milk glass on the upper left. For the most part however, Hoppy clear glasses (like the above center and right) would carry a value range of $95 to $135.

he above is a "Hollywood Auto-'aph" glass that has a "Bill Boyd" opalong Cassidy signature. While ıt an official Hoppy item, it still is ce for $120. From the Jon & harlie Cheek collection.

The above ornate glass set is from the 'Hopalong Cassidy Western Series' of glasses. The four shown are part of the five or six that made-up the set. Each had a different theme. (These glasses were also used to contain endorsement products, please refer to the "endorsements" chapter). The 'Western Series' was also a store item that was reportedly sold in a boxed set. I have never seen any evidence of such a box. The Hoppy Western Series glasses are valued at $85 to $100 each, regardless of theme.

The popular Hoppy china mugs that seem to be in endless supply came in four colors: red, blue, black & green as shown above. Each color depicted a different Hoppy image and scene. Even though the values of these mugs are quite low because of the amount that still exist, a stalwart entrepreneur decided to "manufacture" two others (shown on the left) which are decidedly different in shape and design features. To forestall a debate about their authenticity, these two mugs (one green, one black) you can clearly see they are both made in Mexico on the mug bottom. The original Hoppy cups or mugs were also used as "Big Top" peanut butter containers (see endorsement items chapter). #1. $50 #2. $35 #3. $20. From the Phil Ellis collection.

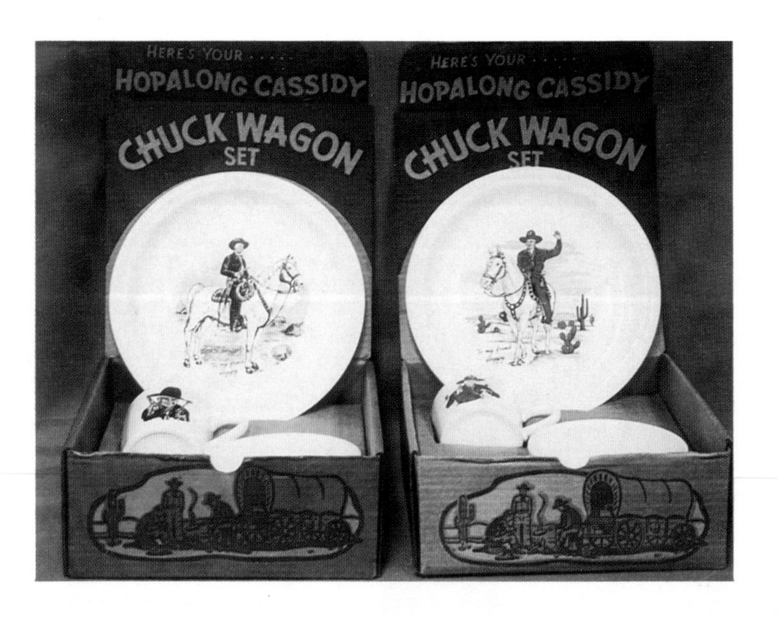

There were three Hoppy plate sets manufactured. The smallest set is the "Bar-20 Chow Set" (above left) which containes a small sandwich plate, small glass tumbler (shown on previous page) and bowl. The graphics were printed only in black. #1. $525 #2. $425 #3. $350 (deduct $200 if no box). From The Phil & Rose Ellis collection. The Hoppy "Chuck Wagon" set (by W.S. George) was made in two versions: Hoppy dressed in black (thought to be the first issue) and dressed in a blue outfit (often called the "blue" set). The "Chuck Wagon" set contained a full-size dinner plate, a milk mug with handle and a bowl. Many collectors consider the black set more collectible, thereby increasing its relative market value: #1. $750 #2. $575 #3. $500 (deduct $300 without box). Blue: #1. $650 #2. $525 #3. $450 (deduct $300 without box). From the Jon & Charlie Cheek collection. Additional photos of these sets are on the following page.

lays of both Hoppy china sets ict different colors and graphics. pieces are often found individually 2 and #3 condition and have been ging: (black) $70-$80 ea. (blue): -$70 ea.

Detail photo of "blue" set bowl graphics. From the Ted Hake Collection.

There is a recent discovery of "blue" graphics china set decal sheets which look to be original and authentic. These 2.5' x 4' sheets are enough for several plate sets and have been selling for $125 to $175 per sheet. Look for these prices to sharply increase as demand builds.

From Ted Hake's "Americana" auctions.

From the Robert Donovan collection

There were two types of Hoppy cookie jars produced (shown above) with th "saddle" version (L) considered the rarest. Lids on both were often broke and glue-repaired, which would drastically affect their value. (short jar): #1 $625 #2. $550 #3. $475 (saddle jar): #1. $825 #2. $725 #3. $650. Note: ther is a difference in the "saddle" cookie jar lid design and graphic paintin Examine jar pictured on the left. from the Jon & Charlie Cheek collection.

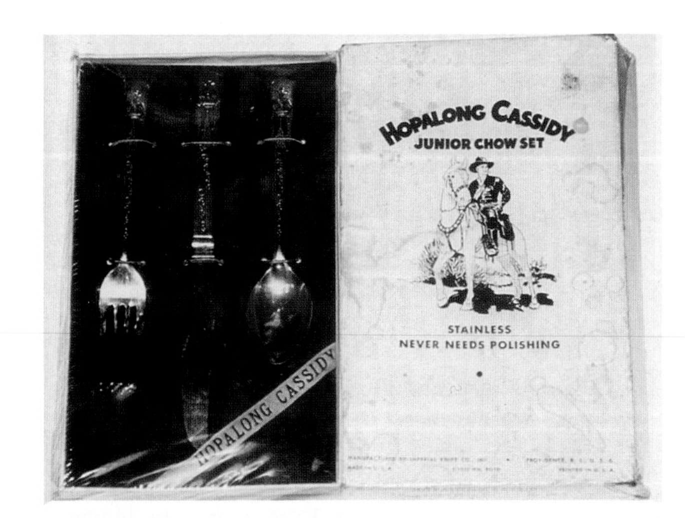

The above pictured "Junior Chow Set" is a boxed Hoppy stainless steel knife, fork and spoon with a standing Hoppy in relief on all three handles. Detail photo (R) shows what must be a very early version. Notice the knife features the engraving of the name "Hopalong Cassidy" and subtle differences in the fork & spoon graphics. (Boxed version): #1. $325 #2. $250 #3. $200 (deduct $125 without box). Individual pieces have been selling for $20 each.

From the Howard Reidinger collection

There is a third Hoppy cookie jar that I would like to bring to your attention and while not "original" it is certainly collectible. Licensed by US Television Office, Inc. these jars were produced in limited quanity (500) and numbered. The selling price was originally $365 and they are already going up in value. Very high quality, very graphic, very nice.

View of limited edition Hoppy collector plates

The two photos above are of a very rare set of ceramic (or plastic) Hoppy salt & pepper shakers, the only set that I have seen or heard about. The top photo pictures them with a Hoppy good luck coin for size. Each "shaker" boasts a color Hoppy decal riding Topper. This set was purchased for a bargain ($50) and is no doubt worth much more.

The Hoppy limited edition display plates have proven to be an excellent value for collectors wise enough to obtain early issues. The first plate (shown on the left) was issued in a lot of 5,000, and originally sold for around $50. The value of this plate today is in the $150-$200 range. The second limited edition plate (Hoppy on Topper) is now selling for $100+ and the newly released (1995) third plate is still available for $60+. All collector plates were made in lots of 5,000 and are individually numbered.

There are several different Hoppy straws boxes and two straw sizes of 50 and 100 to the box. In my opinion, all have similar values. Shown in the samples on this page, Hoppy straws had either color cut-outs or color-in areas. I have been able to ascertain the existence of six different boxes, but there may be more. #1. $200 #2. $150 #3. $100

Detail photo of 100 straw box and back panel cut-out

Detail photo of color-in back panel of straws boxes

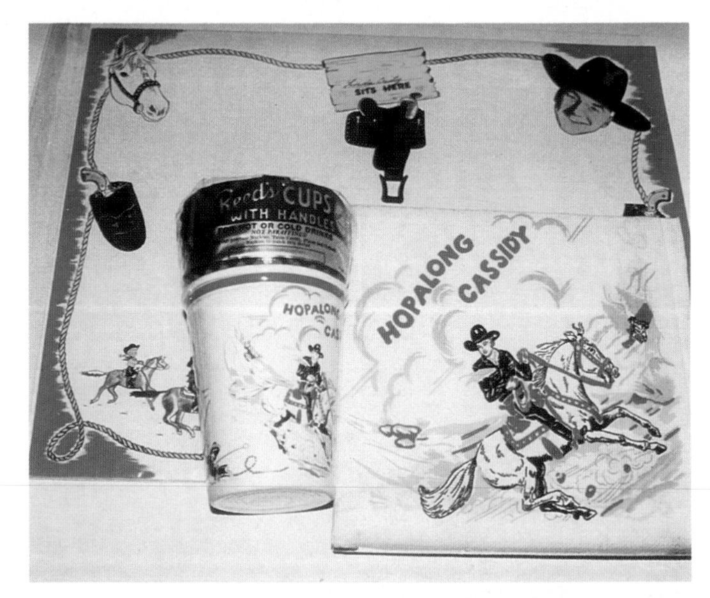

Hoppy party and picnic items included paper straws, two sizes of plates, cups, a table cloth, place mats and party favor containers. Made by Reed Paper and bearing a label (not shown) the Hoppy napkins came in a package of 32: #1. $240 #2. $200 #3. $175. Interestingly, single napkins are selling for up to $15 each. Hoppy paper cups (with fold-out handles) were sold 8 to a container (see photo) which bore the Reed's label: #1. $275 #2. $240 #3. $200. The paper place mats are generally sold individually in #1 or #2 condition for $85 to $120. They are quite rare.

Above photo is a colorful plastic Hoppy place mat usually used for home dining. Plastic composition is brittle and subject to cracks and corner breaks. #1. $225 #2. $150 #3. $100.

Detail photo of napkin package (32) with label. #1. $240 #2. $200 #3. $175.

Paper place mat (above) was made by Buzza Cardozo (Hoppy greeting cards) who also made the very rare party kit shown below. There were 12 place mats included in the party kit and each had a "sits here" area where the child's name could be written. As stated on the previous page, these place mats have been selling for $85 to $120 each.

e Hopalong Cassidy Party Kit (shown below) was made Buzza Cardozo Company, who made all of the Hoppy eting cards. This very, very rare item in addition to ing 12 paper place mats, a pin-the-tail game, party itations and reply cards also came with several Hoppy loons (also found on special greeting cards) and a special ppy pin to be worn by the party recipient. The Party Kit learly an "investment value" item because there are only r known to exist that contain all listed items. #1. $1,350 $1,150 #3. $975. From the Jon & Charlie Cheek lection.

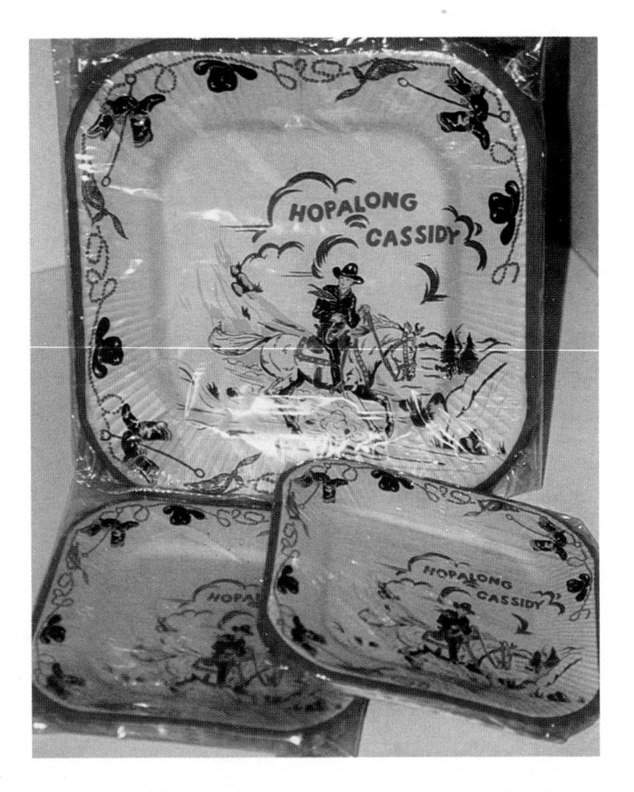

There are two sizes of Hoppy paper plates (shown above) one for the main party course and one for dessert. Both were sold in see-through cellophane packages with the Reed's label generally on the back. Packages contained either six or eight plates. (large) #1. $220 #2. $190 #3. $170 (small) #1. $200 #2. $170 #3. $150

The Hoppy paper party table cloth is a very in-demand collector piece but quite hard to find unused. They are thought to have been cellophane packaged, and sold one to a package. The cellophane easily became brittle and fell apart, so finding them complete is difficult. #1. $325 #2. $275 #3. $245.

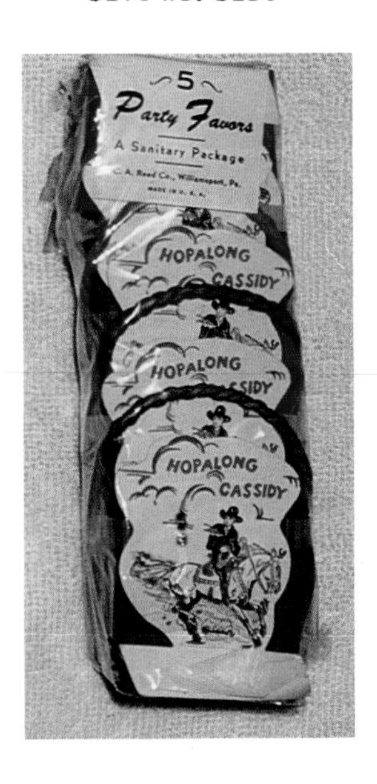

The photo on the left shows a rare set (5) of Hoppy party favors made by Reed's Paper, in their original cellophane package with label. When package is opened, party favors become small baskets that may hold a variety of treats. The photo on the right shows the detail of the opened baskets and the attached Hoppy graphics. #1. $325 #2. $275 #3. $250 (individual party favors are occasionally found selling for $25 to $35 each. From the Dennis Smith collection.

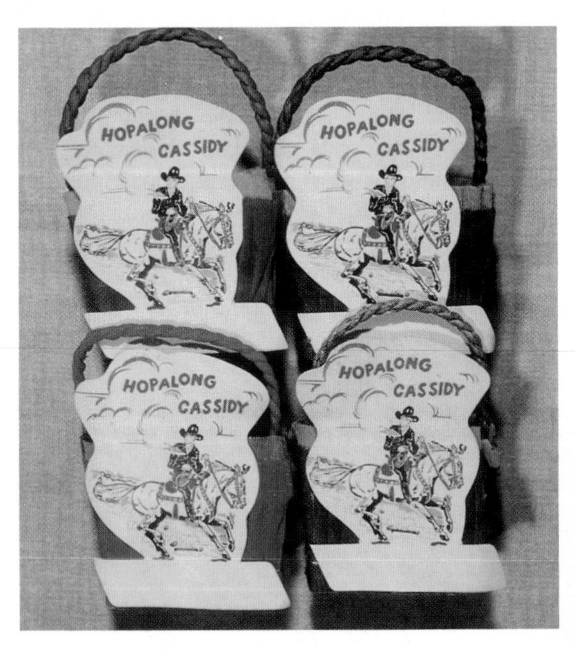

From the Phil Ellis collection

POSTERS
LOBBY CARDS

#1. condition: mint, showing no use #2. condition: excellent to near mint #3. condition: good to very good

This chapter, "Posters & Lobby Cards" generally deals with showing the collector a small part of the wide selections available. Values remain quite stable with Hoppy lobby cards (film advertising cards often shown in theatre lobbys) but values of film "posters" (meaning one-sheets, and the rarer three and six sheets) are quickly increasing. Like comic books, film collectibles have become very popular and as such, specialized. Collectors are advised to seek comparative values when dealing with these items. Due to the limited space available, we will only refer to "one-sheets" when valuing film posters.

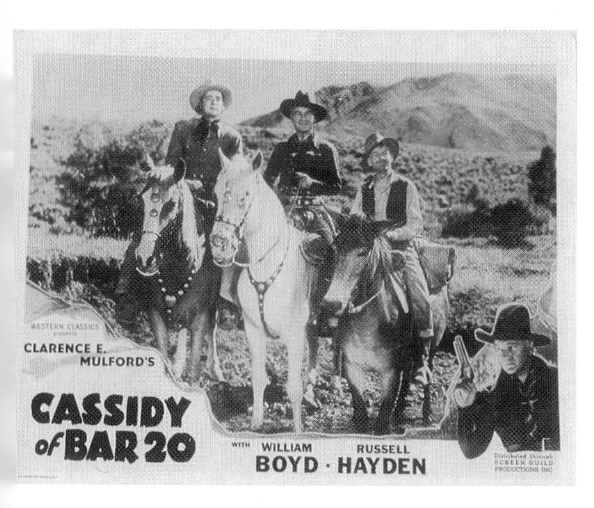

'Cassidy of the Bar 20" was produced in 1938 vith most lobby cards in b&w: #1. $45 #2. $30 #3. ;20.

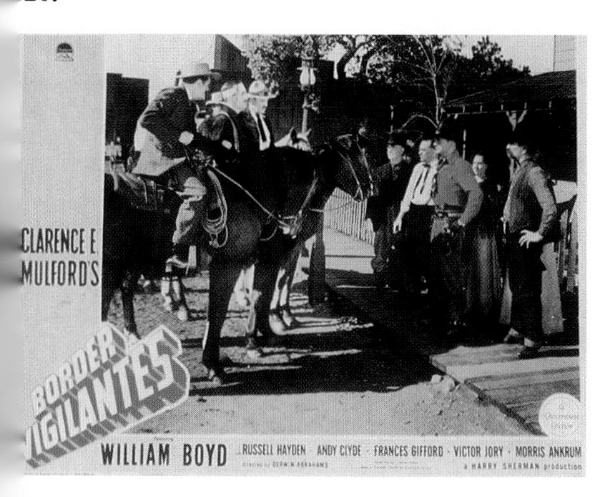

Border Vigilantes" was produced in 1941 with ıost lobby cards in color: #1. $35 #2. $25 #3. 20.

"Dangerous Venture" was produced in 1947 with color lobby cards: #1. $35 #2. $25 #3. $20.

"Bar 20" was produced in 1943 with George Reeves and Robert Mitchum: #1. $40 #2. $30 #3, $25.

While most film posters prominently show Hoppy, not all lobby cards did. Collectors feel that lobby cards without Hoppy shown are worth $5-$10 less. "Dead Don't Dream" (1948) #1. $35 #2. $25 #3. $20.

This "Dead Don't Dream" lobby card shows a scene with Rand Brooks and Mary Ware. The value on this card is less: #1. $30 #2. $20 #3. $10. This seems to apply to most other lobby cards as well.

Foreign lobby card values: #1. $45 #2. $35 #3. $25

There are a number of Hoppy posters and lobby cards printed in Spanish, German and other languages. Collectors generally place a higher value on "imported" lobby cards: #1. $45 #2. $30 #3. $25. The above card is from the Dick Stevens collection.

"Forty Thieves" was produced in 1944 with most lobby cards in color: #1. $35 #2. $25 #3. $20.

"Stick to Your Guns" was produced in 1941 with color cards: #1. $35 #2. $25 #3. $20. From the Dick Stevens collection.

Rustler's Valley" was produced in 1937 and had any color cards: #1. $40 #2. $30 #3. $25. From the ick Stevens collection.

'King of the Range" is a mystery as it isn't listed by his name in the production films. Showing Rand Brooks on the card, it is later than 1946. There are everal Hoppy films during this period which have een released under different titles. "King of the Range" was actually "The Marauders" (1947)

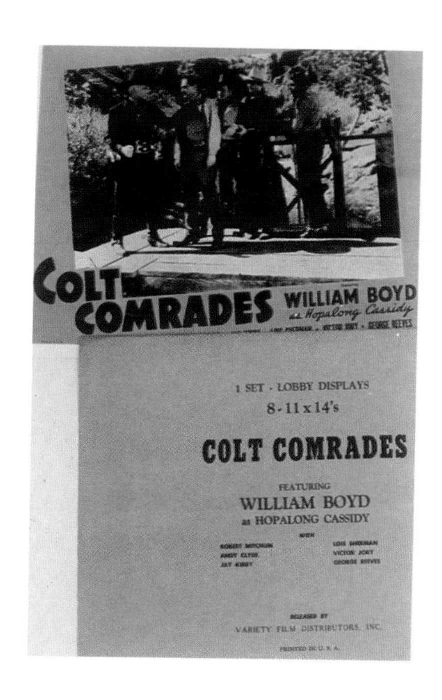

Lobby cards were generally sent to the theatre in sets. A complete 8 card set (and envelope) is shown for the film "Colt Comrades" produced in 1943. Complete, mint card sets are a great item to find: #1. $375 #2. $300 #3. $260. From the Dave Brobeck collection.

"Partners of the Plains" had b&w and hand-tinted lobby cards, It was produced in 1938: #1. $35 #2. $25 #3. $20.

"Heart of the West" (1936) had great coloration in the lobby card: #1. $45 #2. $30 #3. $25

"Hoppy's Holiday" (1947) #1. $35 #2. $25 #3. $20.

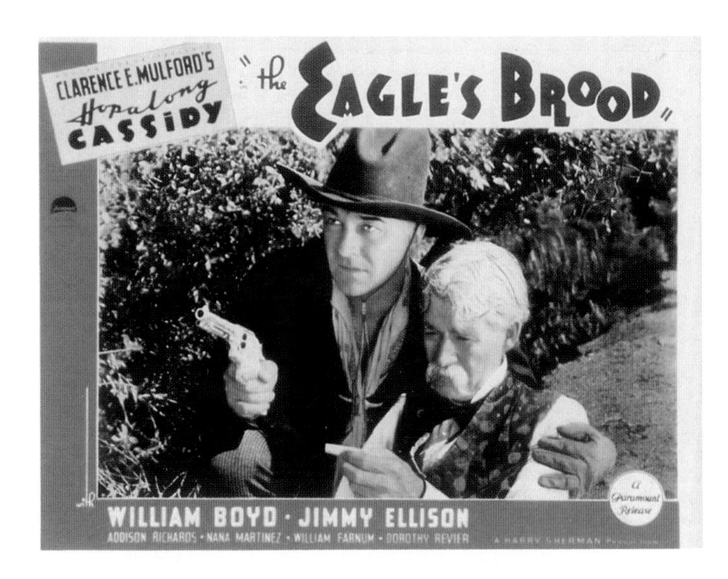

"Eagles Brood" (1935) is a great card of the 2nd. Hoppy film made: #1. $50 #2. $40 #3. $30. From the Ted Hake, Hake's Americana, collection.

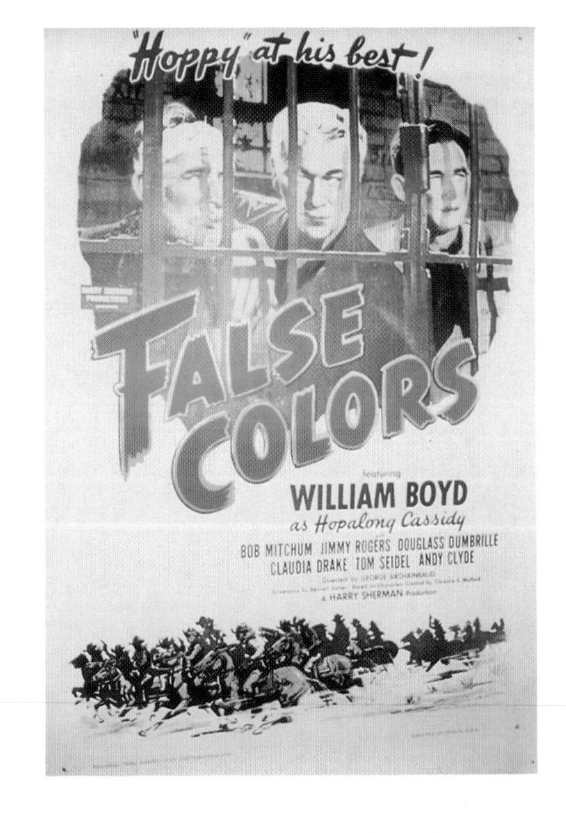

"False Colors" (1943) theatre one-sheet with hand-tinted color. Most one-sheets were folded with heavy creases. Rolled posters (without creases) are valued 35%-40% higher. #1. $400 #2. $325 #3, $250.

"Unexpected Guest" (1947) was a very popular later Hoppy film with good card graphics: #1. $35 #2. $25 #3. $20.

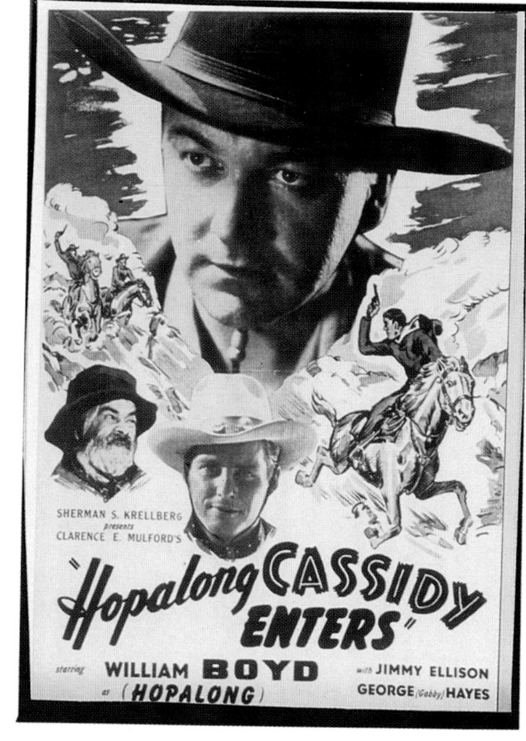

Hopalong Cassidy Enters" was the first Hoppy film, and was released in July, 1935. Above is a b&w film poster of the first film. There were several poster versions of this film and several re-release versions. 1996 auction results list the sale of one of the "Enters" posters at over $1,000 (without describing condition or type). Any "Hopalong Cassidy Enters" one-sheet or theatre poster would be considered a premium item, probably in excess of $500. From the Gene Douglass, M. Saxen collection.

The above Hoppy display was photographed at the 1991 Hoppy Lone Pine Film festival and shows a re-release theatre poster of "Hopalong Cassidy Enters" Several different others also exist.

A passing note regarding one-sheets is important for proper identification. There have been several film releases as "Hopalong Cassidy Enters" pictured above. The original was a Paramount Studios release, the one shown was released by Goodwill Pictures. If it is not Paramount, it is probably not a first run.

Theatre "flyers" or "programs" were often distributed in advance of a film. Note the program on the right advertises "Hop-A-Long Cassidy" which was the original name and hyphenation of the first Hoppy film. Value on the "Bar 20" program is around $100 and the original Hoppy would bring $200 at auction. From the Brian Beirne collection.

"Riders of the Deadline" (1943" had very strong graphics and coloration. A very collectible poster: #1. $350 #2. $275 #3. $220.

"The Fighting Cowboy" one-sheet may very well have been "The Dead Don't Dream" original release. This sheet has poor graphics and quality. #1. $275 #2. $200 #3. $160.

"Gunpowder Valley" was originally released as "Devil's Playground" (1946) #1. $350 #2. $275 #3. $225.

"Mystery Man" (1944) poster had tinted colors and fair graphics. #1. $300 #2. $225 #3. $175.

Theatre color slides (below) were used as an "on screen" promo of upcomming Hoppy films. "Hidden Gold" (1940) slide, as well as others, is a rare collector item. #1. $100 #2. $65 #3. $45.

"Texas Masquerade" (1944) h great color graphics: #1. $350 $275 #3. $225.

RECORDS AND GAMES

#1. condition: mint, showing no use #2. condition: excellent to near mint #3. condition: good to very good

e record shown above is a radio station public service ıouncement platter about forest fire prevention. It was not ıilable retail. In all likelihood, it was produced when Hoppy did color TV forest fire prevention film with Smokey The Bear. e record came with four different "announcements." This is an estment value item with a value of $450. in #2. condition. From Jon & Charlie Cheek collection.

he record album (R) is a unique "Bozo" and "Hoppy" combo ıat features the "Square Dance Holdup." and "Bozo Has a arty." The album also contains story books (with photos and ıustrations) for each record. #1. $200 #2. $160 #3. $125.

The "Two Legged Wolf" sleeved single records were offered in 45 rpm and 78 sizes. The photo (R), shows the "Sheep Rustlers" offered in a similar fashion. Values are similar for both titles: (45 w/sleeve) #1. $125 #2. $90 #3. $70 (deduct $30 without sleeve) (78 w/sleeve) #1. $105 #2. $80 #3. $60 (deduct $40 without sleeve). From the Jon & Charlie Cheek collection.

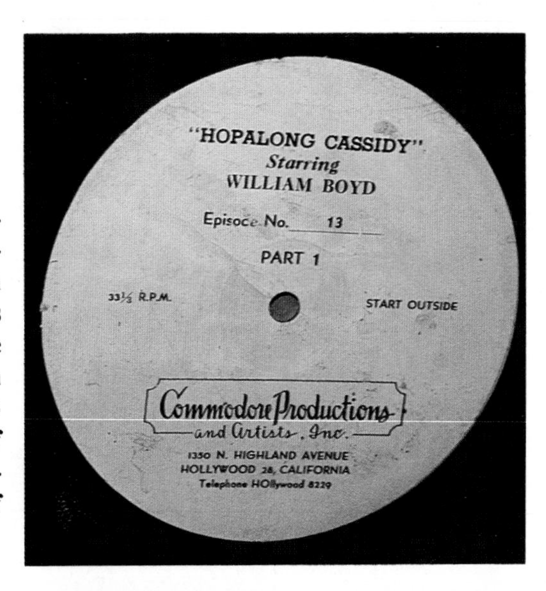

The unusual record label (r) is a radio station Hoppy program long before stations used tape systems. The record is a huge 14" in diameter and 331/3 RPM speed. Value of such records range between $150 and $200 if you can find them.

More easily found than studio records but still qu rare, are the colorfully sleeved single Hoppy reco produced by Capitol Records in the 1950's (shown 78RPM versions). Different regions have vastly w value ranges on single or album Hoppy records. C thanks to Mike Pellow for this great photo.

"Boy's Best Friend" is a very sought after Hoppy record, usually found in 78RPM. We have no value comparisons for the 45RPM version: #1. $150 #2. $120 #3. $100 (deduct $70 without sleeve). From the Hoffman collection. (This record was made in England)

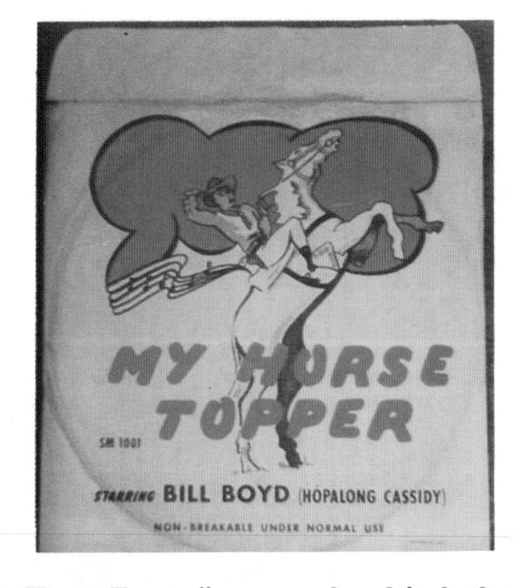

"My Horse Topper" was produced in both earlier and later version. Shown is the ea version with a folding sleeve with plain grap ics. #1. $175 #2. $145 #3. $120 (deduct $ without sleeve). From the Dave Brobeck colle tion.

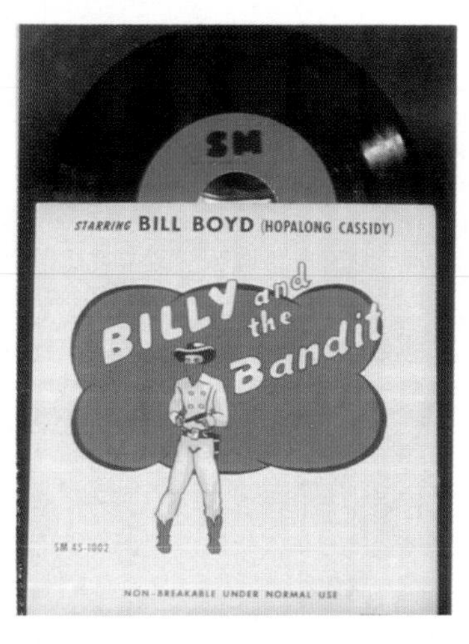

One of the earliest produced Hoppy records is this "78" version containing two short stories; "Good Luck Coin" and "Legend of Phantom Scout Pass." Due to his distinctive voice, only Bill Boyd portrayed Hoppy on the records and radio shows. #1. $175 #2. $145 #3. $120. (Deduct $85 without sleeve) "Billy and the Bandit" (r) is shown in "45" size and was produced by SM records. #1. $125 #2. $90 #3. $70 (deduct $30 without sleeve).

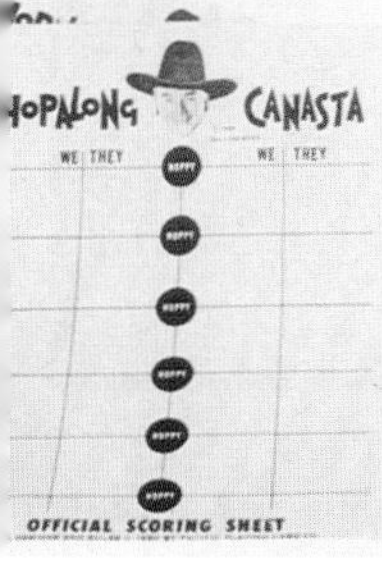

The Hoppy Canasta set came boxed with swivel plastic saddle and two decks of colorful Hoppy Canasta cards, plus instructions and score cards (shown on left). A rare item to find is the boxed Hoppy Canasta saddle alone (above). Hoppy Canasta playing cards were also sold seperately in a two deck box (not shown). Complete set: #1. $425 #2. $370 #3. $350 (with box) The Hoppy saddle-in-box is: #1. $300 #2. $270 #3. $250. Game pad is #1. $50 #2. $30. Thanks to Dennis Smith for the photo of his saddle-in-box. Two deck Hoppy card set is: #1. $150 #2. $100.

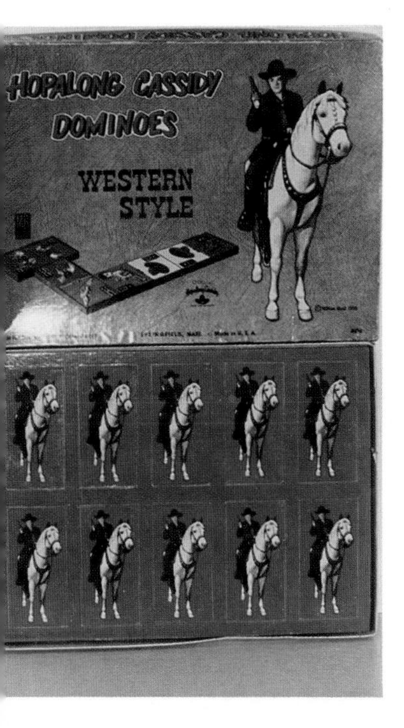

ppy Dominoes contain colorful ich-out cardboard playing pieces h Hoppy on each one. There are ee sheets of punch-out pieces plus tructions. While a common ppy collector item, it is very diffi- t to find in mint condition. #1. '5 #2. $275 #3. $245.

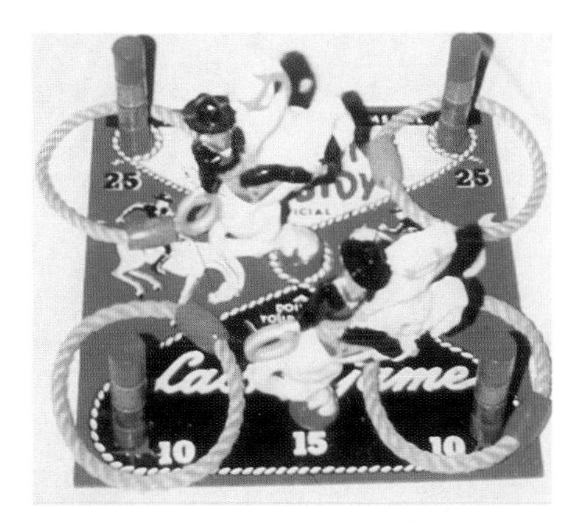

Shown above is a detail photo of the large Hoppy Lasso Game from Transogram. Notice the difference between the two. #1. $550 #2. $480 #3. $400. (including box)

The smaller version (r) of the Transogram Lasso Game as it appears MIB. Larger version (above) had a similar box, but slightly larger. Small set values: #1. $420 #2. $350 #3. $280. (including box)

Hoppy Chinese Checkers came with a cardboard base where the marble holes had to be punched-out. The colored marbles came in a plastic bag. The game was made by Milton Bradley: #1. $400 #2. $300 #3. $260.

A very rare Hoppy collectible, the "Bar Twenty" shooting game was made in England and is rarely found in the US. Rubber band powered to shoot cardboard "bad guys," this is an investment value item due to the condition and rarity. A value opinion would be: #1. $1,500 #2. $1,300 #3. $1,000. From the collection of Jon & Charlie Cheek.

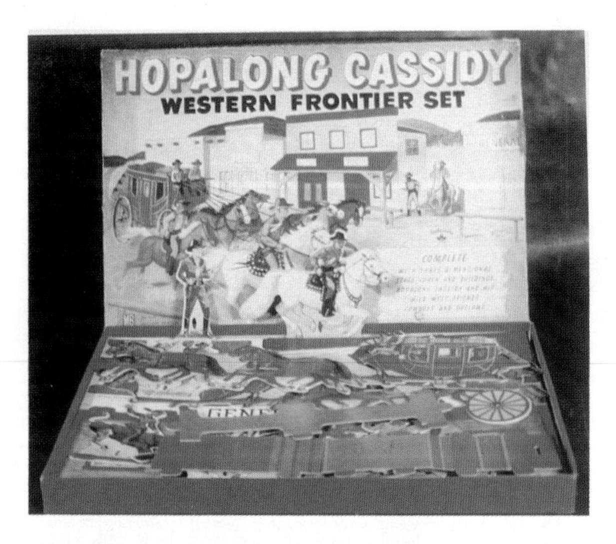

The Western Frontier Set had tremendous "play value" and there are few remaining sets intact. Each set contained cardboard buildings, a stagecoach, horses, "bad guys" and "good guys." There was much to assemble. Made by Milton Bradley, it is a "demand item" for serious collectors. #1. $950 #2. $750 #3. $600.

Hoppy target practice game included three magnet "darts" and a metal target (as shown). There were several different sizes made, the one shown would be called a "small" #1. $325 #2. $250 #3. $200. (deduct $100 without box).

uch larger version he target game fea- d on the previous e, it is difficult to l this collectible the original box. s version had an at- ed metal fold-out d. #1. $385 #2. 5 #3. $240. Deduct 0 without box.

Hopalong Cassidy board game was made by Milton Bradley and there are quite a number in circulation. The game contain s cardboard punch-out game pieces, special Hoppy play money and a card spinner. A very good investment for a starting collector. #1. $275 #2. $150 #3. $95.

ppy bean-bag toss game (large) called "Stagecoach s" Pressboard game came with three dowels to p it stand, and three plain brown "bean-bags" to s in the holes. #1. $275 #2. $225 #3. $185. (without deduct $100)

Smaller version of the Hoppy bean-bag game is "Pony Toss" as shown above. game is similar in all respects to "Stagecoach Toss" but smaller in size and harder to find. Both games share similar values: #1. $275. #2. $225 #3. $185.

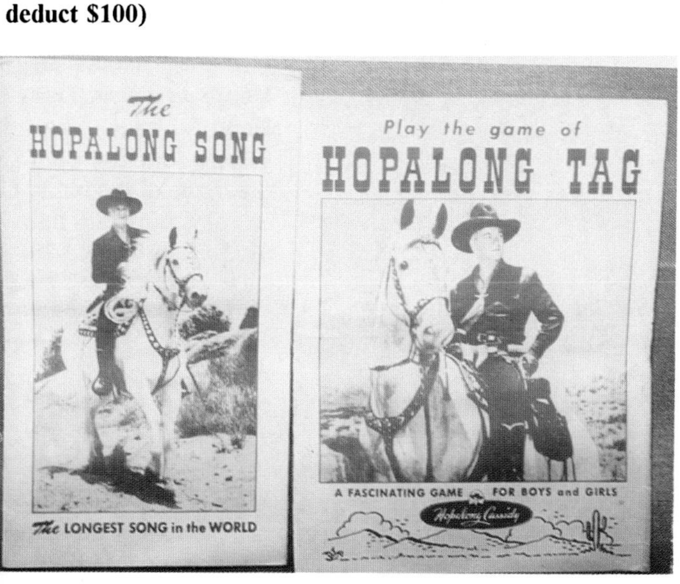

The Hoppy "tag" game (L) was really a promotional item give-away used by many stores. It is a paper "tag" game that followed a trail. The "Hopalong Song" is another give-away promo piece. They are both very rare items with similar values: #1. $95 #2. $70 #3. $50. From the Jon & Charlie Cheek collection.

SAVINGS & TROOPERS CLUB

#1. condition: mint, showing no use #2. condition: excellent to near mint #3. condition: good to very good

A very collectible area is, and has always been the Hoppy Savings Club information and badges, Hoppy letters and membership cards and savings books. This chapter includes complete Savings Club sets and ads and promotions. It also contains what "Troopers Club" information we could find. The traditional Hoppy banks however, are to be found under "Jewelry."

Bank window Hoppy "Savings Club" color decal let kids know this was the place to join. #1. $135 #2. $120 #3. $100. from the Mike Forthun collection.

"Savings Club" bank folder to mom & dad explained the program and the "Saving Rodeo" which got kids their badges based on levels of savings. #1. $65 #2. $50 #3. $40. From the Mike Forthun collection.

"Savings" coin containe shiny new penny enclos in a brass donut and w given by banks to n Hoppy accounts. Front h Hoppy's code, rear h "Hoppy Savings Club" a the name of the bank. C is very hard to find. $125 #2. $100 #3. $75

Section (L) are the incentives to get kids to save. The "Bar - 20 Foreman" badge was yours if you saved $500. Which was a considerable amount in 1950!

Cover of Hoppy promo brochure to banks for sign-up in the Hoppy Savings Club program.

"Savings Club" flyer announcing over a million kids have signed-up, and that you can open your new account for just a dollar! A rare collector find. #1. $70 #2. $50 #3. $40. (shows levels of badge earnings detailed on previous page.)

After kids join the Hoppy Savings Club, they are sent an "official" membership kit and a letter from Hoppy (R). A membership kit, complete with mailing envelope includes: mailing envelope - personalized letter - a rule book - and an arcade card with photo of Hoppy & Topper. #1. $200 #2. $175 #3. $160. This is not the "Rodeo Kit" with badges, nor does it contain the savings "passbook."

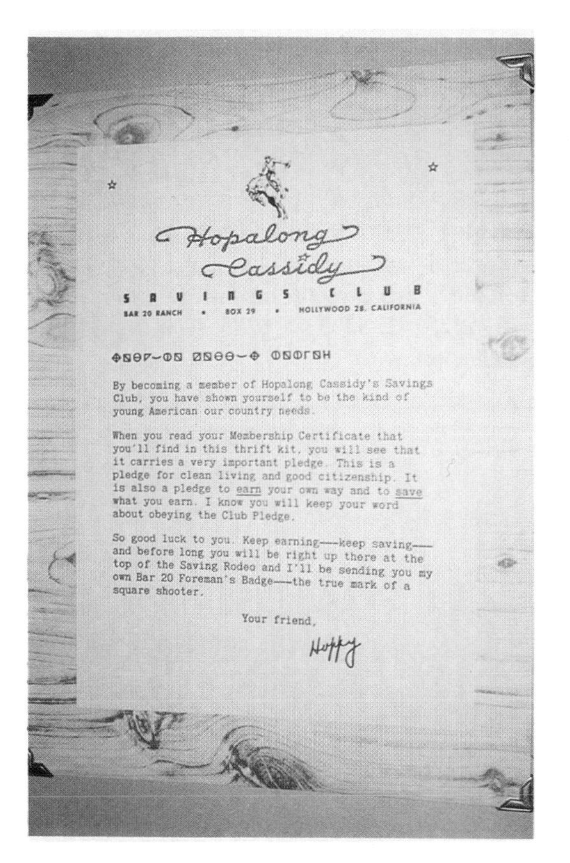

Hopalong Cassidy

SAVINGS CLUB

BAR 20 RANCH • BOX 29 • HOLLYWOOD 28, CALIFORNIA

By becoming a member of Hopalong Cassidy's Savings Club, you have shown yourself to be the kind of young American our country needs.

When you read your Membership Certificate that you'll find in this thrift kit, you will see that it carries a very important pledge. This is a pledge for clean living and good citizenship. It is also a pledge to earn your own way and to save what you earn. I know you will keep your word about obeying the Club Pledge.

So good luck to you. Keep earning---keep saving---and before long you will be right up there at the top of the Saving Rodeo and I'll be sending you my own Bar 20 Foreman's Badge---the true mark of a square shooter.

Your friend,

Hoppy

Savings Club Hoppy letters are $15-$25 each.

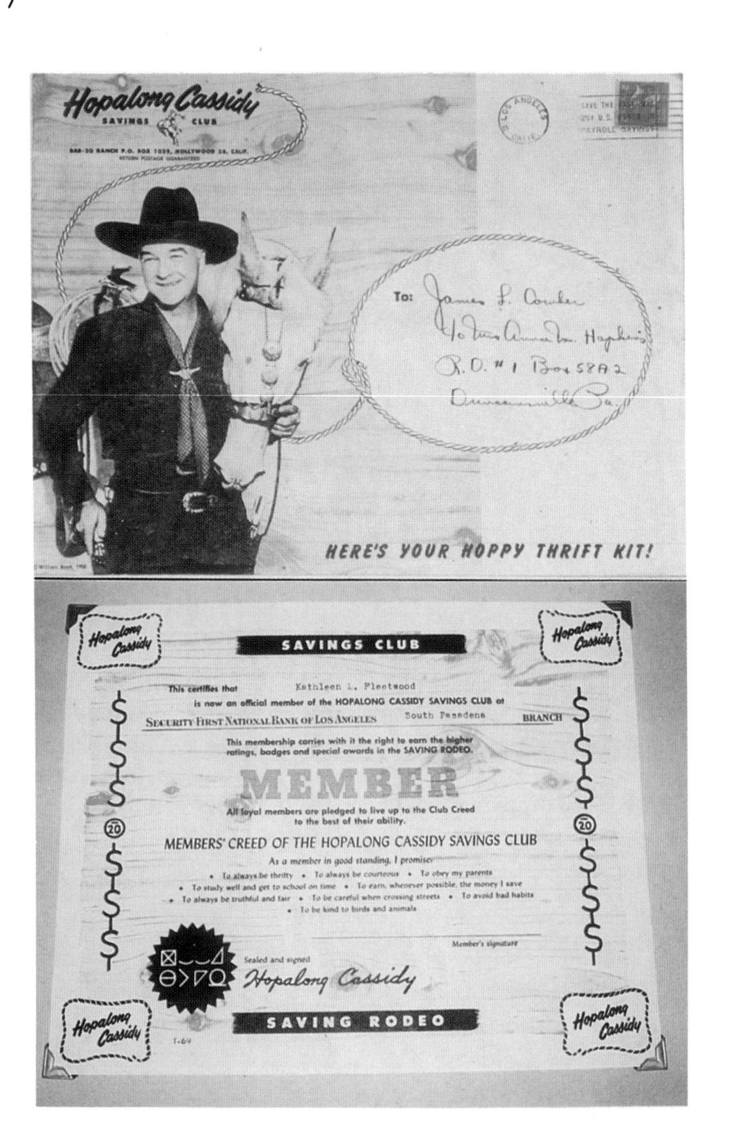

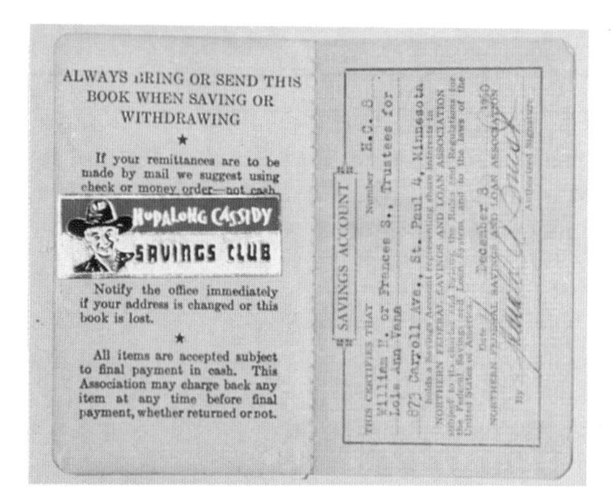

Hoppy Savings Club account book and holder (sleeve). Several account books came with foil "Savings Club" attachment on inside cover (as shown.) #1. $325. #2. $300 #3. $275. from the Mike Forthun collection.

Many savings rodeo badges are being reproduced. Check the "Cameras Pins, Badges" chapter for details.,

Detail photo of envelope and membership "Savings Club" (that could be framed) paper. The Happy Birthday card (bottom) was sent by the participating bank to keep club members enthused. The birthday cards are available for $10 - $15. From the Mike Forthun collection. Kit envelopes (top) are valued at $35 -$60 and membership paper is $30 -$40.

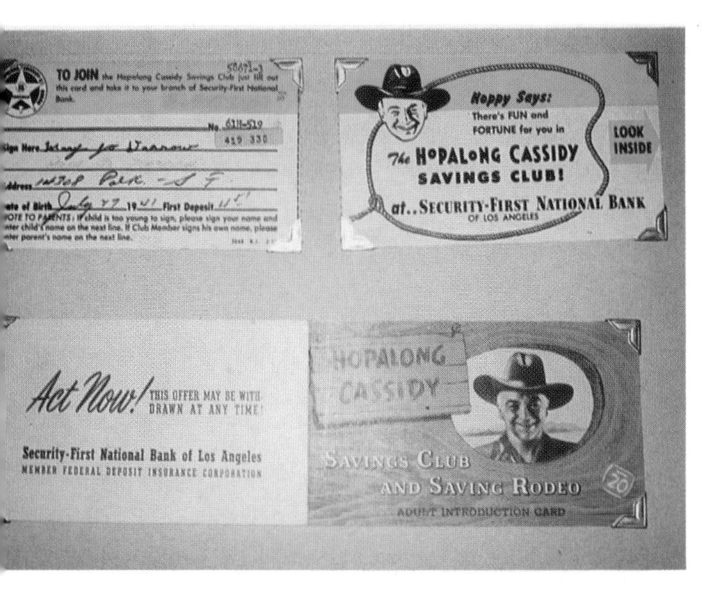

:s offering Savings Club memberships used a variety of nders and promotions to get kids to join. Also, a nembership card (above) which carried the account ›er. From the Mike Forthun collection.

The Hoppy Savings Club Kit has become quite controversial over the past two years based on wide discrepancies in its value. Much of this controversy deals directly with the huge amount of reproduction badges lowering the overall value of the "genuine" collectibles. There are reports that complete "genuine" kits have sold for as high as nearly $2,000 and as low as $900. Each collector must judge for himself.

ile the "Troopers Club" didn't live very long, it : a good promotion vehicle for the many bread ıpanies that endorsed it. The club membership d shown above, was sponsored by Butter-Nut :ad. Cards like this are valued at $25-$35. From Mike Forthun collection.

Many Hoppy wallets found today contain the wallet "Special Agent Pass" and may contain a "Troopers Club" or "Savings Club" membership card as well. Such cards are valued at between $25 and $35. From the Mike Forthun collection.

YIPPEE! BIGGEST NEWS IN HOPALONG CASSIDY TROOPERS CLUB HISTORY!

Hopalong Cassidy

TROOPERS NEWS

HOPPY ANNOUNCES BIG CONTEST!
1001 PRIZES in Southern California Alone!

THIS CONTEST FOR OFFICIAL TROOPERS CLUB MEMBERS ONLY!

Any Boy or Girl who is an OFFICIAL MEMBER of the Hopalong Cassidy TROOPERS CLUB may ENTER this EASY CONTEST. YOU may be one of the HAPPY WINNERS! Full Details and OFFICIAL ENTRY BLANK in this SPECIAL CONTEST ISSUE. LET'S GO... AND GOOD LUCK PARTNERS!

Just Look at all these Wonderful Prizes... More Than A Thousand!

ON TELEVISION Hopalong Cassidy KTLA

If YOU are not yet a MEMBER there's still TIME to join the CLUB so YOU can TAKE PART in this TREMENDOUS CONTEST!

Troopers News was a membership newsletter sponsored by various bread companies. They are very hard to find in complete condition. This issue features a California contest and has a higher value: #1. $250 #2. $200 #3. $150. From the Jon & Charlie Cheek collection.

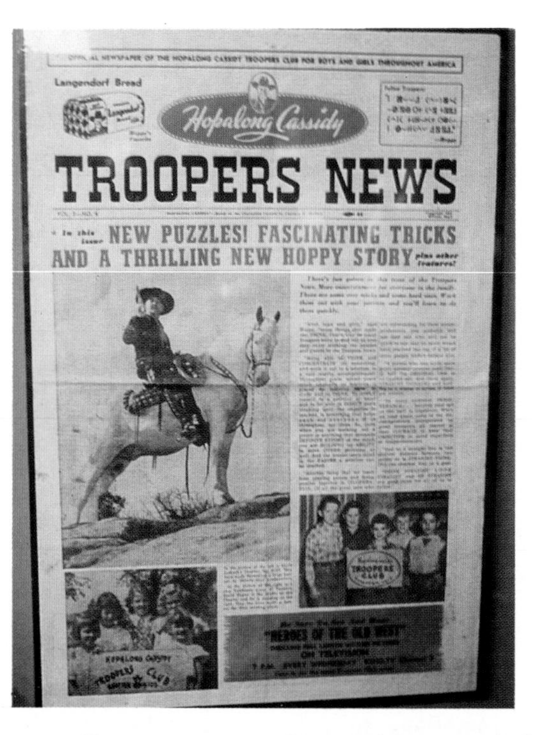

Langendorf Bread

Hopalong Cassidy

TROOPERS NEWS

In this issue NEW PUZZLES! FASCINATING TRICKS AND A THRILLING NEW HOPPY STORY plus other features!

"HEROES OF THE OLD WEST"

ON TELEVISION

Troopers News was an excellent vehicle to remind kids to do the "right thing" in daily life as well as an opportunity to promote Hoppy and other sponsors. Many carried special photos and articles. #1. $200 #2. $175 #3. $100.

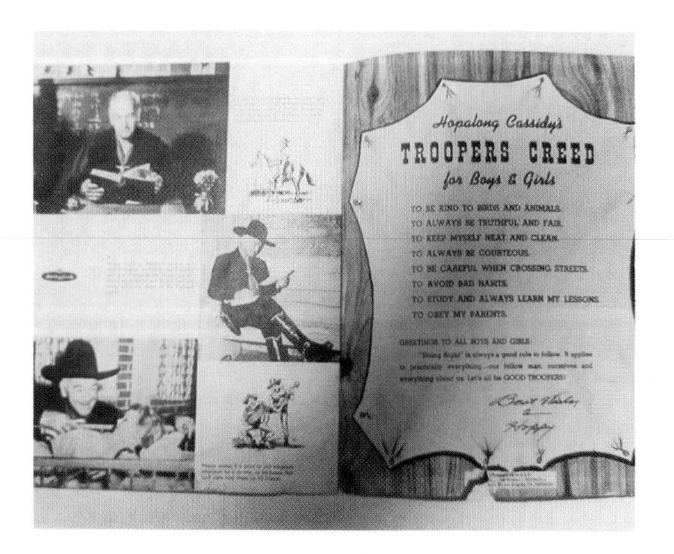

Hopalong Cassidy's

TROOPERS CREED

for Boys & Girls

TO BE KIND TO BIRDS AND ANIMALS.
TO ALWAYS BE TRUTHFUL AND FAIR.
TO KEEP MYSELF NEAT AND CLEAN.
TO ALWAYS BE COURTEOUS.
TO BE CAREFUL WHEN CROSSING STREETS.
TO AVOID BAD HABITS.
TO STUDY AND ALWAYS LEARN MY LESSONS.
TO OBEY MY PARENTS.

GREETINGS TO ALL BOYS AND GIRLS:
"Doing Right" is always a good rule to follow. It applies to practically everything...our fellow man, ourselves and everything about us. Let's all be GOOD TROOPERS!

Display of the Hoppy "Troopers Creed" a must for all young cowpokes.

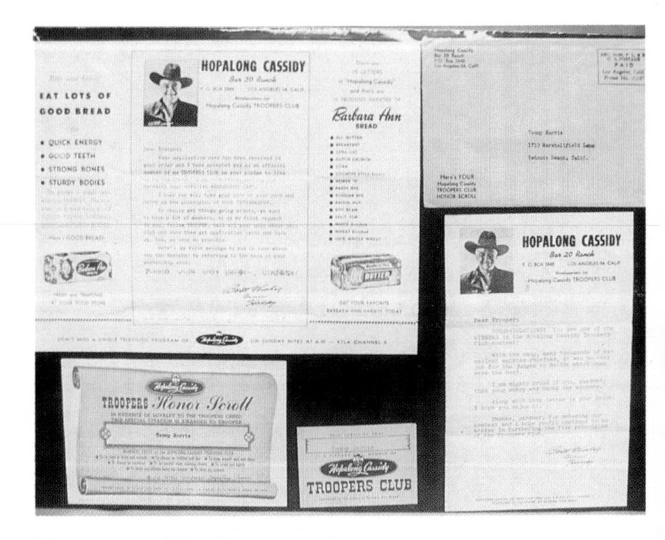

HOPALONG CASSIDY
Bar 20 Ranch

EAT LOTS OF GOOD BREAD

- QUICK ENERGY
- GOOD TEETH
- STRONG BONES
- STURDY BODIES

Barbara Ann
BREAD

TROOPERS Honor Scroll

TROOPERS CLUB

Troopers kit has card, honor roll certificate, brochure and envelope and a "winners" letter from Hoppy. A collection like this is valued at $250.

SCHOOL ITEMS

#1. condition: mint, showing no use #2. condition: excellent to near mint #3. condition: good to very good

Kids in the "50's" were definitely "cool" if they brought Hoppy items to school. Bill Boyd developed the first "character" lunch box with Hoppy in 1949, so when you see Ninja Turtles and all the other collector school lunch boxes, you'll know they are all followers of a great Bill Boyd marketing plan. Hoppy school items are difficult for collectors to find these days because they enjoyed so much use back then. Good luck in your quest!

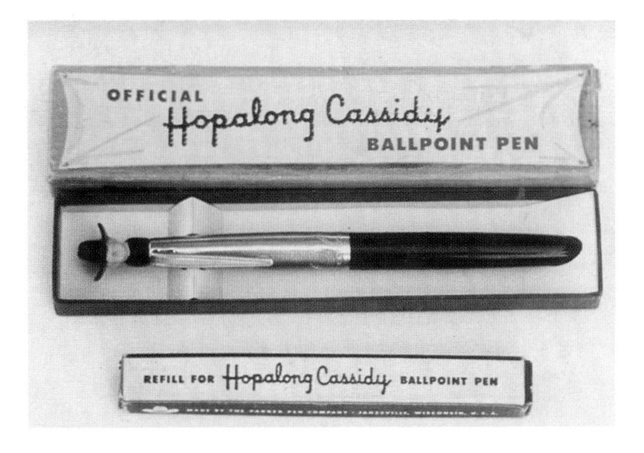

The Hoppy ball-point was marketed two ways, the boxed pen (above) and the store pen display (L). Made by the Parker Pen Company, Hoppy pens were first class! The store display (L) is from the Aileen Buck collection and contains the original 24 pens. This is an investment item with a value in excess of $3,000. The boxed pen (above) is also shown with boxed pen refill: $250 for a #1. pen & box and $60 for the refill and box.

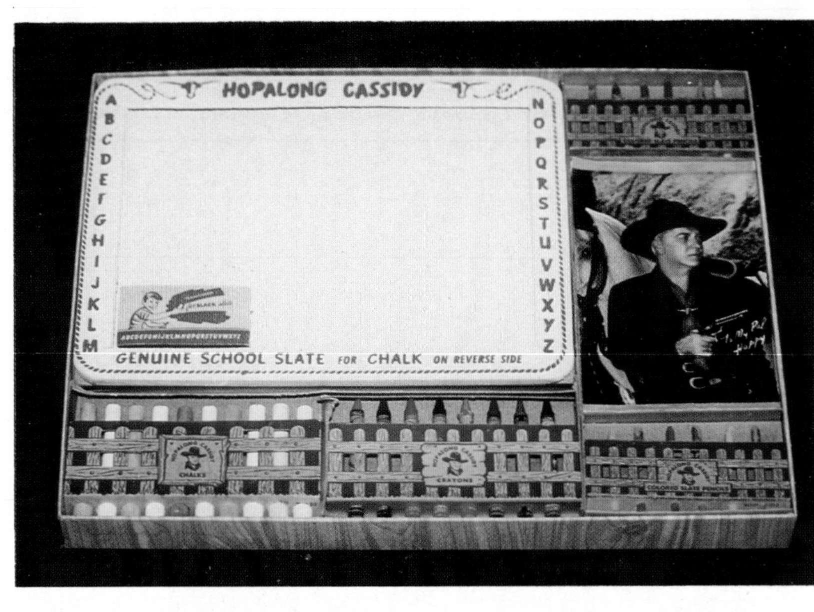

One very rare and desirable collector item is the school slate outfit (above) which contains a two-sided board for crayons and colored chalk and an eraser, slate pencils, stencils, etc.. Set shown is in #1. condition, which is very hard to find: #1. $550 #2. $400 #3. $325. From the Bill Larzelere collection.

Hoppy stationary folio was actually for writing personal letters and is very colorful. Hoppy note paper came in three different colors with three small design changes. #1 $275 #2. $220 #3. $175.

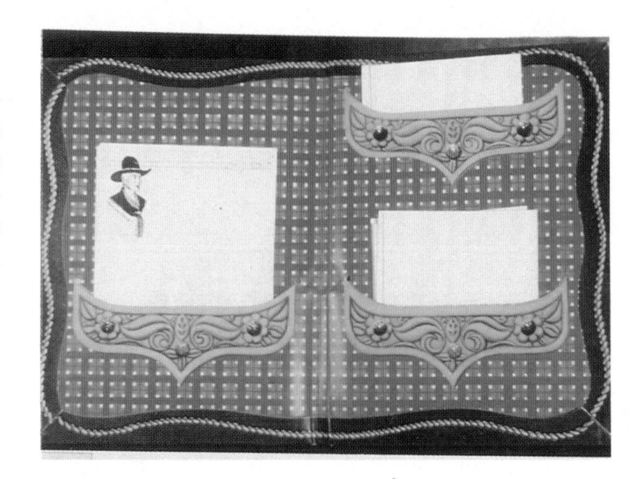

The rare Hoppy mechanical pencil (L) is often called a phoney by some experts, but is actually genuine, due to the amount of them around. The pencil has a battery inside that lights a small Hoppy bust in the nose of the pencil when activated. It is shown next to the Hoppy pen for size. #1. $325 #2. $250 #3. $200.

The first Hoppy lunch pail is thought to be the blue cloud or "scalloped" decal design (above). This metal box and thermos was made by Aladdin Industries. For several years (1949 - 1951) they were produced in red & blue. Evidence below shows the yellow thermos with a black plastic top which was soon changed to the red top version. Hoppy thermos bottles came with the boxes and also boxed (below left & center). Note the difference between the two box styles. "Cloud" lunch box & thermos sets are: #1. $575 #2. $450 #3. $325 (Deduct 35% if no thermos).

oxed Hoppy thermos: #1. $375 #2. 300 #3. $250 (values are for box and ermos in stated condition)

Rare black topped yellow thermos and boxed 1954 litho thermos (R) are from the Phil Ellis collection. Value of a "loose" yellow thermos is: #1. $250 #2. $200 #3. $160.

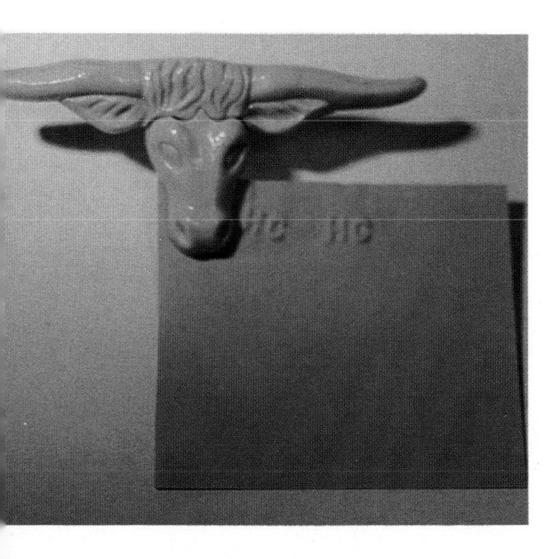

Plastic steer head stationary embosser would leave a "HC" when pressed. Not sure of packaging other than card. #1. $150 #2. $125 #3. $100

Square decal Hoppy lunch pails were made between 195 and 1954. Some collectors value the earlier versions at higher value but purchase records show no noteabl difference. #1. $575 #2. $450 #3. $325 (with thermos).

The 1954 lithographed Hoppy lunch pail & thermos was made in 195 and 1955 against popular belief that it was made for one year only. It i much more rare than the decal versions and hard to find in pristin condition because it scratched so easily. The quality was poor, compare to the others, but it maintains higher collector interest and value: #1.$65 #2. $500 #3. $400. (deduct 40% if no thermos). Loose thermos values are #1. $225 #2. $185 #3. $125.

Above chuck wagon decal came with all Hoppy boxes but rare to find in original glassine: $125 From the Jon & Charlie Cheek collection. Pencil sharpeners (below) came in various colors and are valued at: $45 to $65. (They were not issued in pencil cases)

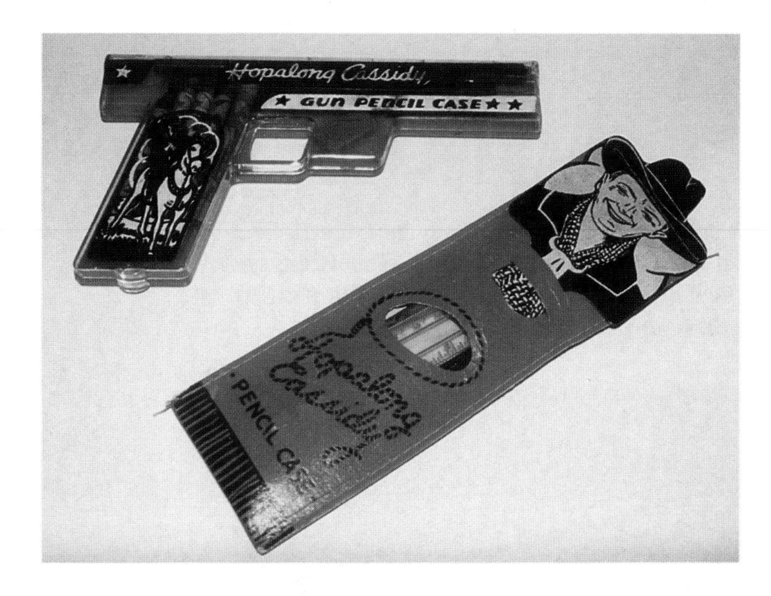

Hoppy gun pencil case came in two different designs - with holster, and without. You will notice the above gun case has graphics molded on plastic while holstered guns only have (pencil sharpener) plastic shield attached. Both designs are in-demand items.

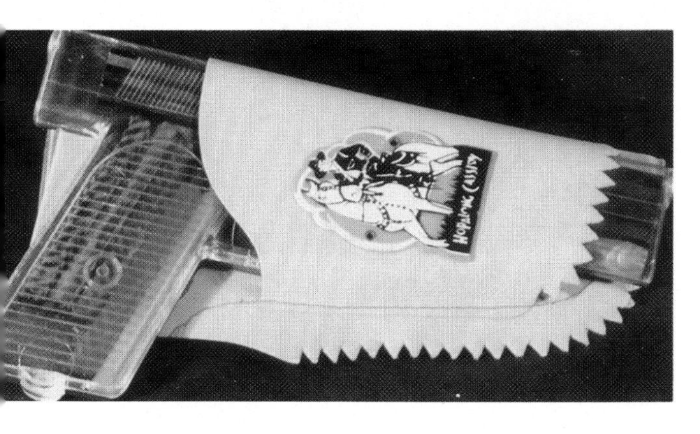

Shown below, plastic gun is top hinged and contains: Hoppy pencils, plastic pen nib holder, eraser and crayons. Holster is made from cardboard. Holstered version: #1. $425 #2. $350 #3. $275. Unholstered version: #1. $340 #2. $275 #3. $200 (both values include all contents)

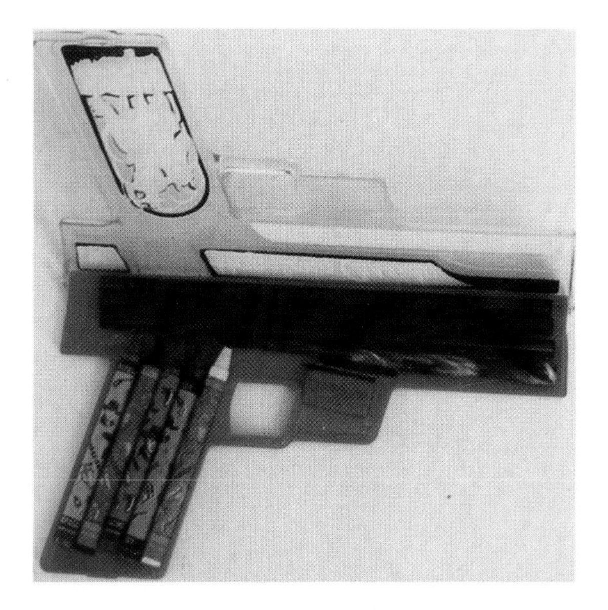

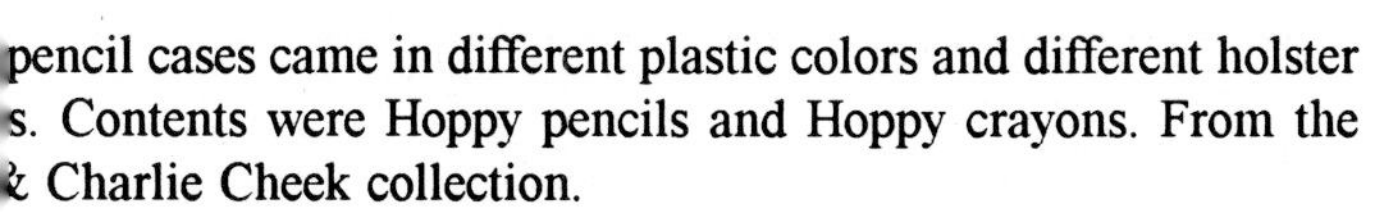

pencil cases came in different plastic colors and different holster s. Contents were Hoppy pencils and Hoppy crayons. From the & Charlie Cheek collection.

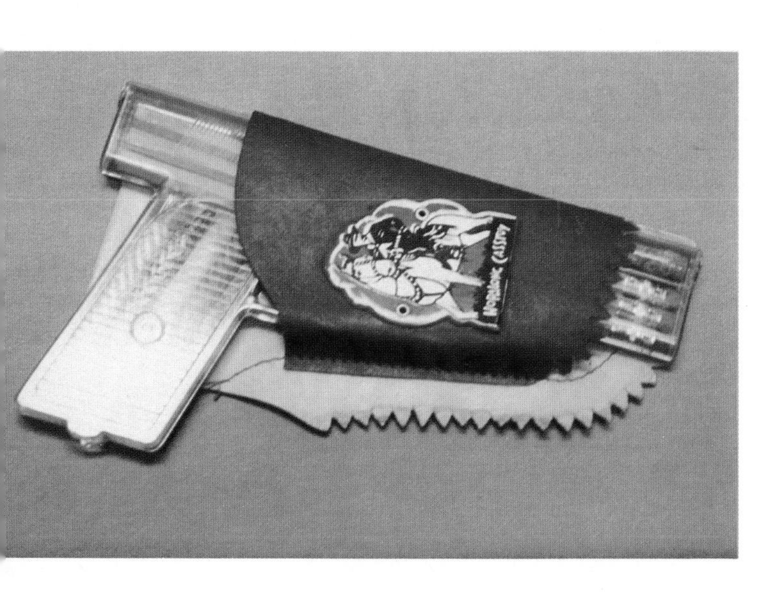

Several different color versions of the Hoppy gun pencil case. On a side issue, it should be noted that many schools did not allow the gun pencil cases in class. (I got caught with mine by Sister Mary . . . three days detention).

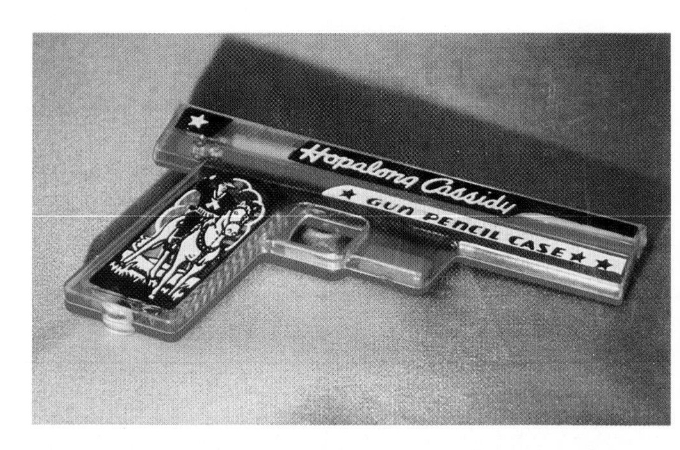

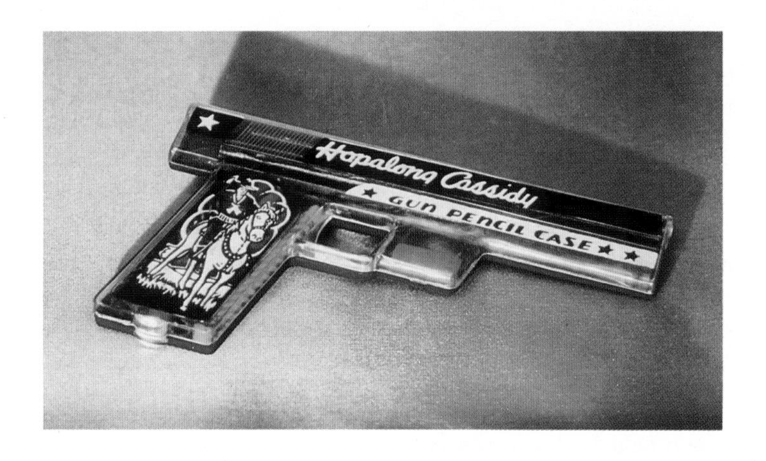

One of the rarest Hoppy school items is the "jumbo" plastic pencil - pencil case. Eraser unscrewed to access contents inside: Hoppy pencils, crayons, ruler, etc. #1. $400 #2. $325 #3. $280. From the Ron Pieczkowski collection. (other pencil cases are in the "Miscellaneous" chapter.

Very rare tan, flip-top pencil case with pencil sharpener graphic on front. Contents include: pencils, plastic ruler, pen holder and Hoppy paper w. photo. #1. $285 #2. $240 #3. $185 (with contents). From the Jon & Charlie Cheek collection.

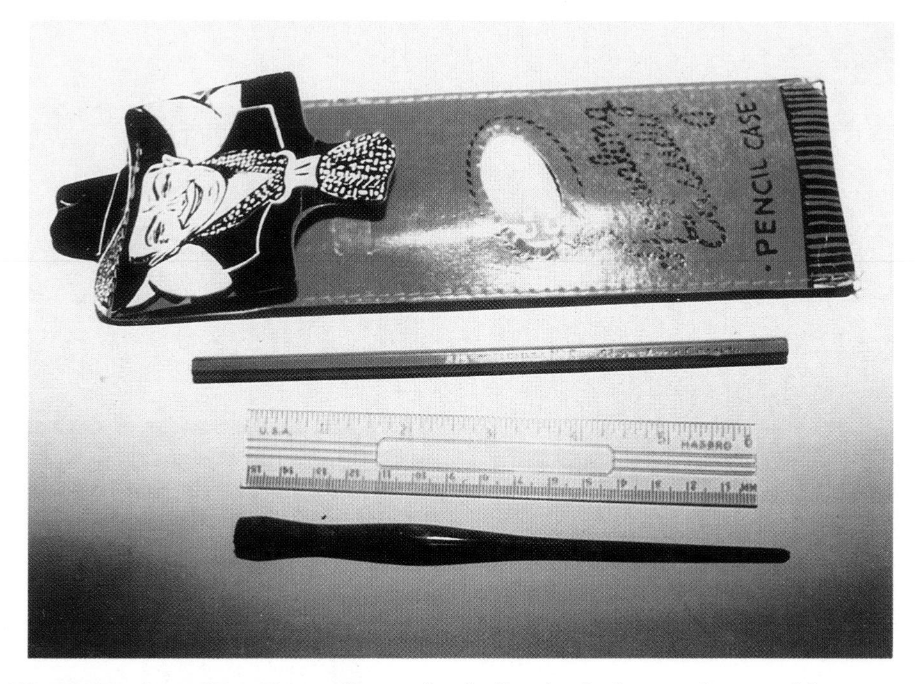

Hoppy-head cardboard pencil case is similar in design as the tan (shown on previous page) except it was more colorful, had a contents view window and, of course, a die-cut Hoppy head. Contents were the same and so is the value: #1. $285 #2. $240 #3. $185.

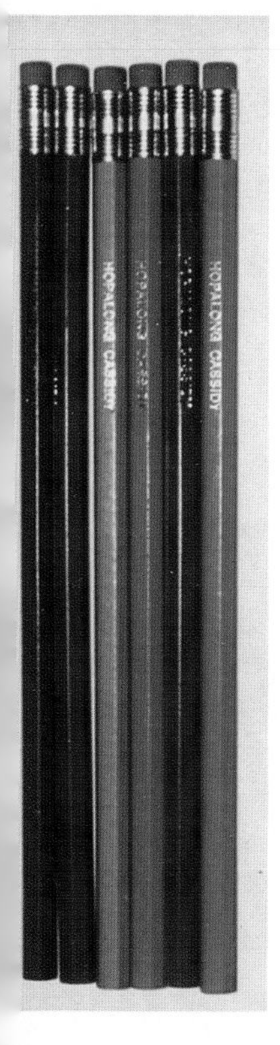

ny pencil cases contain a few "Hopalong ssidy" pencils, but if you find them loose expect to pay $15 to $20 each for one t is in #1. condition. The wrapped pencils are rare and are worth $125 as shown. m the Phil Ellis collection.

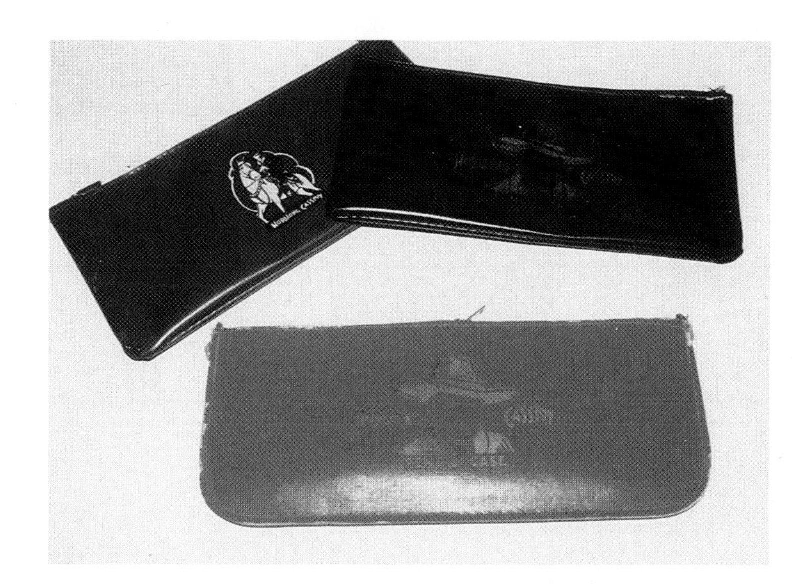

The least expensive of all the Hoppy pencil cases was the plastic or cardboard pencil bag (shown above and left). Both kinds had a zippered top and standard contents of the "flip-top" In addition, each bag had a Hoppy photo paper along with pen and pencils. Values are similar for plastic or cardboard. #1. $185 #2. $140 #3. $100. (with contents).

There are a wide variety of drawer Hoppy pencil cases (cardboard) with three different graphic designs (above). Some are single drawer which slide sideways to open and some are the tool-box type with a front snap. From the Jon & Charlie Cheek collection.

Tool-box type single drawer pencil case had several pencils, eraser. ruler, pen holder and five crayons:#1. $270 #2. $200 #3. $160 (with contents).

Single sliding drawer pencil case has same value as tool-box single drawer (above left).

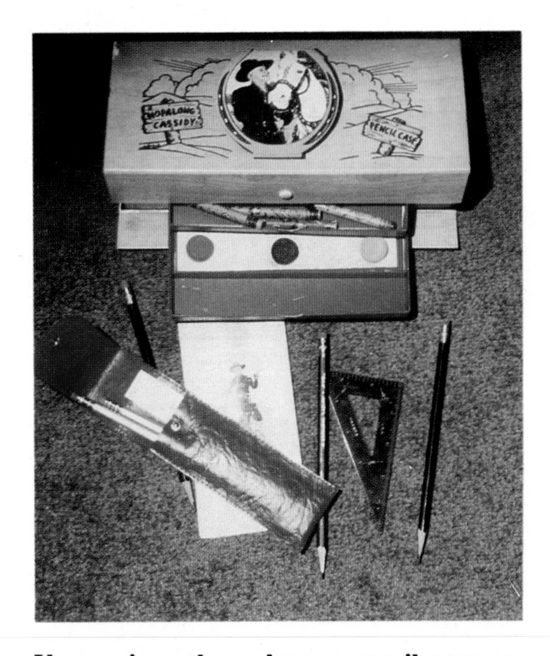

Very unique three drawer pencil case contained water color paints, and a smaller flap case to carry in your pocket. Case also had ruler, eraser, plastic straight edge, crayons and several pencils and Hoppy instruction book w/ photo. #1. $550 #2. $425 #3. $350.

Photo (R) shows single drawer (bottom) 2 drawer (center) and three drawer (top) pencil cases. The value for the 2-drawer is: #1. $375 #2. $300 #3. $250

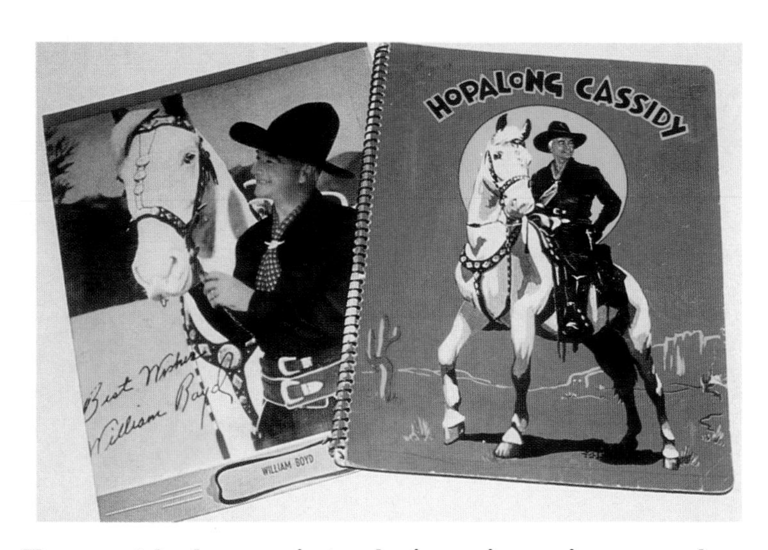

Hoppy notebooks came in two basic versions: wire-wrapped composition (R) and flip-up note pad (L). They are both highly sought by collectors. Each contain about 50 lined pages. Wire: #1. $125 #2. $85 #3. $60. Note pad: #1. $80 #2. $60 #3. $45.

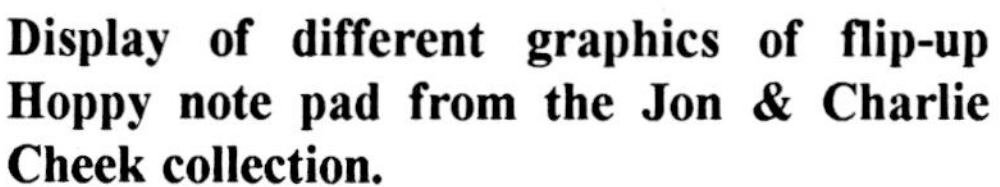

Display of different graphics of flip-up Hoppy note pad from the Jon & Charlie Cheek collection.

"Movie Star" Hoppy two-ring binder paper came with various colored sleeves (R) and different views of same Hoppy photo. A NOS (new old stock) find several years ago, values have increased to $35 to $45 for a sleeved paper packet.

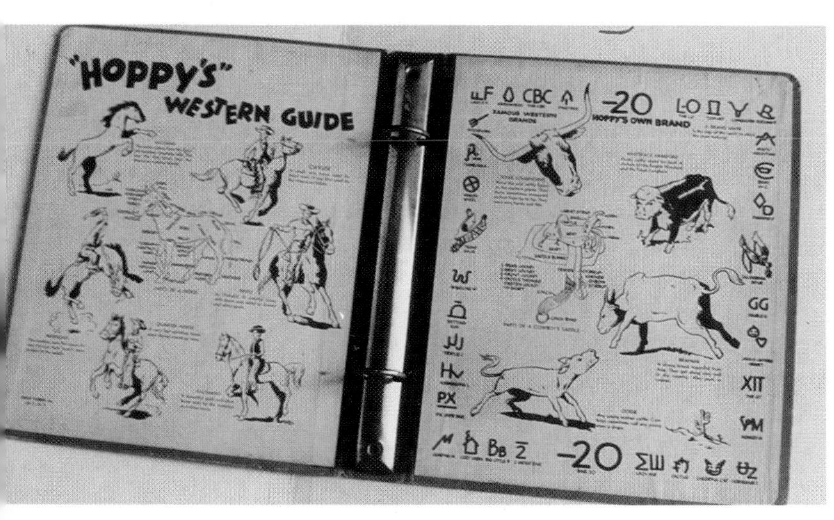

Two-ring binder (L) has interesting western graphics on both inside covers (cover on next page). Binders took "Movie Star" paper as well as others. #1. $185 #2. $140 #3. $100.

Selection of stiff cover Hoppy binders (R) showing a three-ring (L) and two, two-ring binders (R) with a wire wrapped notebook on the bottom. Value of two-ring binders are similar: #1. $185 #2. $140 #3. $100. From the Jon & Charlie Cheek collection. #1. condition binders have price tags attached (see below)

Detail photo of two-ring binder inside covers and Hoppy "Movie Star" paper. Please note price tag attached to binder ring: "Hopalong Cassidy Ring Binder 49 cents." Deduct $25 if price tag is not attached to #1. binders.

The above Hoppy book bag is a well constructed leather version brief case which could be used by adults as well as children (no kidding). While not graphically appealing, it is in demand by collectors. #1. $475 #2. $350 #3. $280. There is no girls version of this particular bag. From the Jon & Charlie Cheek collection.

While not a wide assortment, there were several versions of the plastic (vinyl) Hoppy book bag made for boys' and girls.' There is a "unisex" bag that has both a shoulder strap and a grip. All are similarly valued: #1. $360 #2. $300 #3. $240. from the Jon & Charlie Cheek collection.

TOYS

#1. condition: mint, showing no use #2. condition: excellent to near mint #3. condition: good to very good

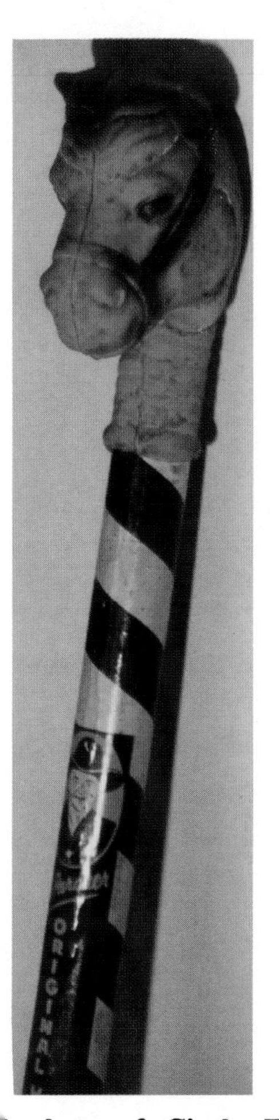

photo of Circle F Toys stick showing Topper head.

Ideal plastic Hoppy & Topper toy. Hoppy is removeable as is his hat. His right arm is moveable. Topper has small chain bridal. #1. $175. #2. $150 #3. $100 Mint in box: $325.

Hoppy Pogo stick from Circle F Toys. Perhaps one of the most rare Hoppy items known: #1. $2,000 #2, $1,500 #3. $1,200. Mint boxed pogo stick (shown above) is valued at $3,500. From the Sharon Delaney collection.

Hoppy plastic "Pistol Flashlight" (L) is a rare collectors item to find with box, and in working condition. #1. $425 #2. $350 #3. $275. (Without original box, deduct: $125).

Inflatable Topper vinyl riding horse. #1. $275. #2. $225 #3. $180. If NOS (new old stock) in box, add $130. "Riding Topper" is more common of the two vinyl inflatables. Also came in other colors.

Strap-on Topper vinyl inflatable horse. Harder to find than the "rider" toy was quite unique (see advertisement). #1. $700 #2. $600 #3. $475. If bo add: $230. From the Jon & Charlie Cheek collection.

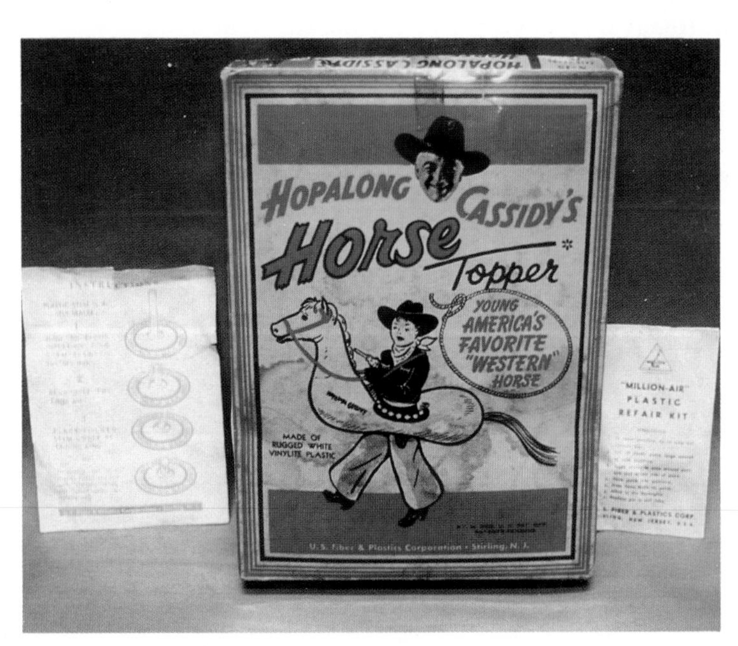

Strap-on Topper boxed item (unopened) shows repair kit a instructions. Extremely rare and considered an "investme item" a value guess would be over $1,000. From the Jon & Char Cheek collection.

Rubico Products Hoppy "Spark Shooter" is a popular collector item but hard to find NOS as in above photo. #1. $275 #2. $230 #3. $190. Mint on card: $450.

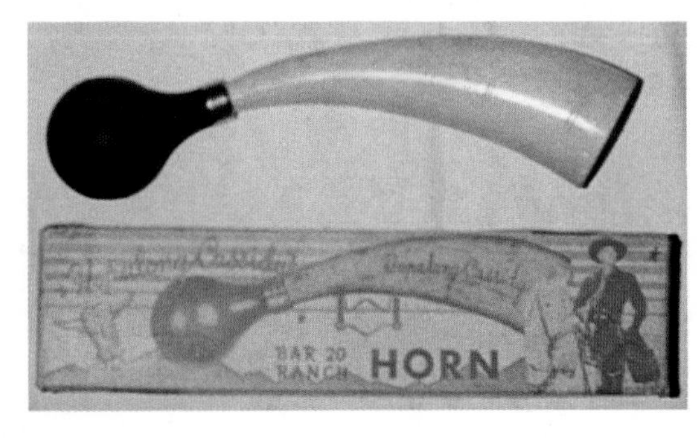

Plastic Hoppy steer horn was made to mount on bicycles of all sorts, but looked best on a genuine Hoppy bike. (mounting bracket not shown) #1. $175. #2. $130 #3. $100 Boxed horn in #1. is: $350

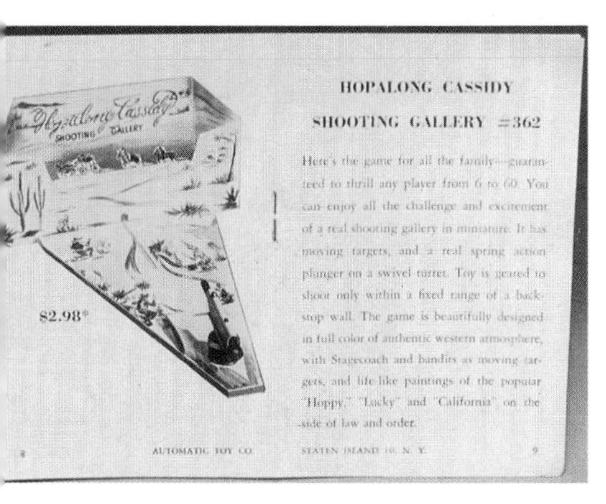

HOPALONG CASSIDY

SHOOTING GALLERY #362

Here's the game for all the family—guaranteed to thrill any player from 6 to 60. You can enjoy all the challenge and excitement of a real shooting gallery in miniature. It has moving targets, and a real spring action plunger on a swivel turret. Toy is geared to shoot only within a fixed range of a backstop wall. The game is beautifully designed in full color of authentic western atmosphere, with Stagecoach and bandits as moving targets, and life-like paintings of the popular "Hoppy," "Lucky" and "California" on the side of law and order.

$2.98*

8 AUTOMATIC TOY CO. STATEN ISLAND 10, N. Y. 9

truction and detail sheet for shooting gallery is y difficult to find even with boxed set. Deduct from boxed value if not included. From the & Charlie Cheek collection.

Hoppy shooting gallery from Automatic Toy Company was one of only three wind-up Hoppy toys know to exist; Hoppy televisions (below) and wind-up Marx Hoppy rocking toys. Values on shooting gallery is with box included: #1. $750 #2. $600 #3. $460.

wer model of the Hoppy TV did not come with top ap or Hoppy image on top. "Action Strips" on this del were in color and not black & white like the lier version: #1. $350 #2. $290 #3. $175. Deduct 0 without box and deduct $50 if the five action ips are missing.

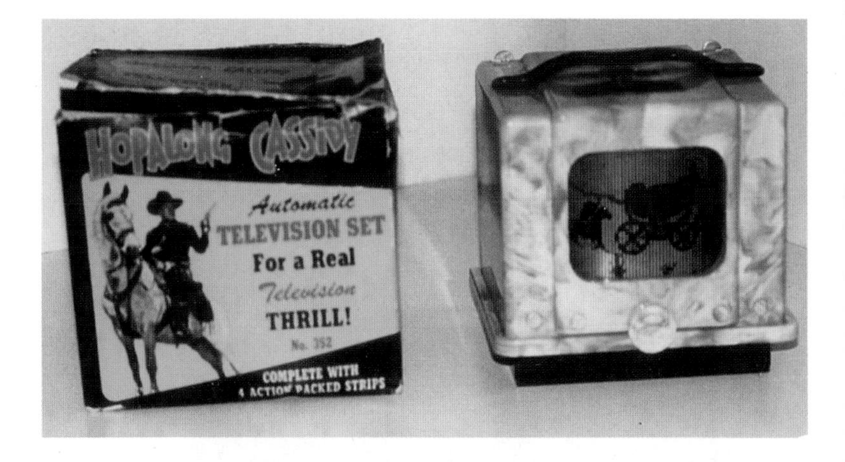

Hoppy plastic wind-up "automatic" television with 6 action strips. Note earlier model (above) has strap and Hoppy image on top. Unit also had only black & white strips: #1. $450 #2. $390 #3. $275. (higher value is for the early version w/ strap & Hoppy image. Deduct $100 without box and $50 without five extra strips.

You will notice subtle differences between solid-core chalks Values are similar. From the Steve Axelson collection

Hoppy "carnival chalk" is really a plaster of paris molded figure that is solid-core. They were occasionally painted differently as shown. #1. $450 #2. $375. #3. $325. They stood about 13" high. From the Jon Cheek collection.

Hollow-core Hoppy chalk (L) stood 16" and generally came wit "sparkles" on his badge and guns. Similar face to Lone Range hollow-core, but without mask. #1. $425 #2. $350 #3. $300.

Rich Toys 22" rocking Topper. There were three sizes of the Topper "rocker" and a large "glider" which moved back and forth. #1. $450 #2. $400 #3. $350. (Check "Miscellaneous" chapter for larger version).

grett Enterprises Company "Zoomerang Gun." Either d or blue gun snapped-out a paper roll. Nice die-cut box. . $375 #2. $325 #3. $300. Deduct $150 if no box.

Tiempo (England) cast metal figure sets. One set standing, the other riding horses. #1. $1,150 (standing set w/ box) #1. $1,500 (riding set w/ box) Individual pieces $25-$50 each. From the Sharon Delaney collection.

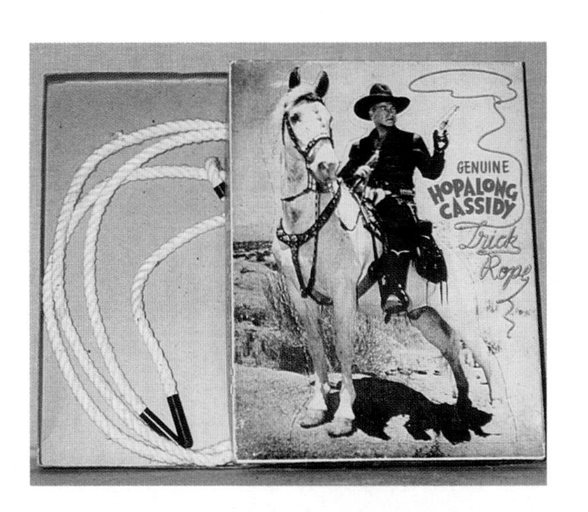

Hoppy "Trick Rope" is a wonderful find, but extremely rare. #1. $750 #2. $600 #3. $540. (Including box) From the Phil Ellis collection.

Hoppy blocks set. 12 Plastic blocks would rattle when shaken for young Hoppy fans. Set is difficult for collectors to find. #1. $950 #2. $870 #3. $775. (including box) From the Phil Ellis collection.

Display of Hoppy & Topper from Tiempo metal figure riding set listed above. Loose riding set figures are selling for $100 each.

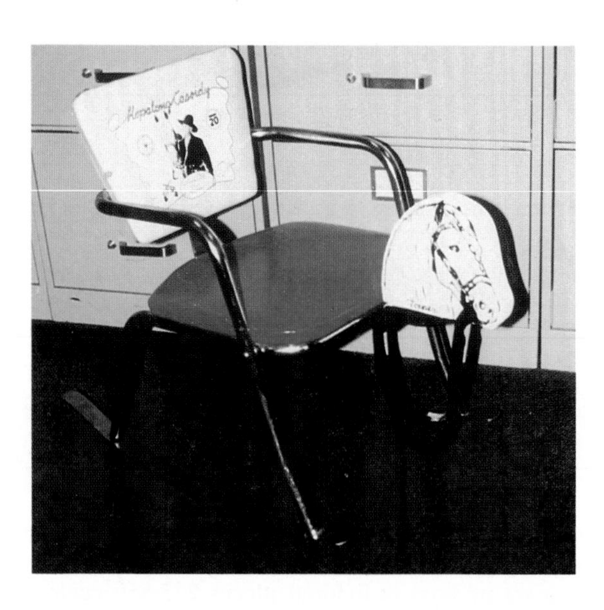

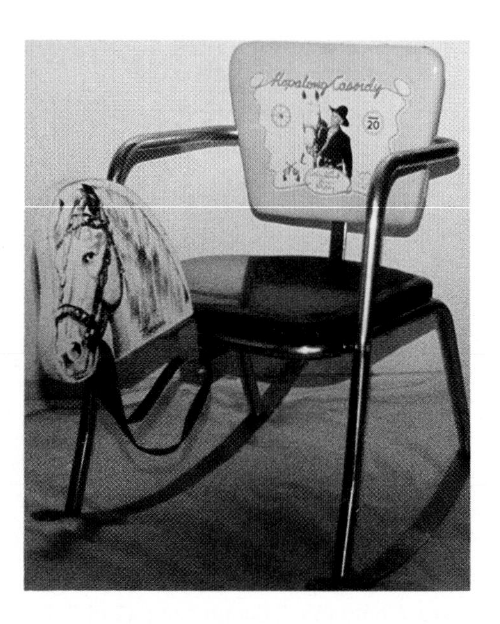

Hoppy 's Topper-head rocking chair came in two colors (as shown) with vinyl seat and seatback with Hoppy image. The wooden Topper head was quickly removeable as child grew. There are more chairs around without Topper-heads, (which were lost over the years) than with. #1. $500 #2. $425 #3. $380 Without Topper head deduct: $150.

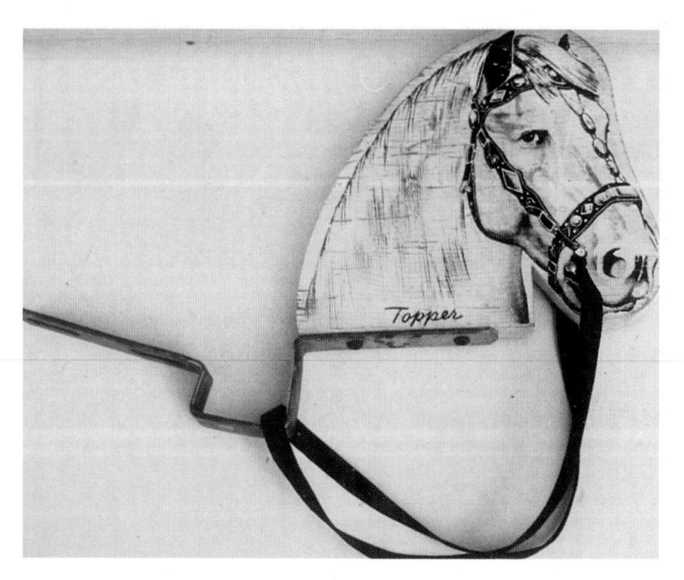

Display photo of wooden Topper head with bridal. Chair heads in this condition bring $150.

Photo of chair without Topper head Chairs in this condition are valued at $200 - $350.

Display set of skates & spurs (#1 condition) from the Jon & Charlie Cheek collection.

Rollfast deluxe roller skates came with fringed Hoppy "kilties," gold colored hubs on the wheels - and removable metal spurs with gold roundels with tip protectors, that attached on skate backs. Metal spur attachments are difficult to find. #1. $850 #2. $750 #3 $650. Deduct: $250 if no spurs, $100 if "kilties" are missing and $400 if no box. A loose pair of skates without spurs or box can generally be found for $150 in #2. condition.

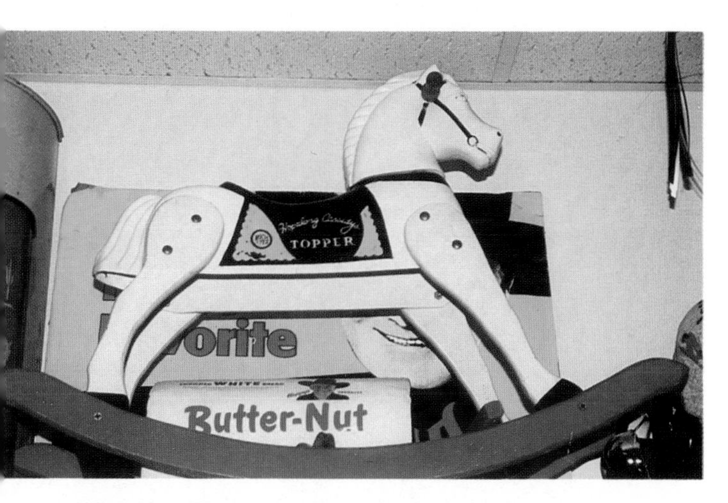

"Standard" version of rocking horse Topper.

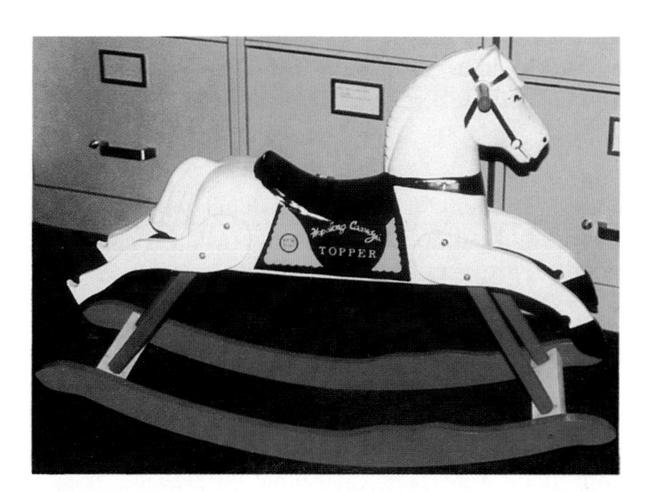

Unusual "running" wooden Topper rocker (above) with legs outstretched (running) compared to "standard" version of same size. Running version is quite rare and is valued at: #1. $600 #2. $525 #3. $425. which is somewhat higher than the standard version shown on previous page.

arx tin wind-up Hoppy: #1. $850 #2. $725 #3. $650. Deduct 00 without box. From the Ron Pieczkowski collection.

Display photo of common hand puppet and Marx wind-up.

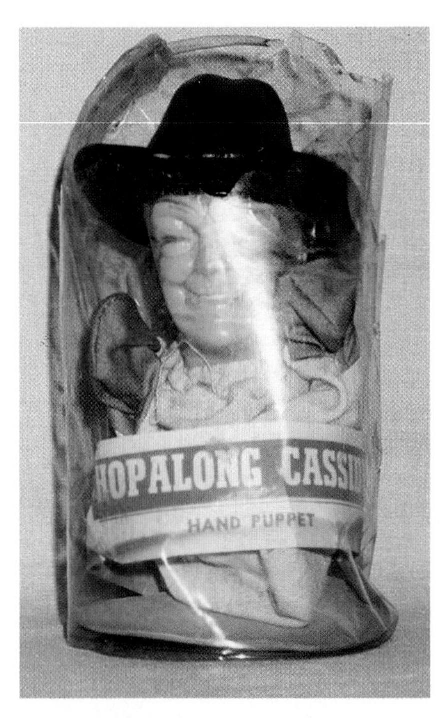

Hoppy hand puppet (above) has never been removed from clear plastic bag. Rare NOS (new old stock) item. #1. $425. From the Phil Ellis Collection. If it has a body design (R) add $125.

The most common Hoppy felt hand puppet is pictured above right, adjacent to Marx toy rocker. Puppet on right is very rare version showing body outline. #1. $350 #2. $275 #3. $225. (without box) From the Jon & Charlie Cheek collection.

Display of three versions of the more common Hoppy hand puppets (below) from the Jon and Charlie Cheek collection. Note face coloration differences. trim and hand configurations. #1. $275. #2. $250 #3. $200.

Hoppy puppets came in a variety of shapes and sizes: hand puppets, marionettes and "stringless" marionettes. Shown on the left is a rare "stringless" marionette with original box. #1. $850 #2. $700 #3. $600. Deduct $250 without box.

Puppet at right is an extremely rare full marionette. Only a few of these are known to exist. #1. $1,300 #2. $1,200 #3. $950. Deduct $300 without box. Very few are found with original box which is similar to "stringless" box shown on left. Look in "Miscelleanous" chapter for a late arrival shown with box from collector Lee Mitchell. The one shown here is from Jon Cheek.

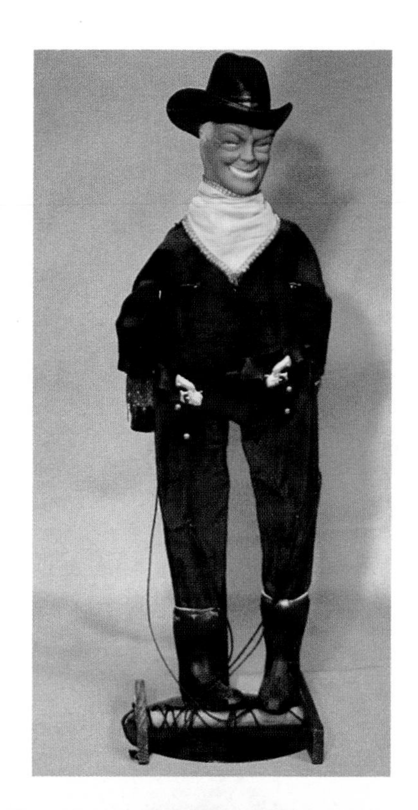

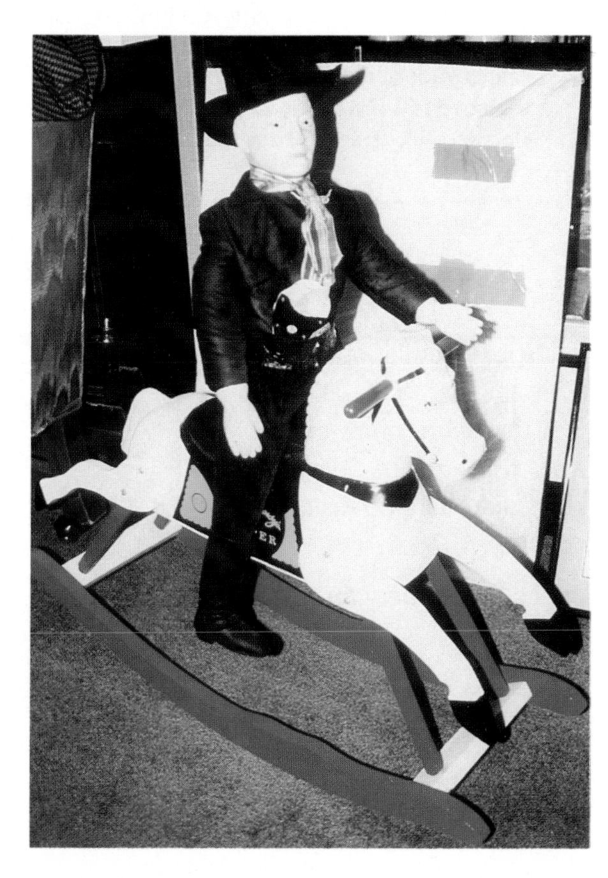

Unusual doll display; large Hoppy cloth and fabric doll on small "running" Hoppy rocker.

View of "stringless" marionette. From the Jon and Charlie Cheek collection.

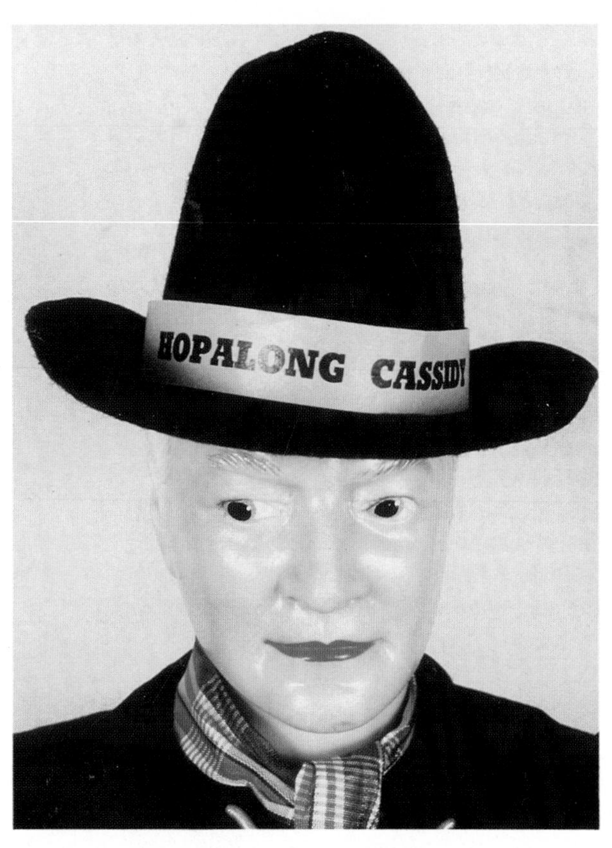

From the Ted Hake collection

Either small or large size Hoppy dolls add dimension to any collection. The doll's gun (below) is most often missing followed by the badge and the belt buckle. For some reason, values of both doll sizes are similar. #1. $970 #2. $835 #3. $750. Deduct $150 if no hat, $200 without vest, $75 for buckle, gun, star or neck slider. From the Jon Cheek collection.

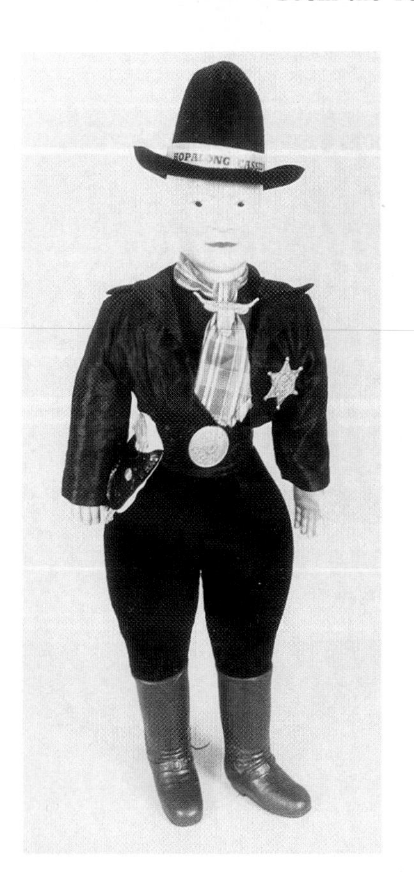

Some of the large Hoppy dolls sported a Hoppy name band on the hat (L) and had life-like facial features that were quite distinctively "Hoppy," down to the blue eyes and white hair. Neckerchief material was usually a red, white and blue plaid.

From the Ted Hake, Hake's Americana Auctions.

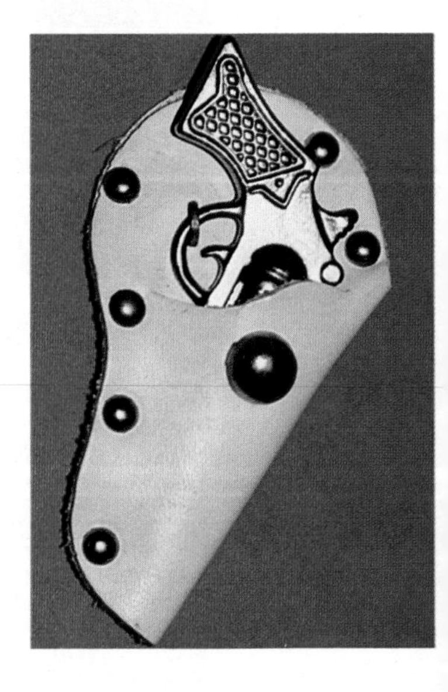

Hoppy metal "clicker" rifle is difficult to find in general, and nearly impossible in the better conditions. #1. $1,000 #2. $850 #3. $700 From the Jon and Charlie Cheek collection.

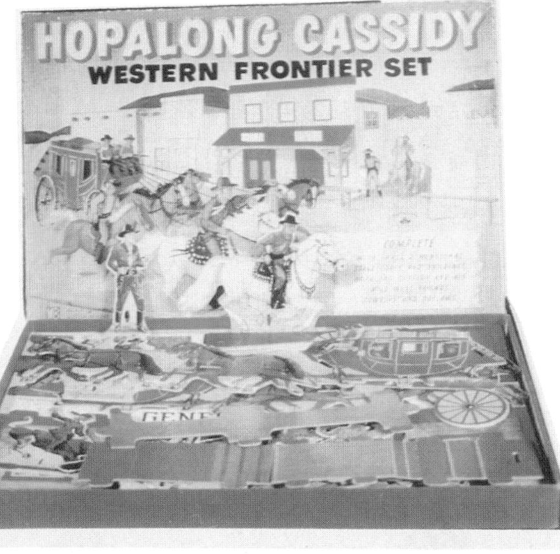

: Hoppy "Western Frontier Set" had a lot of play ıe in its numerous cardboard pieces and is hard to l in good condition. #1. $950 #2. $750 #3. $600.

Controversial Hoppy "baby face" doll that looks more like a plush toy is the genuine Hoppy article. Doll comes with distinctive chaps and vest. #1. $725 #2. $650 #3. $550). With box, add $200). From the Jon and Charlie Cheek collection.

The Hoppy 5 piece rubber gym set is still a collectors favorite, even though the item is somewhat pricey. There are only eight known to exist. #1. $1,475 #2. $1,225 #3. $900. From the Ron Pieczkowski collection.

The Hoppy drum was sold separately from the "Big Chief" Indian outfit, and is hard to find with the original skin intact. Drums had full color different Hoppy images on each side. #1. $425 #2. $375 #3. $300. Deduct $150 if the skin is not original. From the Jon & Charlie Cheek collection.

The two Hoppy felt pennants pictured above came in size lengths from 14" to 30" with the two designs shown. #1. $75 #2. $60 #3. $50. Larger sizes are worth 20% more.

Hoppy metal figures (3") with guns drawn came from Tiempo of England, but were not part of a set. #1. $45 #2. $30 #3. $20

Hoppy owned part of Cole Bros, Circus for several years, and would often make a guest appearance. Kids could buy a memento felt 28" banner. #1. $240 #2. $175 #3. $120 (also came in blue and purple).

Hoppy staff mounted pennant with bell. #1. $200 #2. $175 #3. $125.

Controversial Hoppy guitar with warranty. They are a genuine article. There is no box. #1. $550 #2.. $475 #3. $425

The elusive "Chuckwagon Garden" will turn collectors green if they don't have one. It is very rare! It actually grew grass! #1. $925 #2. $800 #3. $725. Empty package is worth $225.

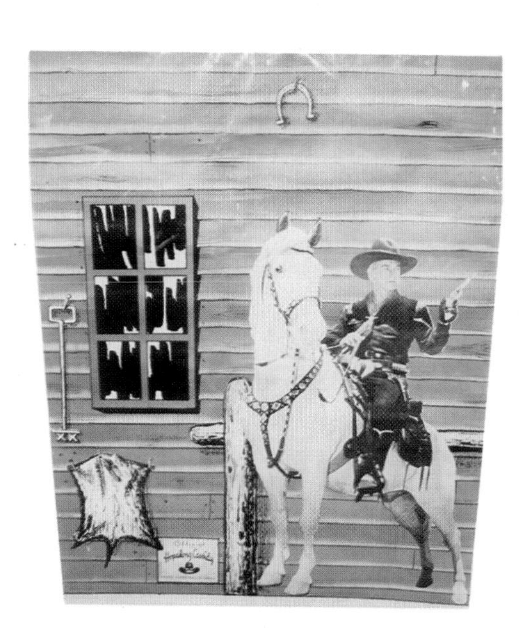

Side panel view (L) of the Hoppy "Western Ranch Playhouse" which was made of heavy paper. From the Dennis Smith collection.

Detail of "Hoppy" image tooled on pony saddle guard.

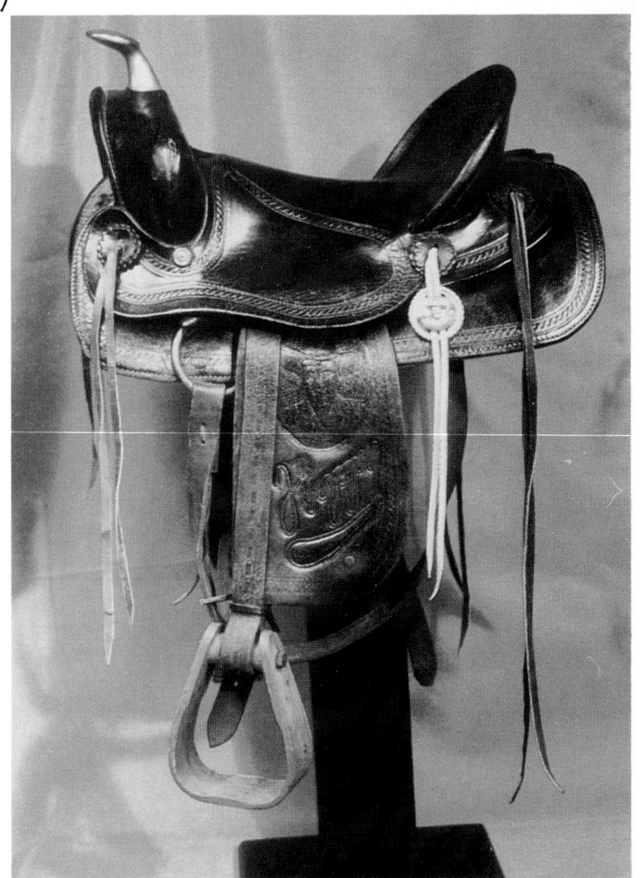
The plain black or brown Hoppy pony saddle (above) was not a "grand prize" contest saddle, but in all likelihood came from Hoppyland Amusement park where it was used on hundreds of ponies. #1. $3,500 #2. $2,800 #3. $2,300. From the Jon and Charlie Cheek collection

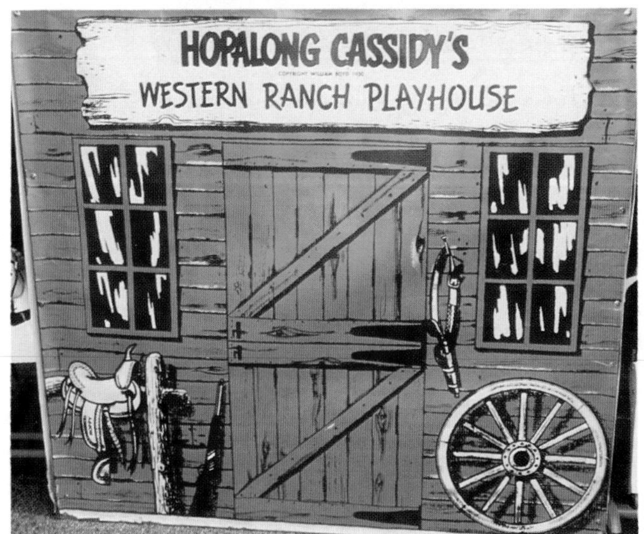

Graphic of front of "Western Ranch Playhouse." There were four panels. #1. $1,300 #2. $1,200 #3. $1,050 Deduct $200 if no tube container. Single panels sell for $200 each in #3. condition.

Hoppy metal fishing pole & reel. Only six are known to exist. Thought to have come in round metal container, but none found to date. #1. $1,400 #2.. $1,200 #3. $1,000 (without metal container). From the Lee Davidson collection.

Controversial Hoppy metal hand-cuffs. Has Hoppy stamped on each cuff but no manufacturer name. May very well be genuine as age and design match 1950's. From the Ron Johnson collection.

Hoppy sleeping bag w/ snap liner from Arnes Harris Nevile Co. #1. $650 #2. $500 #3. $400. Top photo shows it in its packaged form.

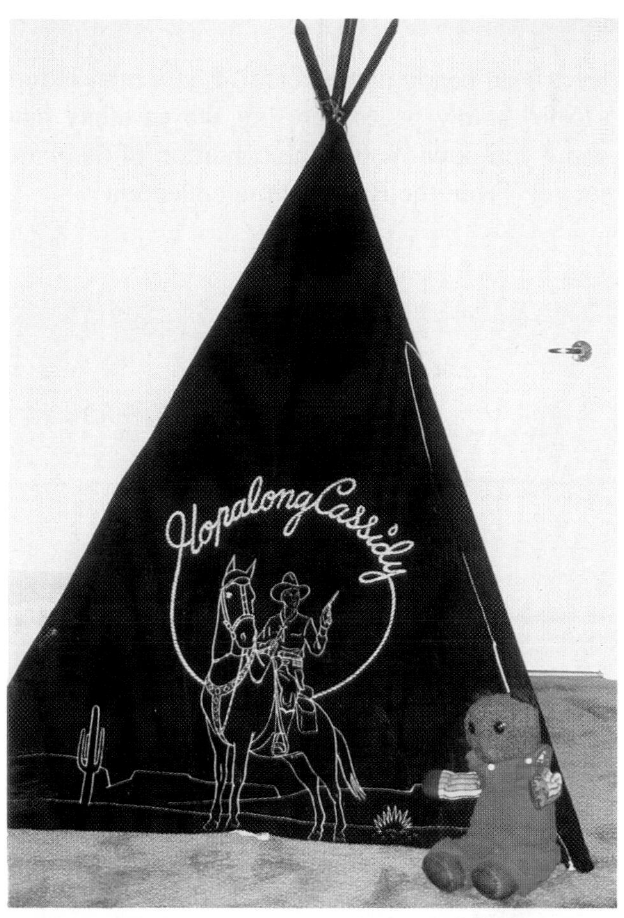

One of the rarest Hoppy collectables is the "Indian-style" tent pictured above. There are so few known to exist that a market value also doesn't exist! Brian Beirne, a popular Los Angeles disc jockey, had a Hoppy tent when a child and when his wife purchased this tent as a birthday surprise, Brian is positive that due to a particular stain and a broken tent pole, it is the same tent he had when a boy! Could this be possible? Brian is sure of it! An investment value item, the Hoppy tent is estimated to be worth $2,500.

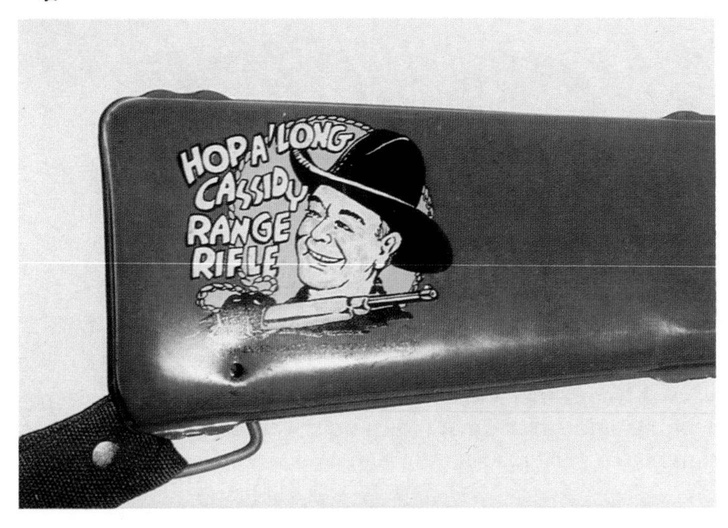

It may have been nearly impossible to find a mint Hoppy "Range Rifle" a few pages ago, but we certainly have one to show you now! Notice the condition of the water decal (above). From the Brian Beirne collection.

Another rare Hoppy item, and the rarest of the hand-puppets is this latex version with neckerchief & slide, gun set and removable hat. The facial expression of the puppet is also quite unique. An "investment value" item, the puppet has an estimated value of $1,500. From the Jon & Charlie Cheek collection.

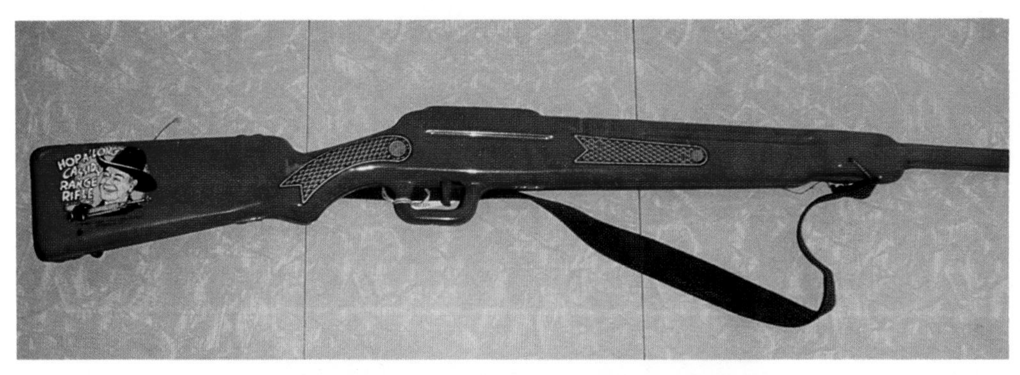

To the left, are two different versions of the Tiempo (made in England) cast-metal Hoppy & Topper. The figure on the right is from the Tiempo "Western Series" set (not shown) which contains riders and their mounts. The figure to the left is also marked "Tiempo" but its origin is unknown. From the Jon & Charlie Cheek collection.

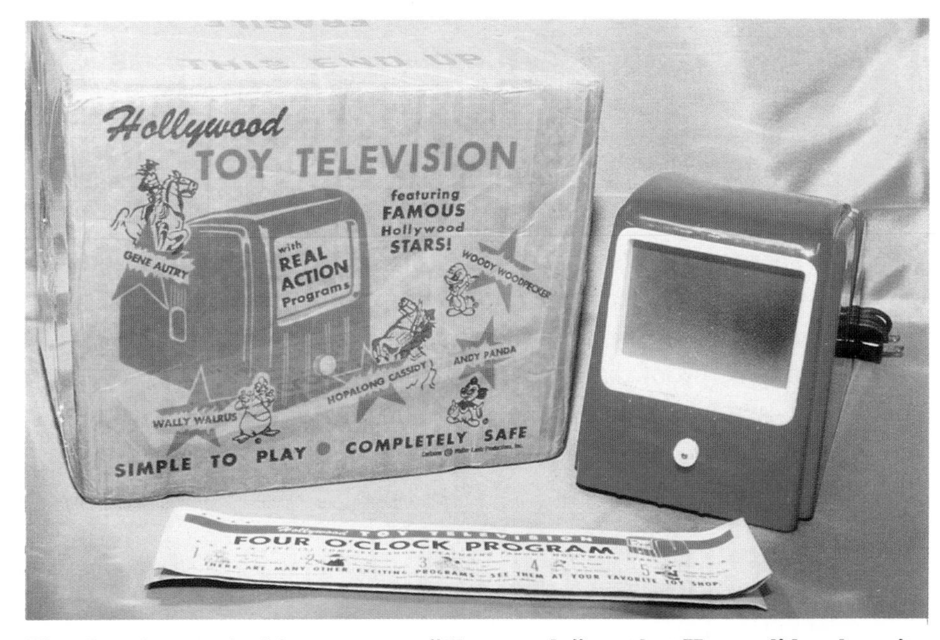

The electric toy television was not a "Hoppy only" toy, but Hoppy did endorse it. The TV came with several "action programs" including one from Hoppy. #1. $375 #2. $320 #3. $270. Deduct $200 without box. From the Jon & Charlie Cheek collection.The dealer ad (L) is from the Brian Beirne collection.

This pristine shooting gallery includes a perfect box, instructions and pellets in original envelope. From the Sharon and Lee Mitchell collection.

The Hoppy fishing pole (R) is a "marbled" version of the one shown on an earlier page. The red reel is also different. The values are the same as the black version: $1,400 in #1. condition. From the Jon & Charlie Cheek collection.

The watch shown (L) is a toy plastic Hoppy watch that is both unique and very rare. The band is similar to the wrist compass. The watch was not designed to work. #1. $500 #2. $425 #3. $385. From the Jon & Charlie Cheek collection.

TOY ADS & PROMOTIONS

#1. condition: mint, showing no use #2. condition: excellent to near mint #3. condition: good to very good

There were over 2,400 licensed Hoppy products and thousands of ads and promotions to sell them. Collecting Hoppy paper products (and ads and promotions) is a high priority for many collectors. The ads on this page show how rare some of these products are, give us graphic proof that they did exist, and probably still do so. Values of paper products will be shown where they are known.

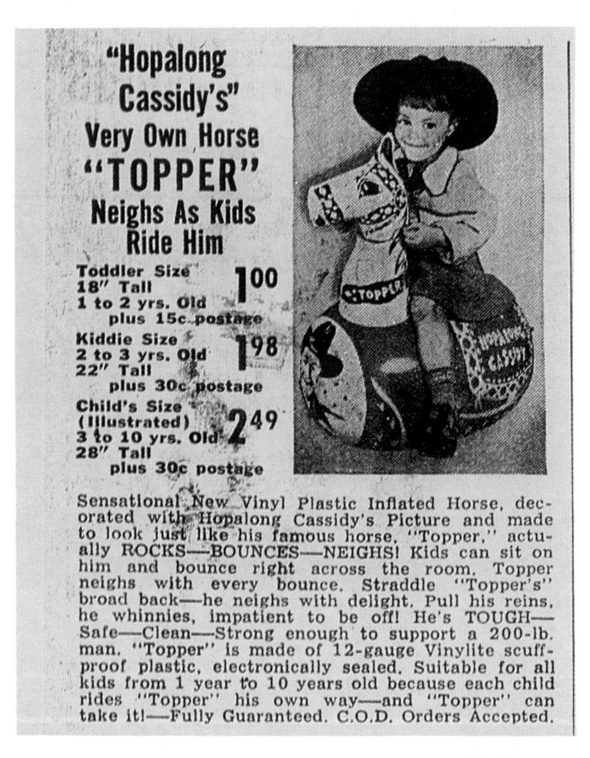

"Hopalong Cassidy's"
Very Own Horse
"TOPPER"
Neighs As Kids Ride Him
Toddler Size 18" Tall 1 to 2 yrs. Old plus 15c postage 1.00
Kiddie Size 2 to 3 yrs. Old 22" Tall plus 30c postage 1.98
Child's Size (Illustrated) 3 to 10 yrs. Old 28" Tall plus 30c postage 2.49
Sensational New Vinyl Plastic Inflated Horse, decorated with Hopalong Cassidy's Picture and made to look just like his famous horse, "Topper," actually ROCKS—BOUNCES—NEIGHS! Kids can sit on him and bounce right across the room. Topper neighs with every bounce. Straddle "Topper's" broad back—he neighs with delight. Pull his reins, he whinnies, impatient to be off! He's TOUGH—Safe—Clean—Strong enough to support a 200-lb. man. "Topper" is made of 12-gauge Vinylite scuff-proof plastic, electronically sealed. Suitable for all kids from 1 year to 10 years old because each child rides "Topper" his own way—and "Topper" can take it!—Fully Guaranteed. C.O.D. Orders Accepted.

Neighing inflatable Topper toy ad. Size and design are very different from those shown in book, or known in collector's circles. Quite unique, and none are known to exist. From the Gene Douglass/M. Saxen collection.

Topper vinyl 54" wading pool ad. The Topper pool plays music, comes with a shower and repair kit. None are known to exist. From the Gary Nichols collection.

Young cowboys can run and gallop with inflatable horse when taking off over the hills after rustlers. Shoulder strap holds featherweight horse at youngster's waistline. Red plastic bridle goes over Topper's nose. Black-trimmed white *Inflatable Topper*, $3.95, ppd. Artisan Galleries, Fort Dodge, Iowa.

12/50 Better Homes & Gardens

Inflatable Topper came in several versions including the "donut" shape which was worn (see "Toys" chapter). This ad was sent to us by Terry Klepey.

BIG AS LIFE—well . . . as tall as a card table, anyway—stands Topper. And astride him sits his beloved Master, Hoppy Himself. Made of full-round, three-dimensional molded rubber, lacquered in natural colors, figure is breakproof, chip-proof, weatherproof. Wonderful for a window display, dentist office, boy's club, milk bar, it's 26" long, 31" high. $59.95 f.o.b. Mold-Craft Co., 3727 N. Palmer, Milwaukee, Wis.

31" high molded rubber Hoppy on giant Topper is another unique ad. From Mold-Craft Company, this supposedly indestructible product is not known to exist. From the Gene Douglass/M. Saxen collection.

"Hopalong Cassidy" Fountain Pen National Dealer-Theatre Tie-Ups

First of a series of "Hopalong Cassidy" merchandise tieups that will continue through all subsequent "Hopalong Cassidy" releases is the "Hopalong Cassidy" fountain-pen. This pen bears the signature of William Boyd and of "Hopalong Cassidy" and is the type of merchandise that kids everywhere will go for.

The pen is manufactured and distributed nationally by Salz Bros., Inc., 44 West 28th Street, New York City, and retails at popular prices. A big merchandising campaign has been scheduled by the manufacturer to put the item across. Everywhere dealers will be ready to cooperate with theatres showing the "Hopalong Cassidy" pictures. Included in the campaign is the cutout counter-card illustrated above. The pens will be displayed in the dark area in the lower left-hand corner. A booklet on lariat-throwing will go with each pen, thus making them even more attractive to kids.

Contact Salz Bros. direct for names of local dealers handling the item. The pens and the accompanying booklets on lariat-throwing will make ideal prizes in lassoing contests, knot-tying contests and other contests of the sort in connection with the showing of the picture. The manufacturer will advise managers of special prices on the item for this use.

Perhaps the rareist of the rare, is this 1935 ad for Hoppy fountain pens to promote the first film. The pens do exist! From the Gene Douglass/M. Saxen collection.

Unusual Hoppy bust made from heavy cardboard. Not known what it was used for. From the Ted Hake, Hake's Americana Auction. No value given.

Contest ad to win many Hoppy products. From "Who's Who in Western Stars" magazine, 1954. From the Mike Merryman collection.

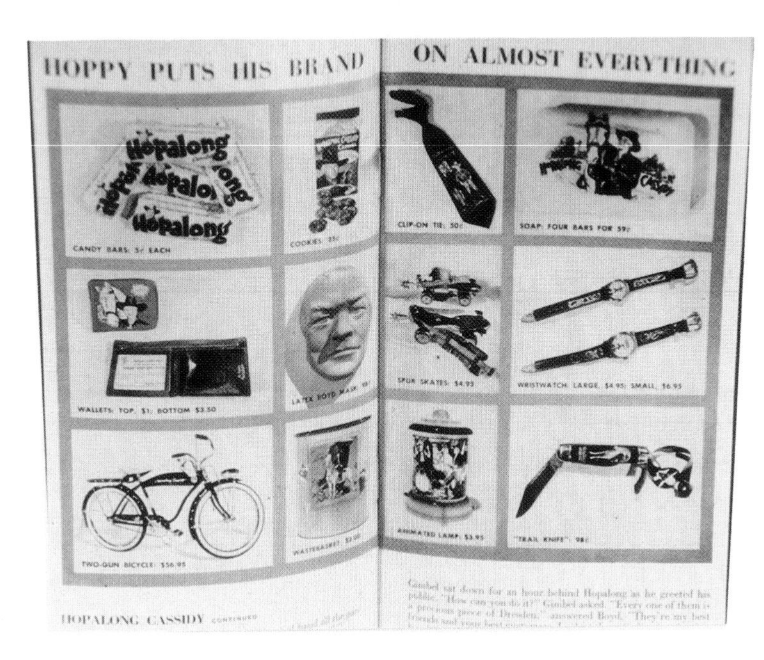

June 12, 1950 Life Magazine Hoppy article shows many products. Magazine has Hoppy on cover and sells for $50 to $75.

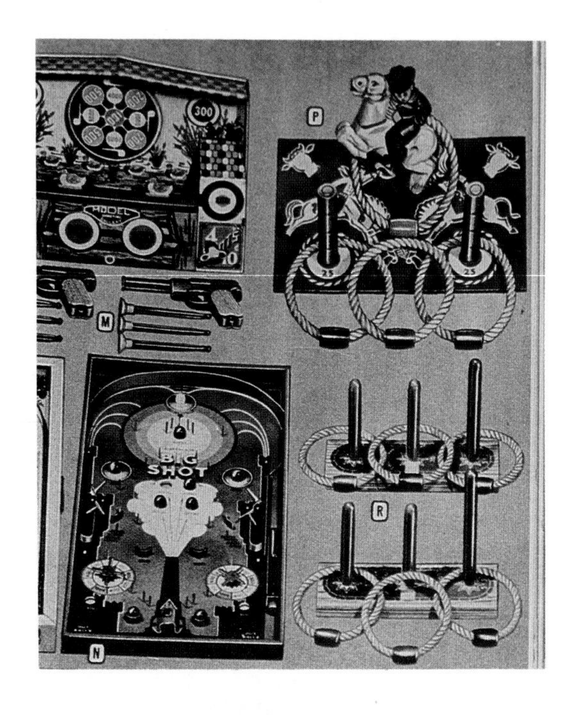

Hoppy ring-toss game was featured, along with many other items, in many catalogs and magazines. The one above is from a 1951 Wards catalog.

Contest rules, entry blanks and prize selections were a part of the "eight prizes" contest in "Western Stars" magazine. This June issue is worth $30. in "fair" condition. From the Mike Merryman collection.

A popular Hoppy products ad was for outfits and clothing. This ad came from Wards in 1952.

Motorola TV ad has also become quite plentiful in past years. Current values are $20 for this great mag. ad.

Which is really "Hopalong Cassidy"..?

Batteries also look alike but AUTO-LITE STA-FUL

NEEDS WATER ONLY 3 TIMES A YEAR!

AUTO-LITE sta-ful

Battery ads from major era magazines are quite plentiful. They sell for $10 to $15. Ads like these make a great wall display.

Saturday Evening Post magazine ran full color Acme boot ads. Valued at: $20.

Two-page Hoppy Gift Round-up Christmas ad is very popular to collectors. Values range between $40 - $65. Saddle bag candy ad (L) was a dealer ad with quantity prices. A nice find for: $50 to $75. From the Mike Forthun collection.

Magnetic Hoppy dart game promotion pages to dealers is a difficult find. There are hundreds of similar dealer program pages on most Hoppy products. The trick is to find them! There are no values or price records available for this promotion set, but I would venture to guess that these two pieces would be worth $80.

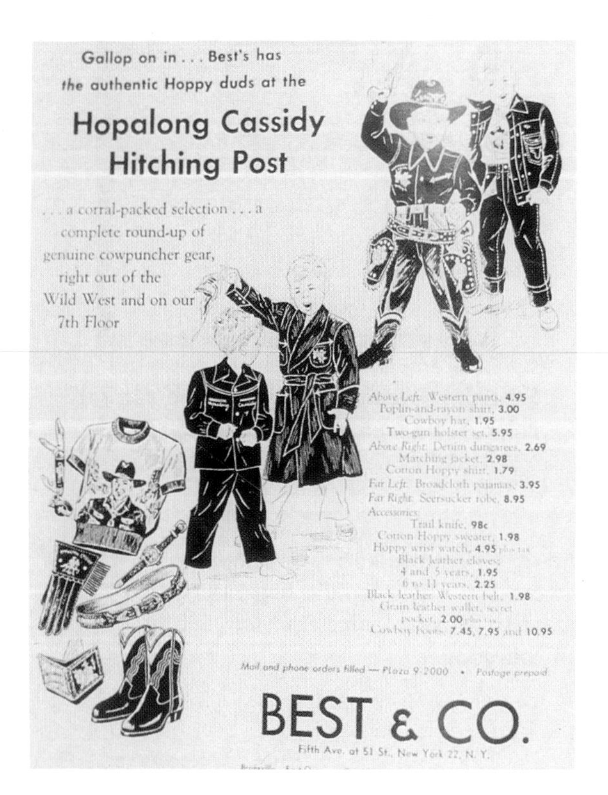

Inside pages of dart game promotion

Hoppy clothing ad from Best, Co. shows Hoppy pajamas and bathrobe, two super rare items that few, if any, have seen. Ad is from the James McLoughlin collection.

above pictured Hoppy tent ad is almost as rare as the tent! There are only two tents known to exist. This ad from n's Hardware store is a nice display of both the sleeping and the Hoppy tent. Ad value is : $100.

Reproduced thermos ad and store display sign is nearly 24" and makes a nice wall display. They are available nationally for $10 to $20 each.

Cardboard Hoppy frame store counter top promotion display that includes a 5x7" photo process. Nice die-cut promo piece. #1. $175 #2. $145 #3, $100. From the Phil Ellis collection.

Poster-sized ad for Colorado Sage calogne. This 1970's ad resulted in a major lawsuit against company. They did not obtain rights to do it. #1. $150 #2. $ 125 #3. $95.

Scoot Had Saved His Money For A Hopalong Suit

Even a few Hoppy books of the 1950's carried subtle buying signals like the one on the left which was printed in England. (see "Books" chapter).

Two magazine page ads(R) show the impact of the Hoppy rage of the 1950's. Ads like this are available and plentiful at $10 each.

This wide variety of newspaper, magazine and catalog ads for socks to television sets show the power of the Hoppy endorsement. Finding the ad for a memorabilia item you have makes a nice display. From the Richard Stevens collection.

Many advanced Hoppy collectors research ads such as these to identify Hoppy products to search for, or to date year of manufacture.

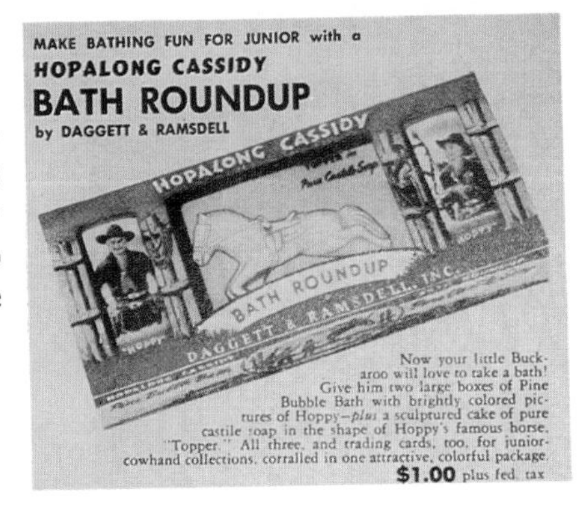

Hoppy paper "popper" gun was a promotion for his Capitol Records albums and singles. Gun is very collectible and there are only a few left. #1. $175. #2. $150 #3. $120.

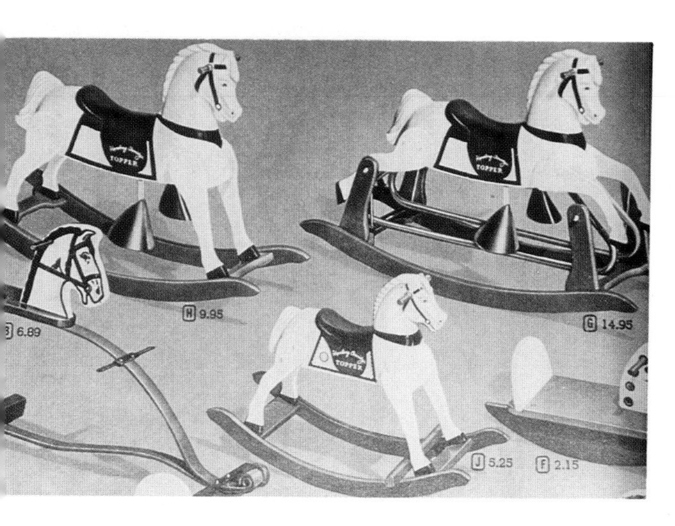

Wards catalog shows several versions of Topper "rock-
Notice large "glider" upper right.

ls catalogs often ran half-page Hoppy products ads. Circa 1952

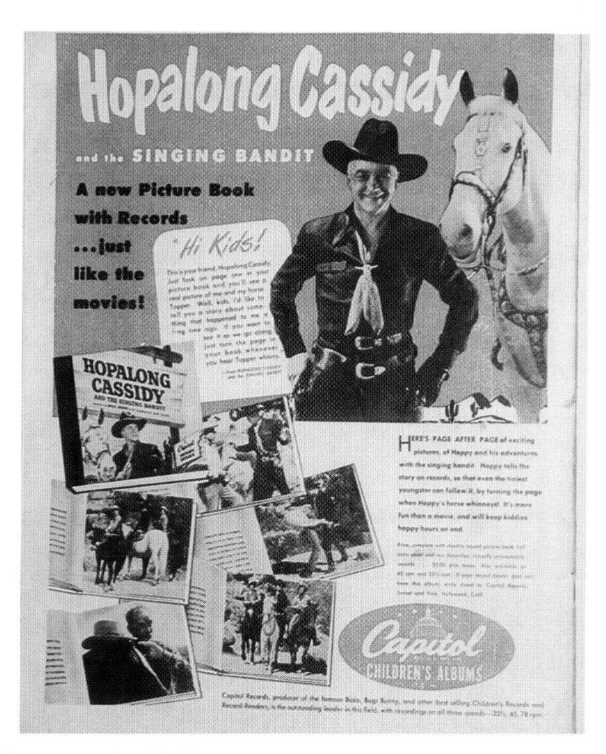

Store ad for "Singing Bandit" album from Capitol Records. Ad is worth $35. From the Mike Forthun collection.

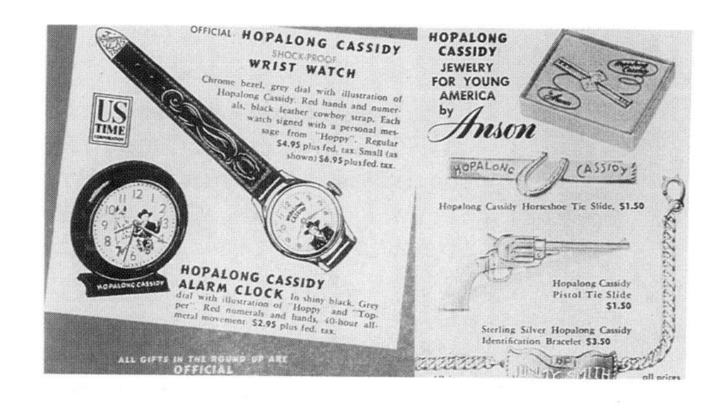

1952 ads show watch & strap design and jewelry made. Rare six-gun tie slide is also shown in "Jewelry" chapter.

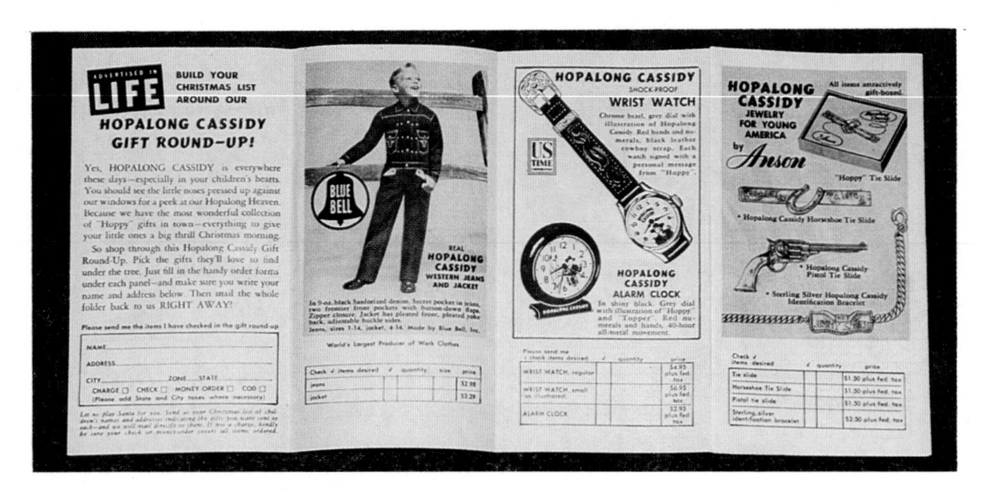

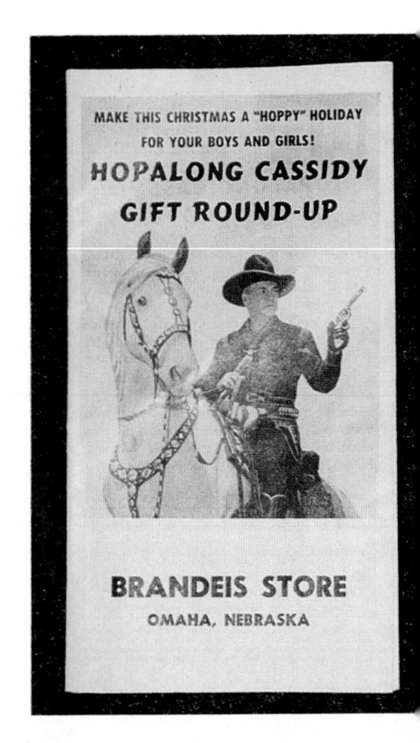

Exclusive Hoppy products Christmas brochures were directed toward the practical side of parents by the listings they enclosed: jewelry, watches, clothes. Note the impossible to find "Slick-Up Kit" (below) which is the rarest toiletries product sought by collectors today. What is one worth? There are several open orders from collectors for $2,500 for a complete set.

Special in-store Hoppy promotio and ads (above) are very collec ible. The Brandies Store Christm brochure is valued at $75 in # condition.

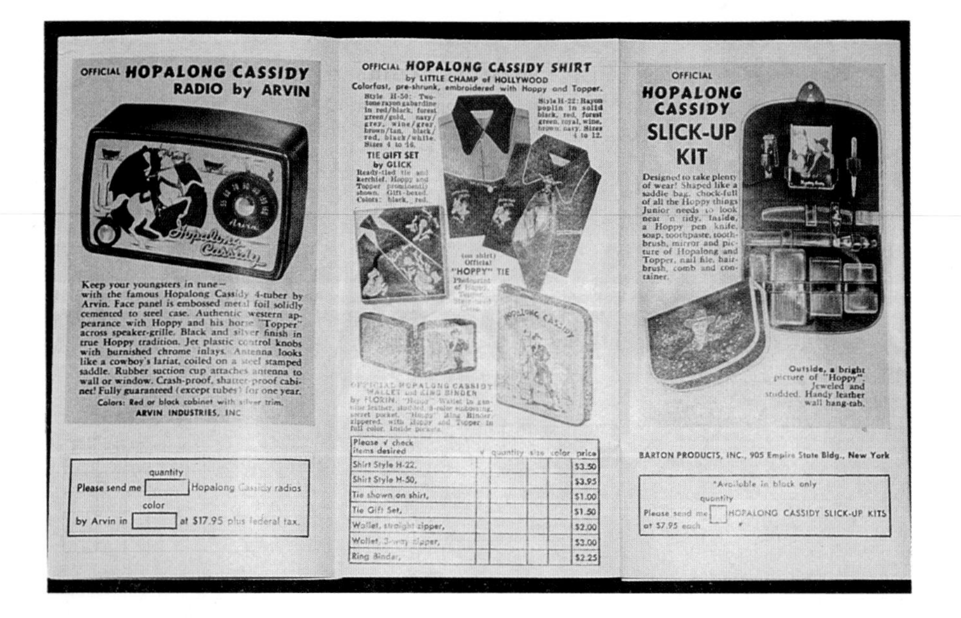

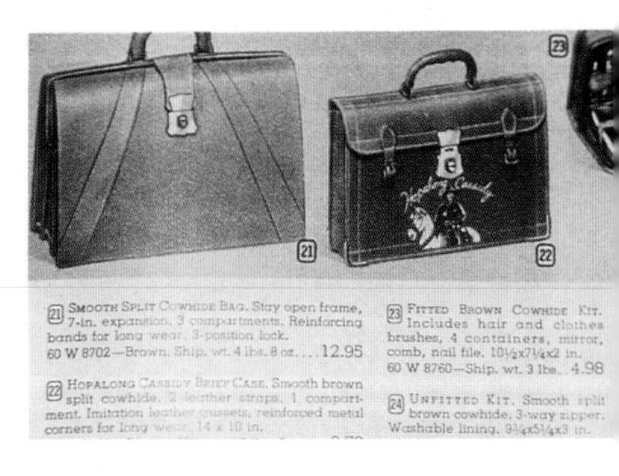

The Hoppy leather briefcase is shown i a 1951 Wards catalog for $3.79. It wa advertised in the "men's" section next t business briefcases. This case today i worth $400 in #1 condition.

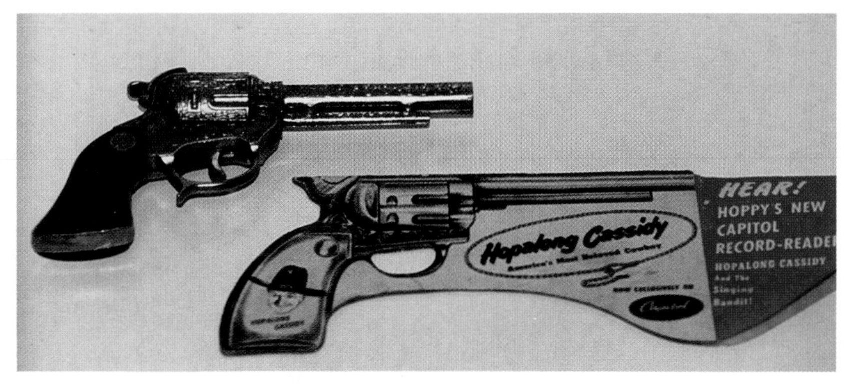

Display of Capitol "popper" gun and Wyndotte cap pistol for size.

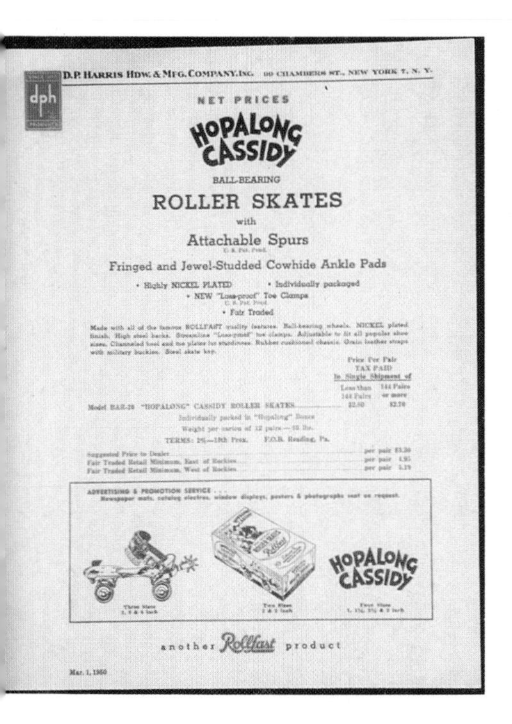

D.P. HARRIS HDW. & MFG. COMPANY, INC. 99 CHAMBERS ST., NEW YORK 7, N. Y.

NET PRICES

HOPALONG CASSIDY

BALL-BEARING

ROLLER SKATES

with

Attachable Spurs

U. S. Pat. Pend.

Fringed and Jewel-Studded Cowhide Ankle Pads

- Highly NICKEL PLATED
- Individually packaged
- NEW "Lose-proof" Toe Clamps (U. S. Pat. Pend.)
- Fair Traded

Made with all of the famous ROLLFAST quality features. Ball-bearing wheels. NICKEL plated finish. High steel backs. Streamline "Lose-proof" toe clamps. Adjustable to fit all popular shoe sizes. Channeled heel and toe plates for sturdiness. Rubber cushioned chassis. Grain leather straps with military buckles. Steel skate key.

Price Per Pair
TAX PAID
In Single Shipment of

	Less than 144 Pairs	144 Pairs or more
Model RAR-20 "HOPALONG" CASSIDY ROLLER SKATES	[illegible]	[illegible]

Individually packed in "Hopalong" Boxes

TERMS: 2%—10th Prox. F.O.B. Reading, Pa.

ADVERTISING & PROMOTION SERVICE . . .
Newspaper mats, catalog electros, window displays, posters & photographs sent on request.

HOPALONG CASSIDY

another Rollfast product

er sales letter for carrying Rollfast Hoppy es (see "Toys" chapter).

Wards catalog often had many children models dressed in Hoppy outfits and clothes. A great help for collectors who want to know what clothes were produced and when.

Unique Hoppy flyer to help promote sales and interest in his comic strips also mentions both the TV and radio shows. Flyers are valued at $45 to $60 each.

Hoppy calenders can be found in all sizes, shapes and designs. They are not very easy to find, however, and are a collectors premium item. They do make a great framed wall display.

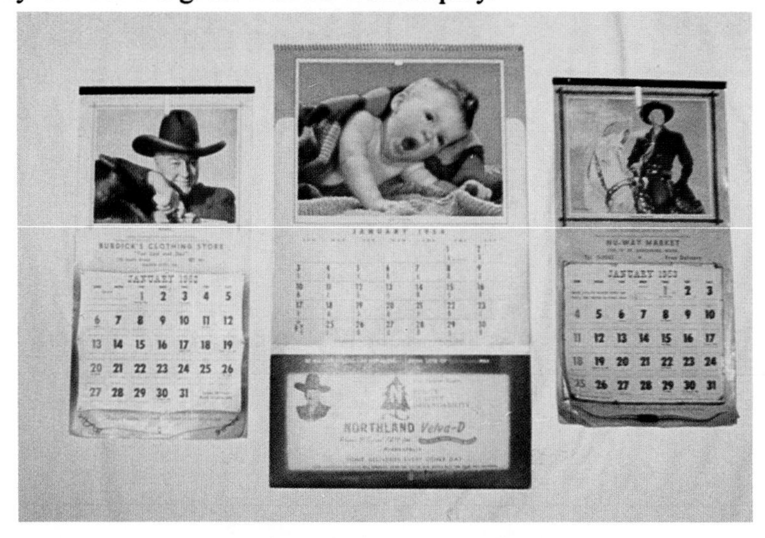

Calenders range in value from $75 to $250 depending on uniqueness.

Calenders above, are complete and in mint condition but they are "standard" designs. Expect to pay $125 in this condition.

VIEWERS AND FILMS

#1. condition: mint, showing no use #2. condition: excellent to near mint #3. condition: good to very good

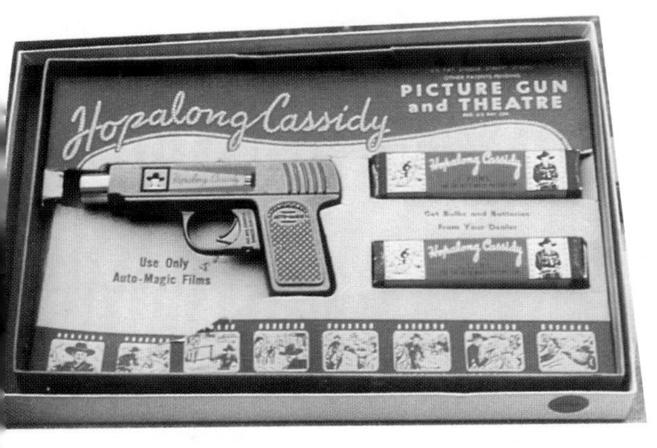

icture Gun Theatre boxed viewer set with folded ardboard to turn box into a "theatre." From the John bramson collection.

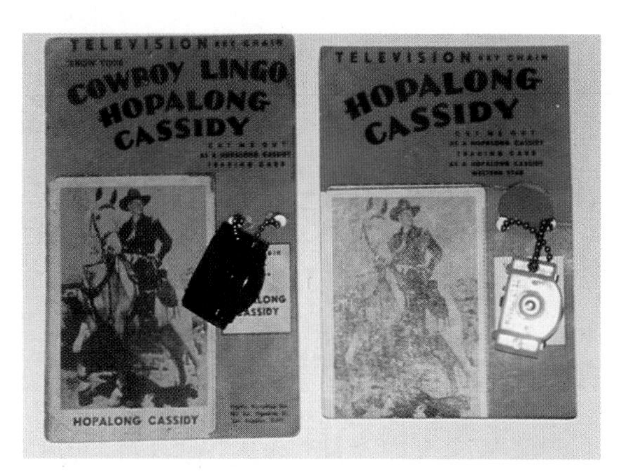

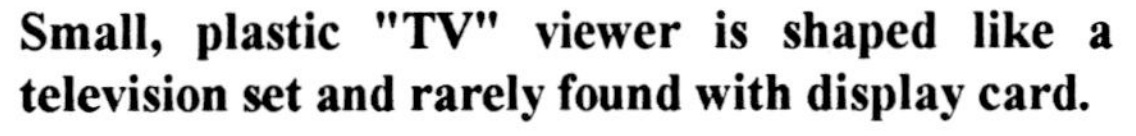

Small, plastic "TV" viewer is shaped like a television set and rarely found with display card.

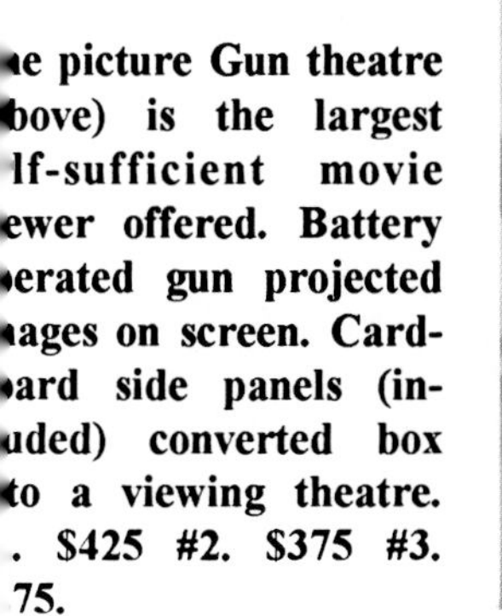

e picture Gun theatre bove) is the largest lf-sufficient movie ewer offered. Battery erated gun projected ages on screen. Card-ard side panels (in-uded) converted box to a viewing theatre. . $425 #2. $375 #3. 75.

Viewer assortment display from the Jon & Charlie Cheek collection

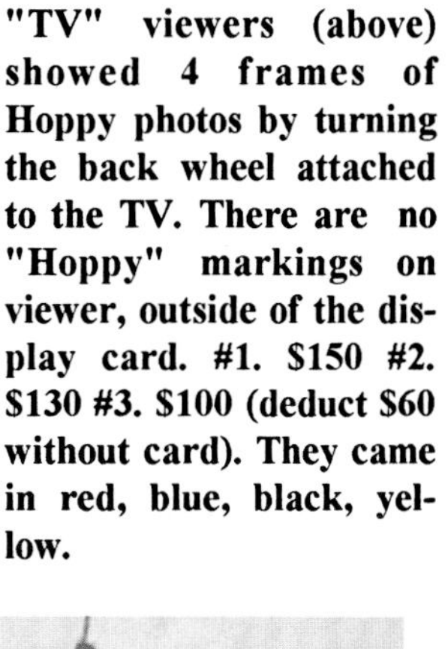

"TV" viewers (above) showed 4 frames of Hoppy photos by turning the back wheel attached to the TV. There are no "Hoppy" markings on viewer, outside of the display card. #1. $150 #2. $130 #3. $100 (deduct $60 without card). They came in red, blue, black, yellow.

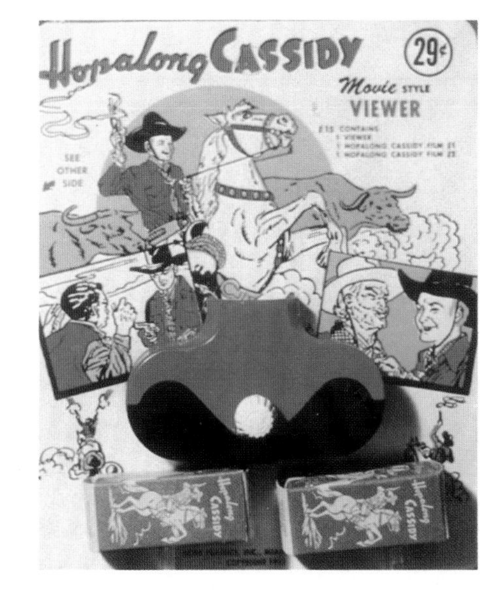

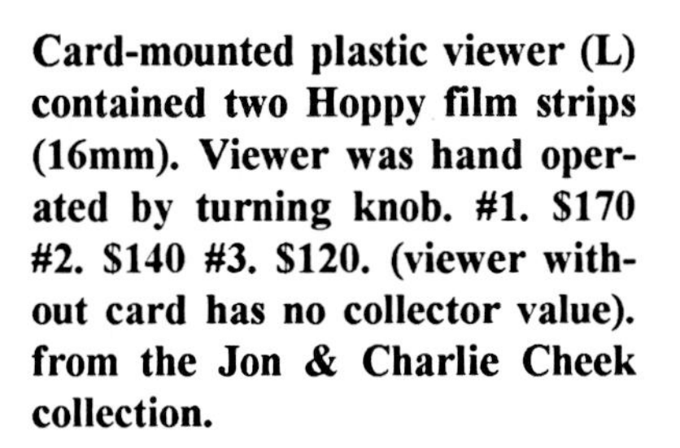

Card-mounted plastic viewer (L) contained two Hoppy film strips (16mm). Viewer was hand operated by turning knob. #1. $170 #2. $140 #3. $120. (viewer without card has no collector value). from the Jon & Charlie Cheek collection.

"Jumbo" Hoppy viewer (r) claims 35mm film viewing with new subjects. It is priced at 49 cents. Has one film in viewer and another in box (shown). #1. $250 #2. $200 #3. $175. From the Jon & Charlie Cheek collection.

Boxed set Hoppy film viewers are very rare and an in-demand item for most collectors. Pictured above is viewer A which is a 16mm viewer with 4 film boxes. It is an earlier version of viewer C shown to the right: #1. $450 #2. $375 #3. $325 (valued only with box). Viewer B (upper right) had a fully closing box lid and itself, was an early version. It only contained two boxes of film: #1. $400 #2. $325 #3. $275 (valued only with box). Viewers A & B are from the Jon & Charlie Cheek collection.

There are an unknown amount of numbered boxed film loops (16mm) that will fit several of the Hoppy viewers. The boxed are distinctive, with Hoppy on each. Boxed film loops have been selling for $25-$35 per box.

The cardboard 35mm Hoppy film viewer (L) is both a rare and controversial item. It is genuine. The film came stored inside the box, and was inserted and fed by hand by pulling on the bottom of the strip. There were only 2,000 of these viewers produced for retail sales. There are only five known to exist: #1. $150 #2. $120 #3. $100.

Early Hoppy 8mm. retail films were offered by Castle Films in a generic box. Castle later introduced the "Hoppy" box. generic box Hoppy films are: $35-$50 in #1 condition.

The man who produced the "Hollywood" viewer was a very close friend of the author, who recently passed on. Gene Lester was a great Hollywood photographer who was instrumental in the discovery of Marilyn Monroe and many others. Gene had his studio next to Bill Boyd's office in downtown Hollywood. Gene even did the photo story of Hoppy & Grace for Saturday Evening Post (1947) which bears his photo credits. He taught the author professional photography and was his mentor, but was always a man with good business sense. Due to his relationship with Bill Boyd, Gene was able to obtain the "rights" to produce this little viewer. He obtained a small contract with a national five-and-dime chain and sold them 2,000. Several hundred others sat in his garage, were damaged by rain and destroyed. Some of the film strips may exist however, I am trying to find them. J. Caro

Castle Films produced Hoppy retail projection quality 16mm films in 100 foot reels and 400' reels, generally, but a few 1,000' reels (1/2 hour) are rumored to exist. 100' reels are widely available with different titles: #1. $45 #2. $30 #3. $20. The 400' reels are more rare: #1. $100 #2. $75 #3. $50. (box included in all values). From the Richard Stevens collection.

Above is a Castle Films catalog which lists Hoppy films in addition to others. Hoppy is on the cover: #1. $75 #2. $50 #3. $25. From the Brian Beirne collection.

Above is shown two 100' reels of the Hoppy film "Bar 20" Rides Again. The only difference is the generic film box. Both films were 8mm, silent. #1. $60 #2. $40 #3. $25.

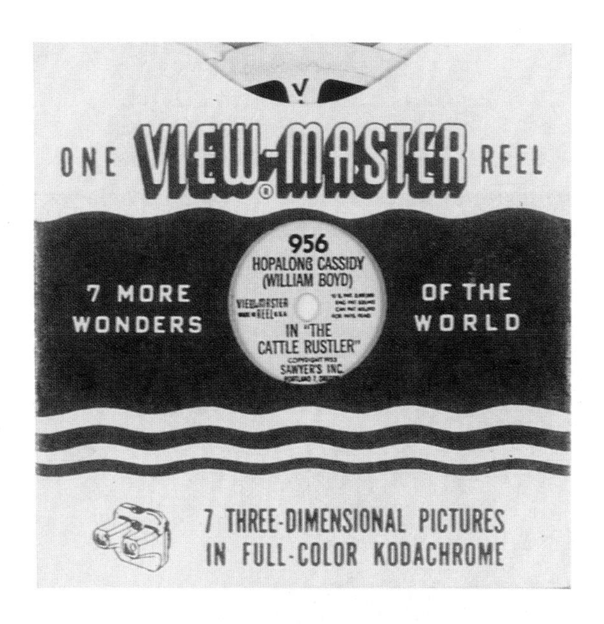

The View-Master reel (above) contains #956 (Hoppy) in the "Cattle Rustler" sequence. There was #955 which was of Hoppy & Topper which can be found everywhere for $20 in the generic sleeve. Note: the photos are in color and a good 3-D version.

View-Master reels shown on the left feature several cowboy stars, especially the "Cowboy Stars" reel that had Hoppy, Gene & Roy plus others. This special reel is valued at $30 with sleeve. From the Brian Beirne collection.

FILM & OTHER PROMOTIONS

#1. condition: mint, showing no use #2. condition: excellent to near mint #3. condition: good to very good

This chapter deals with a potpourri of ads, promotions, articles and other things that I can't find a home for: Hoppy's college and the "Gold Star" children's charity to name just two. Many will feature Hoppy, his films and exhibitor promotions.

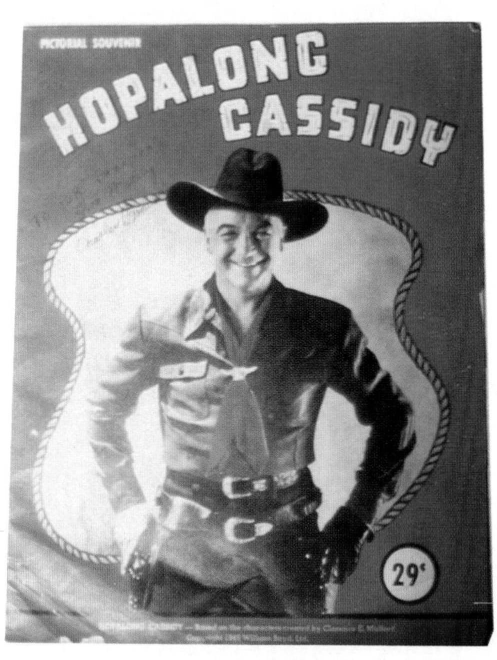

Hoppy pictorial souvenir book (29 cents) is believed to have been sold at the Circus and other events where Hoppy appeared. #1. $125. #2. $90 #3. $70

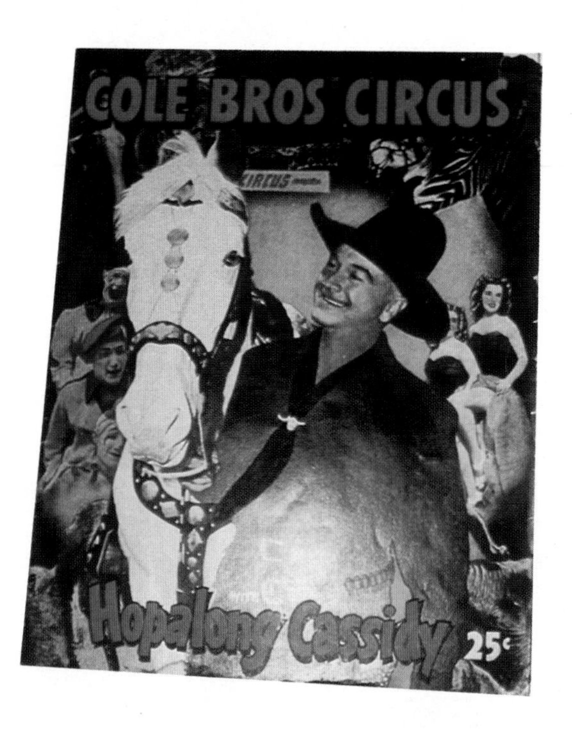

Cole Bros. Circus program with Hoppy on cover is a demand item not easily found. #1. $225 #2. $200 #3. $175.

Dear Friend:
I appreciate your writing for a photograph and do hope you like this one.
I'm happy to tell you we are starting a new series of "Hopalong Cassidy" pictures which will be coming to your favorite theatre soon, the trade mark you see below will appear on the screen and on all lobby displays, please watch for it.
Thanks so much for your loyalty,
Good Luck
William Boyd
"Hopalong"

Fans writing for photographs were sent this letter - photograph in 1948 about "new" Hoppy films and the using of the new Hopalong Cassidy Productions seal on the bottom of lobby cards, etc. This was after Bill Boyd purchased the "rights" to all of the Hoppy films. Item is valued at $30.

Theatre operators 15 page publicity and exploitation manual was designed to promote Hoppy films. A recent "find" has brought the value of this item to $75 in mint or near mint condition.

Rare theatre operators promotion on the advantage and use of Hoppy lobby cards and posters. Notice film is Hoppy's first. Investment value for this item may be $500. From the Gene Douglass, M. Saxen collection.

Satin theatre banner was used to promo early Hoppy films. Gold-fringed banners were hung in key theatre locations prior to, and during showing Hoppy films. Very rare item From the John Rizzo collection. Values are in "Miscellaneous" chapter.

A theatre preview card (R) (4x6") for Forty Thieves was handed out to audiences prior to show. Has empty block for the starting date. Item is considered rare. In some cases, promo was used as a post card as part of a audience mailer. Valued at $35. From the Mike Forthun collection.

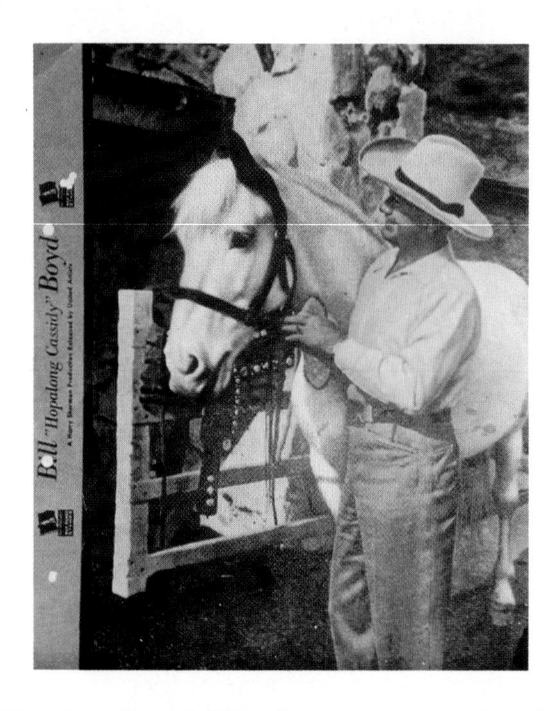

Bill "Hopalong Cassidy" Boyd promotion color flyer for War Bond Stamps during WWII. Came in nearly a dozen poses. #1. $125 #2. $95 #3. $70

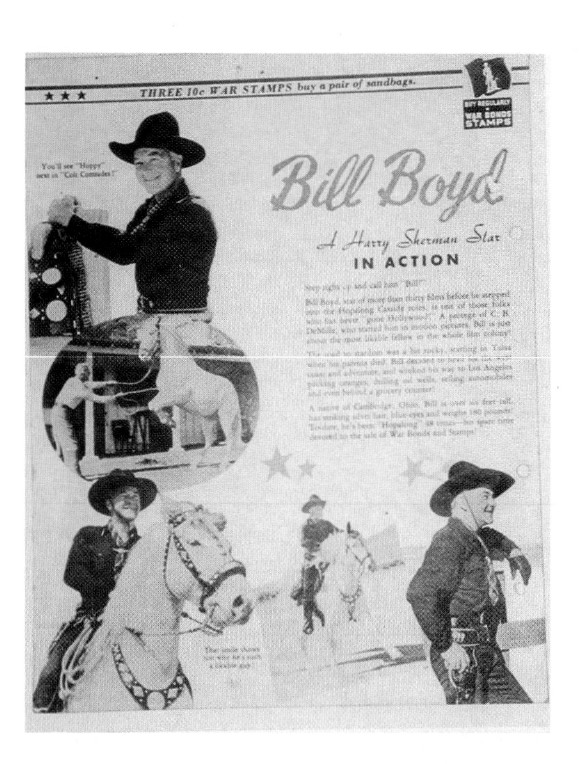

Reverse side of War Bond stamps promo Hoppy page during WWII, calls Bill Boyd a Harry Sherman star. Sherman produced the Hoppy films until 1946. This rare piece is valued at $70 in #2. condition. From the Mike Forthun collection.

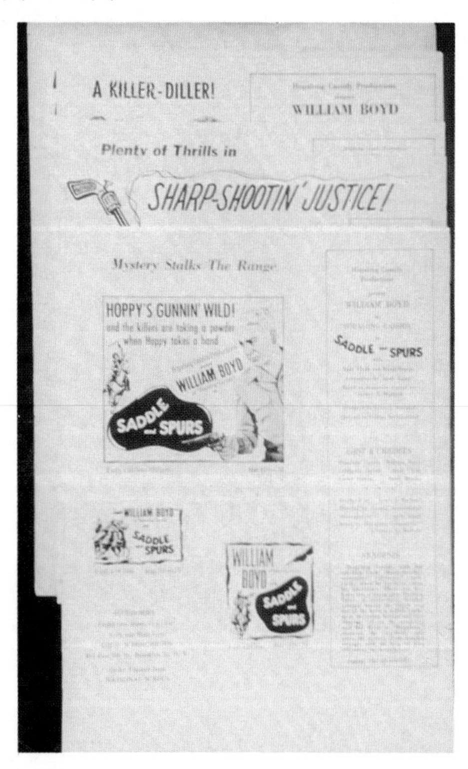

Part of a dialogue continuity kit for theatre operators the kit contained information about each film and ways to advertise. Each contained ad graphics. In #1 condition, they are worth $20 to $25 per page.

Colorful theatre promo flyer contained selling points to show Hoppy films. Sales info. was on reverse side #1. $50 #2. $35 #3. $30.

Rare Hoppy comic strip promotion from the NY Mirror. Enclosed pin stated "Hopalong Cassidy In The Mirror." #1. $175. #2. $140. #3. $100. (including envelope) From the Bill Hoffman collection.

side pages of the 15 page "Publicity & Exploitation" theatre ners manual shown on previous page.

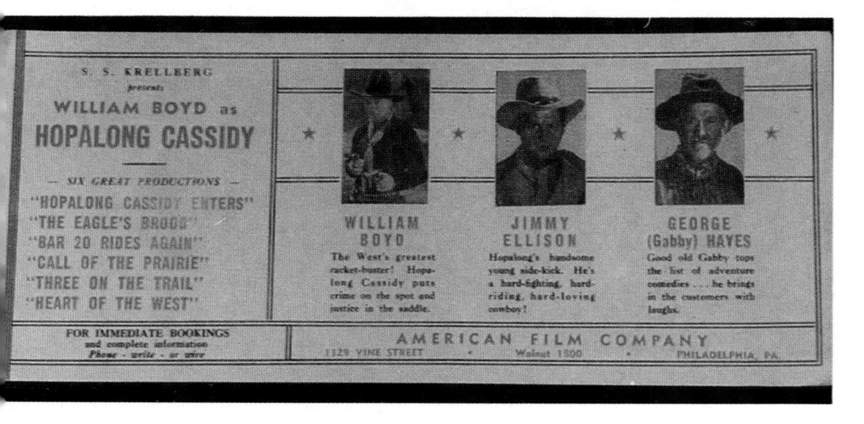

erican Film Company promotion blotter (1930's) lists the first six Hoppy ns. Recent find of original blotters reflect a good value at $50 each.

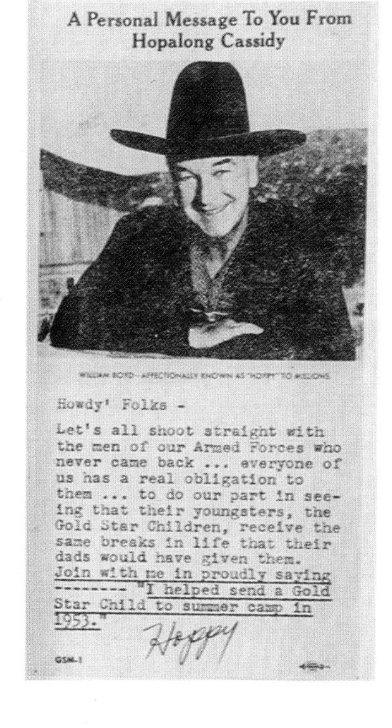
A Personal Message To You From Hopalong Cassidy

WILLIAM BOYD—AFFECTIONALLY KNOWN AS "HOPPY" TO MILLIONS

Howdy' Folks -

Let's all shoot straight with the men of our Armed Forces who never came back ... everyone of us has a real obligation to them ... to do our part in seeing that their youngsters, the Gold Star Children, receive the same breaks in life that their dads would have given them. Join with me in proudly saying -------- "I helped send a Gold Star Child to summer camp in 1953."

Hoppy

GSM-1

Rare "Gold Star" children's camp program (1953) was promoted by Hoppy to send children of deceased veterans to summer camp. This was a theatre program used during intermissions as well as mailed to audience homes. Shown at left are the Gold Star stamps. Letter and stamps as shown: $150. from the Dennis Smith collection.

One interesting and unique "find" was this souvenir program for the "Hollywood Movie Star World Series" for charity. It pitted the "Comedians against the "Tragedians" of which Hoppy was the official umpire of the game, and is shown in this illustration arguing with Eddie Bracken. Containing many stars of the 1940's, it would be a great find for any paper collector. Photos shown are from various pages. #1. $175 #2. $150 #3. $135. From the Bill Hoffman collection.

ppy TV show promo featuring the Meadow ld song. The song is contained inside. #1. $40 . $30 #3. $25. From the Mike Forthun collec- n.

everal song sheets used Hoppy on cover. This "Take Me Back to the Wide Open Spaces" y Harry Tobias. #1. $35 #2. $30 #3. $25

Promo ad for the Chicago Daily Tribune Hoppy comic strips is a nice find for paper collectors. Expect to pay $35 -$45. From the Mike Forthun collection

Castle Films magazine ad announcing Hoppy films on 8mm reels. Advertises: "Three on the Trail," "Heart of the West," and "Bar 20 Rides Again." Full page ads like this are selling for $20. From the Mike Forthun collection.

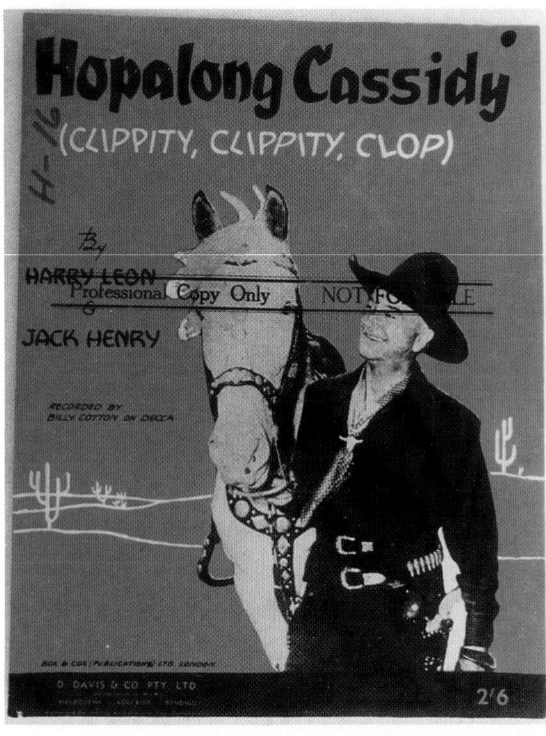

Another unusual song is actually entitled "Hopalong Cassidy" and pictures Hoppy & Topper on cover. Note stamping "Professional copy - not for resale" (Wonder what it sounds like). Note: this is a British song, which is even more unique. from the Bill Hoffman collection. Value: #1. $70 #2. $50 #3. $30.

DIPLOMA

HOPALONG COLLEGE

CAMELBACK INN — PHOENIX, ARIZONA

HOPALONG CASSIDY (WILLIAM BOYD) — A SYMBOL TO YOUNG PEOPLE

THIS IS TO CERTIFY THAT

Date:

has graduated with honor from Hopalong College; having demonstrated these qualities of courage and resourcefulness which are a tradition of Western ranch life; having enjoyed good informal ranch fun and companionship; having learned many ranch arts; having proven worthy of the respect and friendship of other young people at Hopalong College

Cordially yours

HOPALONG COLLEGE PHOENIX ARIZONA

GRADUATION APPROVED BY:

Hopalong College diploma is dated 1953 and is a genuine article. Camelback Inn in Phoenix AZ, was often a resting place for Hoppy & Grace all the way back to the 1930's. The college idea was a promotion for the kids of hotel guests. The above diploma has been signed by Hoppy himself and is quite rare. Hoppy College is still in business after all these years! #1. $275 #2. $250 #3. $225. (must have authentic Hoppy signature)

Similar to the War Bonds Stamps promotion this Hoppy film promo photo (above) and flip-side details (L) are a very popular collector item. #1. $70 #2. $50 #3. $30. From the Mike Forthun collection.

The Official

Hopalong Cassidy™ Tribute

Recently, we celebrated the 100th anniversary of William ***"Hopalong Cassidy"*** Boyd's birth. Revered for his honesty, integrity and patriotism, Hopalong Cassidy was so respected that parents encouraged their children to watch his show.

Dressed in black from head to toe, Hopalong Cassidy quickly became America's first television superstar. William Boyd also starred on the silver screen in 66 movies. His first movie was **"Hop-A-Long-Cassidy."** Winchester rifles were featured in the first Hopalong Cassidy movie, and in subsequent films.

In his show, Hopalong Cassidy was a clever and kindly defender of truth and justice. As foreman of the Bar 20 Ranch, he tracked down all manner of unsavory characters - from cattle rustlers to desperate killers.

William Boyd was recently inducted into the prestigious Hall of Great Western Performers at the National Cowboy Hall of Fame in Oklahoma City. This permanent tribute to William Boyd ensures that future generations will recognize the importance of William Boyd, and Hopalong Cassidy, in our American heritage.

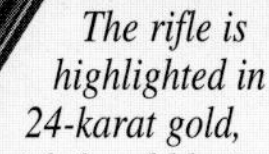

The rifle is highlighted in 24-karat gold, nickel and blueing with artwork honoring Hopalong Cassidy and William Boyd. The detail in the artwork is powerful, and the spectacular blend of nickel, blueing and gold perfectly highlight this officially authorized Tribute.

Right side of receiver features a detailed portrait of William Boyd in nickel and blue, framed in a 24-karat gold shield. The name William Boyd is etched permanently in gold, and a banner with his dates of birth and death are featured. Hoppy called the Bar 20 Ranch home, so you will also find "Bar 20" on the receiver.

The Tribute

The Hopalong Cassidy Rifle is a masterpiece, from the gold and nickel embellished receiver to the handsome walnut stock. The lever-action, Model 94 Winchester rifle has a 20-inch barrel. This Tribute includes the large loop lever.

The rifle's receiver is etched with incredible detail by craftsmen commissioned specifically by America Remembers for this project.

Left side of the receiver features "Topper", Hoppy's faithful horse. Note detail on the image of Topper. A saddle with the "HC" initials and a banner reading "Hopalong Cassidy", are highlighted in gold, nickel and blueing. The large loop lever is decorated in nickel and blued and features the well-known trademark of Hopalong Cassidy, the steer head from his bolo tie.

Rifle Description

Make: Winchester Model 94 Rifle

Caliber: .30-30

Edition Limit: 500

You are invited to view this handsome firearm before making your final decision. We will arrange delivery of your rifle through a licensed dealer of your choice. If for any reason you are less than satisfied with the rifle, you may return it within 30 days for a full refund.

The Hopalong Cassidy™ Rifle is issued under a license granted by U.S. Television Office, Inc.

I wish to reserve ___ of the **"Hopalong Cassidy Tribute(s)"**, a working Winchester Rifle, at the advance issue price of $1595. (Official price: $1850). Each rifle is numbered within the edition limit of 500. Certificate of Authenticity included. Thirty day return privilege. My deposit of $195 per rifle is enclosed. I wish to pay the balance at the rate of $100 per month, no interest or carrying charges.

❒ Check enclosed for $ ___________. *Virginia residents please add 4.5% sales tax.*

❒ Charge payment of $ ___________ to:

❒ VISA ❒ MasterCard ❒ AMEX ❒ Discover ❒ Diners Club

No. ______________________ Exp. ________

Name ______________________ Telephone (   )

Address ______________________

City/State/Zip ______________________

America Remembers®

8428 Old Richfood Road • Mechanicsville, Virginia 23116

To place your reservation toll-free call 1-800-682-2291

Joe Caro's Exclusive interview with "Hoppy" illustrator Dan Spiegle

I first met Bill Boyd after graduating art school, a few years after my Navy discharge from WWII, and of course, after graduating art school on the GI Bill. There was a newspaper ad for an illustrator at Capitol Records, and I applied for it. That was in July, 1949. They wanted someone to draw Bozo The Clown stories, but what I had in mind were westerns, so there was no match. As I was leaving, one of the executives stopped me and told me that a new productions company was looking for a western illustrator just a couple of blocks away. That's when I met Bill Boyd.

I showed him some of my western sketches and told him about my idea for an authentic western comic strip. He liked the idea, and asked me to put something together, commenting "I sure like the way you draw horses." With a warm smile on his lips and a twinkle in his eye, he stood and shook my hand saying "the rest will come with practice, and I think you'll be getting a lot of it around here."

Dan Spiegle at work on Hoppy comic strips in 1950

The first Hopalong Cassidy daily comic strip appeared in the Los Angeles Mirror Syndicate newspaper in January, 1950 and did so well that by summer, it was syndicated in over 200 papers nationally. The success of the daily Hoppy strip was soon followed with a Sunday color strip. Bill was right, with no assistants to help, I certainly was getting a lot of practice! I worked with Bill until he retired in 1956. Then I went to Western Publishing. The rest, as they say, is history.

Doing this limited edit
Hopalong Cassidy comic book
like turning back the clock
me, and perhaps the best way
thank Bill Boyd for taking
chance on an "unknown" and s
a little wet-behind-the-ears ill
trator who was just starting c
He was the genuine article, an
pleasure to work with. I hope t
he still likes the way I dr
horses.

Dan Spiegle today, is a widely known and well respected illustrator with an awesome list of credits: Disney's Pocahontas and The Hunchback. Indiana Jones Adventure books, Mary Poppins, Maverick, Classics Illustrated, Sea Hunt, The Green Hornet, Spin & Marty, Herbie the Love Bug, Lawman, The Rifleman, Rawhide Annie Oakley and Wells Fargo, just to name a few. Dan and his family lives in the beautiful and secluded Santa Barbara Mountains, near Carpenteria, California.

Hopalong Cassidy

HOPPY COLLECTORS WANTED!!
$24. FOR A YEAR!
COWBOY COLLECTOR NEWSLETTER
New publication specializing in Hopalong Cassidy "collectibilia" contains information on Hoppy collecting for beginning and advanced collectors -"new finds" - classified ads - item values - current prices and collecting tips and auction results! Published by Hoppy authority Joe Caro
COWBOY COLLECTOR PUBLICATIONS
P.O. Bx. 7486 Long Beach, CA 90807
Yes! I would like to subscribe to CCN for a year and get all kinds of great Hoppy info on a bi-monthly basis. Here is my check for $24.00 and I would like the publication sent to:
name...........................
address............ ....
city............ ....
state...............(zip)........

COLLECTOR'S DREAM
ANTIQUE TOY SHOW

Jon & Charlie Cheek (910) 674-3431

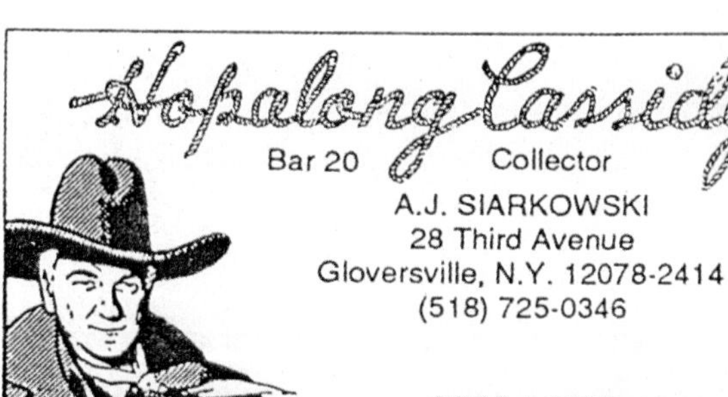
Hopalong Cassidy
Bar 20 Collector

COWBOY COLLECTOR

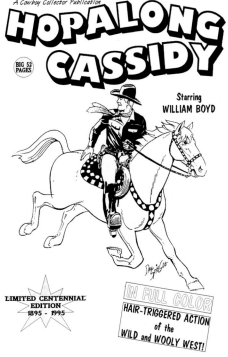

NOTES